Parent Child Excursions

Parent Child Excursions

ADHD, Anxiety, and Autism

Dan Shapiro, MD

and a section on

Autism, Sexuality, and Gender Identity with Aaron Shapiro, MD, MPH

Illustrations by John Watkins-Chow

DAGMAR MIURA
LOS ANGELES

Published by Dagmar Miura
Los Angeles
www.dagmarmiura.com

Parent Child Excursions: ADHD, Anxiety, and Autism

First published 2019

ISBN: 978-1-951130-10-7

To Robin, my hiking partner, with love.

Acknowledgments

———— ◆ ————

Throughout the book, I provide vignettes from my parent training groups and from my private clinical practice. All are true. Sometimes, for the sake of demonstrating a point more clearly, I have taken the liberty of blending some cases together. Of course, the names have been changed to protect the privacy of patients, parents, and others. Thanks to all of these children and families for sharing their lives with me and teaching me so much.

How wonderful to collaborate with my son Aaron on Excursion 5! Truly, I could not have done it without him. I am pleased beyond words that each of my four sons has taken his own career path. As adult professionals, they have all been generous with their wide-ranging expertise. Here, Aaron shares his with you and me.

As with my first book, again it has been a true pleasure to work with John Watkins-Chow, my amazing illustrator. I hope that you enjoy his drawings as much as I have marveled at their creation. Thanks, John, for bringing to life Raph, Dog, and Turtle.

Also reprising his role from my first book, thanks to my dear old friend Bruce Louryk, for his meticulous work on the footnotes.

And thanks to Danny Solomon for his expertise creating the medication coverage curves in Excursion 1—one month before his wedding!

Thanks to Teja Watson (Two Birds Editing) for her substantial assistance preparing the manuscript.

Huge thanks to my publisher, Christopher Church at Dagmar

Miura. Chris is a consummate professional. Throughout this daunting process, I have appreciated his meticulous attention to detail, expert advice and unflagging support. I am grateful beyond words.

Heartfelt thanks to the following friends and colleagues who reviewed various drafts and sections of the manuscript: Dr. Polly Panitz, Dr. Bonnie Zucker, Dr. Rachel Rubin, Dr. Veronica Raggi, Dr. Tom Holman, Dr. William Stixrud, Dr. Mary Alvord, Dr. Carey Heller, Dr. Roby Marcou, Dr. Naveena Hemanth, Dr. Rebecca Edelson, Dr. Sarah Berger, Dr. Lisa Sanchez, Dr. Michelle Forcier, Dr. Lem Yutzy, Dr. Lance Clawson, Dr. Hector Parada, Dr. Dan Wojnilower, Annie Glanville, Albert Monroe, Kathryn Spindel, and Emily Siegel. All of you were extraordinarily generous with your time, expertise, and honesty. I deeply appreciate your many thoughtful suggestions. You made the writing of this book a much deeper learning experience for me. You challenged me, held me accountable, and improved tremendously the quality of these excursions. Please do consider yourselves co-authors.

Disclaimers

This book contains a considerable amount of specific advice. I hope it helps parents become more educated consumers of developmental-behavioral care. I also hope that it helps clinicians become more expert providers. However, I must emphasize, none of the information provided here should take the place of regular reassessment, clinical experience, or more up-to-date research. Parents must stay in touch with clinicians. Clinicians must stay in touch with parents and children.

This need for close communication is especially true regarding medication management. Pharmacotherapy is a rapidly changing field; much of what's here will become out-of-date. Although many of the medications I discuss are approved by the FDA for use in children, others are not. Medications recommended in this book that are not FDA-approved are commonly used in children based on clinical experience, community standards, pediatric research, and extrapolation from adult studies. Nonetheless, parents should be fully informed regarding the current evidence base and FDA-approval status before making any decisions with a properly licensed clinician.

This is a book for both parents and professionals. As such, I will sometimes refer to "your child" and other times refer to "the child."

Contents

———— ◆ ————

INTRODUCTION

Stop, Go, Balance, Change, and Discover

———◆———

For many years in the greater Washington, DC, area, I have offered Parent Child Journey and Parent Child Excursions parent training programs. These large pay-what-you-can groups evolved in response to a crisis of affordability and availability in developmental and behavioral pediatrics.

My first book, *Parent Child Journey: An Individualized Approach to Raising Your Challenging Child,* was based on my ten-session parent training program (Shapiro, 2016). It was designed to give parents a comprehensive and integrated set of strategies for raising children with developmental and behavioral differences.

This second book, *Parent Child Excursions: ADHD, Anxiety, and Autism,* is based on other seminars I've offered over the years. Careful evaluation is always essential. But the primary focus of this book is management, not assessment.

Why Not Five Smaller Books?

1. Many children have coexisting conditions or at least features of more than one diagnosis.
2. ADHD, anxiety, and autism can be seen as disorders, with overlapping presenting symptoms, that all lie along the same

spectrum of self-regulation differences. Variations in sexuality and gender are commonly intertwined.

3. With treatment and the passage of time, "hidden" tendencies often come out. Issues may evolve along a predictable developmental trajectory as demands change. A child who starts with one diagnosis may transform. Therefore, readers will find many sections to be of surprising relevance over time— perhaps even before they turn the last page.

4. Putting all of these topics between two covers helps me keep down the cost and remain true to the spirit of the pay-what-you-can parent training programs upon which my books are based. (See ParentChildJourney.com.)

The "Stop And Go" Theme

In the pages that follow, we will discuss ADHD as a problem with stopping, anxiety as a problem with going, and autism as difficulty balancing these competing biological tendencies. Despite their differences, ADHD, anxiety, and autism are complementary disorders of self-regulation, commonly co-occurring, each affecting the other. Although these issues can be complicated, this book is also, quite simply, a story of red light and green light, braking and accelerating, holding back and forging ahead.

The stop and go theme is not at all unique to ADHD, anxiety, and autism. Stop and Go defines all of biology, psychology, and sociology. In many ways, health can be viewed as a functional balance—and disease as imbalance—between inhibition and excitation. Human physiology, development, and behavior are not normally smooth and linear. Throughout life, beginning at the simplest level and moving outward, there are sputters and spurts, offs and ons, pauses and plays, rests and notes.

At the level of biology, atoms repel and attract. Genes are turned off and on. Cells withdraw and approach. Spermatozoa are rejected and accepted. Growth occurs in fits and starts. We alternate between sleep and wakefulness, satiety and hunger, accumulation and expulsion. Nerves rest and fire. Hormone production is shut down and cranked up. Muscles relax and contract. Heart and respiratory rates go down and up. Cells die and reproduce. Species become extinct and evolve. In these ways and more, stop and go suffuses all of genetics, chemistry, physiology, and evolution.

At the level of psychology, we stay and follow, look and leap, obey and rebel. Rules are embraced and rejected. We seek sameness and novelty. Our behavior is modified by punishment and reward. We doubt and believe. We keep it real and play pretend, find patterns and break molds. We think slow and fast, rationally and instinctually. We are pessimists and optimists, conservatives and radicals. We are depressed and manic, anxious and risk-seeking, stuck and disconnected, obsessive-compulsive and psychotic. Stop and Go permeates all of cognition, emotion, and behavior.

At the level of sociology, parent-child attachment ranges between anxious and secure. Parenting style can be authoritarian and permissive. In communities, there are constraints and freedoms, prohibitions and exhortations, standards and autonomy, communitarianism and individualism. Behavior can be normative and non-categorical. We are affected by scarcity and plenty, isolation and collaboration, peaceful coexistence and war. Culture can be fixed and fluid, stable and changing, tradition-bound and revolutionary. Stop and Go pervades all of interpersonal relations, society, and culture.

At all these levels—biology, psychology, and sociology—we strive for flexibility and moderation along a continuum of thought, emotion, and behavior. In other words, between stop and go, we struggle to find the right balance. We change. We discover.

Excursions, Signposts, and Trail-Ends

As we shift from ADHD to anxiety to autism, we will take five excursions. With each successive excursion, we will move from individual nervous systems to family systems and then to larger social systems. At the beginning of each excursion, readers will be oriented to the material with "SIGNPOSTS," which summarize the main features of the path ahead.

Excursion 1: Stop—Medication for ADHD

ADHD is a disorder of under-inhibition. People with ADHD have inconsistent self-control. This is because their "brain brakes" do not work well enough. We will explore the many different types of inattention. For the most common type of ADHD, the core feature is impulsivity. For properly diagnosed ADHD, medication to improve self-inhibition should be part of a comprehensive treatment plan. For those of you with fears or biases about medication management, the reasons for this strong statement will become clear as you read on. We will take a deep dive into important details that are crucial for effective medication management, but generally missing from other books on this topic.

Excursion 2: Go—Parallel Exposure Therapy for Anxiety

Anxiety is a disorder of over-inhibition. People with anxiety have "brain brakes" that work *too* well. The core feature of anxiety is inflexibility. When anxiety is persistently impairing, avoidance is the number one challenge. It is crucial to face anxiety triggers. Real-life exposures to just-right doses of anxiety produce the most durable results. Unlike traditional cognitive-behavioral therapy, the parallel exposure therapy approach outlined here includes the child and family members, as well as the school, community, and other larger systems.

Excursion 3: Balance—Combined Medication and Parallel Exposure Therapy for Coexisting ADHD, Anxiety, and Autism

Children with complicated profiles often have conflicting tendencies. When ADHD, anxiety, and autism coexist, we need to find a functional balance between under-inhibition and over-inhibition. Here, the trick is combining therapies to find "the golden mean." By using just-right combinations of medical and psychosocial interventions, we can hit the sweet spot between stop and go.

Excursion 4: Change—Social Engineering for Autism

Just like neurotypical people, individuals with autism, and other differences in social development, must change and grow. The world in which they live must change as well. The trick is finding the right balance between intervention and accommodation. Parents and professionals worry about helping the individual with neurodevelopmental difference better fit into the "real world"—but it's at least as important to change the "real world" to better fit all individuals.

Excursion 5: Discover—Autism, Sexuality, and Gender Identity

In this final excursion, we will explore how autism and other developmental differences affect sexuality. We will also discuss the overlap of gender-nonconformity with autism and other developmental differences, and apply management principles from previous sections to the challenge of cultural transformation for sociosexual-minority individuals.

These are complicated and controversial issues. There's a lot to cover.

Our Story Continues

But before we get going, allow me to make some introductions. As in my first book, we will be accompanied by Raph, a bird of a different feather, plus his new friends, Dog and Turtle. Their tale is added for some much-needed levity and another chance for me to work with the incomparable John Watkins-Chow. I hope that you enjoy their story and John's wonderful illustrations.

Those of you who have read *Parent Child Journey* recall that Raph, a young dodo bird, was saved from going over the waterfall by Hawk. They became good friends. Together, they traveled up the river, sharing many adventures. Raph loved to eat fruit from the Tambalacoque tree. Hawk loved to fly. They both enjoyed resting on shore and kicking pebbles into the water. Along the way, Hawk helped Raph learn to navigate. But one day, quite mysteriously, Hawk flew off.

Our story picks up there. It will weave in and out of the entire book.

The Tale of Raph, Dog, and Turtle

Onshore, Raph looked around and wondered, How did I get here? Hawk was gone. Their boat was gone. Somehow, Raph must have survived the falls and drifted down river. But Raph could not hear

the falls anymore, and he did not see even one Tambalacoque fruit tree.

Raph wondered, "Where am I? What can I eat?"

Raph's wings were too small for flying. But his legs were strong and sturdy. So Raph started to walk. And walk. And walk. After a long time, Raph's legs got tired, and his tummy got hungry. What to do?

Just then, a dog appeared. Running circles around Raph, the dog barked, "Ruff!"

Raph said, "My name is not Ruff. It's Raph."

The dog repeated, "Ruff!"

Again, Raph said, "My name is Raph!" Even though the dog couldn't say Raph's name right, at least Raph wasn't alone anymore.

The dog was happy to meet Raph too, and jumped and ran and barked. The dog came close to Raph, barked, then ran away again. Raph said, "I'd like to play chase but I'm too tired." Then Raph said, "That's what I'll call you: Chase. Chase the Dog."

The dog growled.

"Okay, then," said Raph, "I'll just call you Dog." Dog wagged his tail in agreement.

Raph saw a smooth bump on a log. A perfect place to sit and rest. Raph settled his tuft down onto the bump.

"Ahh," sighed Raph. "What a nice bump for sitting."

With a muffled voice, the bump protested, "Get off of me, you strange bird! I'm not a bump on a log. That's my shell. I'm a turtle, warming myself in the sun. You are too heavy and you're blocking my ultraviolet light!"

Startled that the bump could talk, Raph climbed off and said, "I'm sorry, Bump. I didn't know you were a turtle."

The turtle said, "Please don't call me Bump. Call me Turtle!"

Raph said, "Okay, Turtle."

Raph was getting hungrier. But he was too tired to walk another step. Raph asked Dog and Turtle, "Can you get me some Tambalacoque fruit?"

Dog barked. Raph looked up the trail.

Turtle said, "I've heard that there is a whole forest of Tambalacoque trees over the mountain." At the end of the trail, far, far away, there loomed a very large mountain.

"Up over that mountain?" Raph asked. "How would we get there? How could we get to the other side?"

Excited for an adventure, Dog ran every which way, barking "Ruff!"

Raph agreed with Dog: "Yes, you're right. It would be a very rough trip. But you sure seem excited to go anyhow."

Turtle was petrified at the thought of leaving his log. Turtle whimpered, "Oh, no," and hid deep within his shell.

EXCURSION 1
Stop—Medication for ADHD

———— ◆ ————

The idea that human self-control is largely
self-determined and largely instilled by one's
parents during childhood should be discarded
on history's conceptual scrap heap.
—Russell Barkley, *ADHD and the Nature of Self-Control*

Just then, Raph saw something on the ground: a unicycle. Raph thought aloud, "That's how I can get to the mountain. I can't fly, and it's too far to walk. But with my strong legs and my hind tuft, a unicycle would be perfect."

Dog barked encouragement. Turtle groaned, "You've got to be crazy. Birds don't ride unicycles!"

But Raph's tuft settled softly onto the unicycle seat. His feet fit on the pedals.

Dog ran ahead, yapping and woofing. Turtle stayed on his log, screaming at Raph and Dog, "Stop, you fools! You won't make it to the mountain. You'll fall off that one-wheeled contraption. Don't leave me here alone!"

But Raph and Dog were too excited. Raph tightened his leg muscles. He sang, "To the mountain we go!" He leaned forward. The wheel turned—but only once. The unicycle hit a rock, and Raph went airborne.

For a moment, he marveled, "Maybe I can fly after all?" But Raph came right down—hard.

With a buried beak but a racing heart, Raph thought, *Rough landing.* Dog agreed: *"Ruff!"*

Turtle said, *"You must be completely dodo! You could have gotten yourself killed!"*

But Raph grabbed the unicycle in his beak, shoved it under his tuft, and got back right back on. Again, Raph leaned forward and pedaled. Dog ran ahead. Turtle pleaded, "Be careful!"

Again, the wheel rolled once, and Raph was thrown to the ground. Boom. Beak-plant.

Again, Turtle protested, "You're going to keep falling! Give up!" Dog ran further down the trail, too impatient to wait for the others. Again and again, Raph mounted, leaned, pedaled, and fell.

Signposts for Excursion 1

This excursion is a detailed discussion of medication management for ADHD, including:

- The case for medication management of ADHD.
- Parent concerns about medication.
- How to do a medication trial.
- How to manage medication side effects.
- How to manage uneven medication coverage.
- Long-term care issues.
- When and how to stop ADHD medication.

Some Background about Medication for ADHD

In any country and socioeconomic group, ADHD affects about 5–10 percent of children (Centers for Disease Control and Prevention, 2016). ADHD is diagnosed when three conditions are met:

1. There is hyperactivity, impulsivity, and/or distractibility that causes a significant degree of impairment.
2. This impairment is present across settings, between observers, and over time.
3. These symptoms are not better explained by some other factors in the child or the environment (Subcommittee on Attention-Deficit/Hyperactivity Disorder, Steering Committee on Quality Improvement and Management, 2011).

ADHD is just one of many reasons a child might have problems with self-control. As part of a comprehensive assessment, an expert should consider other conditions that could mimic ADHD, coexist with ADHD, and potentially complicate treatment (Nigg, 2017). Although careful diagnosis is of the utmost importance, it is beyond the scope of this book. I will touch on some issues regarding assessment but will go into much greater detail on practical aspects of management.

According to the fifth edition of the *Diagnostic and Statistical Manual of the American Psychiatric Association (DSM5)*, there are three different subtypes of ADHD: predominantly hyperactive/ impulsive, predominantly inattentive, and combined. Some people still use out-of-date language and refer to the predominantly inattentive subtype of ADHD as ADD. In this book, beyond these three subtypes of ADHD, I will gradually broaden the discussion to encompass a fuller spectrum of self-control and attention disorders. But most of this first excursion will focus narrowly on a very specific formulation of ADHD.

Following Russell Barkley (1997), the leading expert, when I refer to ADHD, I will mean the kind of poor self-control that results from poor inhibition. Barkley explains that the problem for people with ADHD is primarily one of executive dysfunction: difficulties with managing time, planning, organizing, initiating, sustaining, inhibiting, shifting; in short, being strategic. According to this view, ADHD is not a disorder of knowing what to do. It is a disorder of doing what you know. In other words, people with ADHD know the script. They just have a hard time following it. They know what to do but have difficulty with implementation. ADHD is all about inadequate self-talk and performance inconsistency. It is this disorder of inhibition that we will be primarily discussing and for which we have the most effective medications.

Paul's parents and teachers described him as "a real live one!" As a toddler and ever since, his body was always moving. Now seven years old, he drummed on tables and ran from one end of the room to another. Paul was always getting into some kind of trouble. Afterward, he knew he'd done something wrong but did not understand why he did it anyway. His mind was always moving. He could not stay on a single task or thought for more than a few seconds. He was constantly shifting from one conversational topic to another. He seemed to notice everything but could not really stay focused on any one thing. His father said, "Paul is like a race car with no brakes."

Becky, a ten-year-old, did not have any obvious problems. However, she was falling behind in school and she had a hard time making friends. Becky just seemed lost in her own thoughts. Her mind flitted from one disconnected thought to another. Her body stayed calm but her eyes were constantly darting around the room. Becky did not pose any problems for others, but her mother said, "Becky seems like a cork just bobbing around on the top of the ocean."

People with ADHD have a serious but treatable neurological disorder, not a primary problem with willful disobedience, laziness, or lack of motivation. Children, adolescents, and adults with ADHD, like Paul and Becky, would exert more consistent self-control if they could.

In the brain, there are two separate networks of nerves: the excitatory brain system, for "go," and the inhibitory brain system, for "stop." People with ADHD have no problem with their excitatory "go" system; their problem is with the inhibitory "stop" system. In neuroscience lingo, ADHD is a brain-based disorder of disinhibition. In plain English, ADHD means "unreliable brain brakes." The result: It is hard for people with ADHD to pause and consider past experience and future consequences. They live too much in the moment.

In my opinion, we should really throw out the name "Attention Deficit Hyperactivity Disorder." It is inaccurate and misleading. For people with a diagnosis of ADHD, the common symptoms of distractibility and motor restlessness are not the *primary* problems. Rather, attention deficits and hyperactivity are *secondary* to problems with inhibition, self-control, or impulsivity; in other words, inconsistent brain brakes.

Even more confusing, "stimulant" medications are also misnamed. Note that ADHD stimulant medications do not rev you up. In fact, too much stimulant medication can make you too stuck and withdrawn. ADHD medication works by "stimulating" the brain's inhibitory nerves to send stop signals and apply the brakes more consistently. It would be more accurate to call them "inhibitory" or "stop and think" medicines.

The Case for ADHD Medication

A mountain of good scientific research offers compelling reasons to treat ADHD (Barkley, 2013; Hamed, Kauer, & Stevens, 2015). In the short term, effective medication improves your child's day-to-day adaptive behavior and availability for learning. Medication for ADHD can make a crucial difference in family functioning, acquisition of self-care skills, peer interaction, and school success. Medication can have a very positive effect on your child's self-image, turning a "can't-do kid" into a "can-do kid."

What is often underappreciated is that undertreatment of ADHD can lead to serious consequences. The impulsivity of ADHD can cause real distress, significant impairment, and serious long-term fallout. Poor self-control often leads to life-changing difficulties in school, family functioning, peer relationships, and work. Adequate treatment is crucial in the prevention of chronic failure and all its consequences. I know it might sound overly dramatic, but undertreatment of ADHD truly fills our basements with failure-to-launch young adults, our underpasses with the homeless, our prisons with those who cannot control their criminal behavior, and our cemeteries with victims of accidental death. This disorder represents a public health challenge.

Over the course of a lifespan, treatment of ADHD has many crucial positive effects. Treatment lowers the chance of the following serious problems (Barkley & Benton, 2010):

- secondary depression and anxiety
- suicide
- family stress
- marital discord and divorce
- substance abuse (McCabe, Dickinson, West, & Wilens, 2016)
- social failure
- dangerous sexual behavior and other risk-taking behaviors
- motor vehicle accidents and other serious accidental injuries (Chang et al., 2017)
- school underperformance
- failure to attend or complete college
- unemployment and poor job performance
- homelessness
- juvenile delinquency

- adult legal problems, criminal behavior, and high rates of incarceration
- significant problems with general health and shortened life-span

On the last point of physical health, Dr. Barkley has recently presented disturbing long-term data about mortality. Untreated ADHD can actually shorten lifespan by nine to thirteen years. In an interview, Barkley explained: "Our research shows that ADHD is much more than a neurodevelopmental disorder, it's a significant public health issue. In evaluating the health conse-quences of ADHD over time, we found that ADHD adversely affects every aspect of quality of life and longevity. This is due to the inherent deficiencies in self-regulation associated with ADHD that lead to poor self-care and impulsive, high-risk behavior. The findings are sobering, but also encouraging, as ADHD is the most treatable mental health disorder in psychia-try (Barkley, 2018a)."

For these reasons and more, treatment of ADHD should not be misrepresented as "cosmetic psychopharmacology," "per-formance enhancement," or "cultural craziness." Some media coverage, Internet rants, and playground conversations portray ADHD as a product of poor parenting or modern culture.

But ADHD is a serious neurogenetic disorder. Proper medica-tion is imperative. Although ADHD medications can be abused to "raise the performance ceiling," proper use of these medica-tions raises the floor. We treat ADHD to help children and adults play their lives on a level field, not to give them an unfair advan-tage or cater to their distorted fears. If medication has adverse side effects, as we will discuss in detail below, you can always stop it. On the other hand, the cumulative life-span consequences of undertreated ADHD are much harder to reverse.

In Barkley's (1997) *ADHD and the Nature of Self-Control,* he quotes Dr. John Weery: "In any other medical or psychiat-ric condition where the evidence for drug efficacy is this sub-stantial and for drug side effects is this benign, the failure of a physician to consider medication treatment for the disorder would be considered tantamount to malpractice." In the same book, Barkley himself writes, "The idea that human self-control is largely self-determined and largely instilled by one's parents during childhood should be discarded on history's conceptual scrap heap. Until such time as more effective treatments having even fewer side effects have been scientifically identified, the use of stimulant medication as part of a larger treatment package for the management of ADHD should be a first-line and mainstay treatment, without apology."

Although much work still needs to be done, we are no longer working in the dark regarding the possible benefits and side effects of these medications. We know that pharmacological treatment for ADHD can safely enhance self-control, improve availability for learning, and facilitate social success. There is no other family of medications where we have better scientific data, a more favorable risk-benefit ratio, or more compelling reasons to treat.

Some History of Medication Management for ADHD

The Bradley Hospital Study

You might be surprised to learn that the first good study of medication for ADHD was done way back in 1938, even if by accident, at the Bradley Hospital in Rhode Island (Strohl, 2011). Children at this residential treatment facility were given a stimulant medication to see if it would prevent headaches from spinal taps. The medication did not help with headaches but the staff noted remarkable improvements in behavior. Since then, the safety and effectiveness of ADHD medication has been well-documented. We now have stacks of well-designed, prospective, placebo-controlled, randomized, peer-reviewed studies.

The MTA Study

Some of our best data comes from the National Institutes of Health–funded Multimodal Treatment of Attention Deficit Hyperactivity Disorder Study (MTA). In this large, well-designed, multi-center study, children with ADHD who received state-of-the-art medication *and* psychosocial supports did *no* better (on core symptoms of ADHD) than children who received medication alone (National Institute of Mental Health, 2009). The conclusions were clear: Medication should be the cornerstone of treatment for the core symptoms of ADHD—hyperactivity, impulsivity, and distractibility. Behavior management, psychotherapy, executive function coaching, educational care, and other psychosocial interventions may also be needed but should supplement medication, not replace it (CDC, 2016). Although medication for ADHD is never the whole answer, a carefully controlled medication trial should be part of any comprehensive treatment plan.

Parent Concerns about Medication

Many parents have serious misgivings about giving their child medication. Parents and doctors should always be skeptical and cautious. But I hope that this discussion eases your fears a bit, or at least helps you feel more in control of the process.

Overdiagnosis and Overtreatment

Parents of children with ADHD often ask:
- Isn't ADHD overdiagnosed?
- Aren't children with ADHD overmedicated?
- Isn't my child too young to be diagnosed?
- Isn't my child too young for medication?
- What about trying other things first?
- What about treating ADHD without medication?

Over the years, proper diagnosis and treatment have improved. However, ADHD is still overdiagnosed, underdiagnosed, and misdiagnosed. Children's struggles are often misinterpreted. The most common cause of overdiagnosis and misdiagnosis is the presence of mimicking or coexisting conditions—learning disabilities, mood disorders, sleep problems, medical conditions— which can lead to inappropriate treatment. For example, anxiety can cause secondary hyperactivity, impulsivity, or distractibility. In these cases, treatment with stimulant medication can make the anxiety worse. Also, anxiety can coexist with ADHD. Then, treatment of both may be necessary.

Consider the inappropriate practice of using antibiotics to treat viral infections. Just because antibiotics are often misused in this way does not mean that they should never be used. Same with ADHD medication. All medicines should be used carefully, after thorough assessment, according to our best scientific knowledge. Thorough assessment does not mean just a computerized test of attention or even a more comprehensive standardized neuropsychological test battery (Barkley, 2019). Although these tools may be helpful, the diagnosis is most reliably made by direct observation, rating scales, and detailed history; from many people, across settings, over time.

The more severe the ADHD, the easier it is to make an early and accurate diagnosis. The milder the ADHD or the more complicated the profile with various other coexisting conditions, the more difficult it is to make a certain and durable diagnosis. The decision to treat ADHD should depend upon both the degree of diagnostic clarity and the severity of impairment. In preschoolers, if there is diagnostic uncertainty, then behavior management and educational care may be appropriate (CDC, 2017). However, if the diagnosis is certain and the child is impaired, medication should also be used (Evans, Owens, and Bunford, 2014). Medication management of younger children can be trickier, but should still be given a careful try (Greenhill et al., 2006).

With his first child, Mr. Jones refused to even talk about ADHD treatment. The doctor was recommending a trial and Jamal was only five years old! But throughout kindergarten and first grade, Jamal fell further behind and got in more trouble. Reluctantly, Mr. Jones agreed to give it a go. Although it took some time to get the right medicine and the right dose, soon positive reports poured in from school. He could see the difference at home too. Most important, Jamal seemed so much happier and more confident, and was even getting along better with his two-year-old brother, Manfred. A few years later, when Manfred turned four and it became clear that he had ADHD too, Mr. Jones called the doctor. Successful preschool treatment spared Manfred a bad start in elementary school too.

If treatment is indicated, then FDA-approved (stimulant or non-stimulant) medication is the way to go. Although behavioral therapy can help, medication is necessary to effectively treat impulsivity. There is evidence that omega fatty acids and gluten-free/casein-free diets may help some—but not much. There's even less evidence for cognitive training such as Cog Med (Orban, Rapport, Friedman, & Kofler, 2014).

Although I have tried, no one person could possibly read the thousands of well-controlled experiments and excellent books currently available. To merely scratch the surface, I encourage interested readers to check out the resources listed at the back of this book. For a much more complete discussion of ADHD in the context of overall development and behavior, see *Parent Child Journey*. Wherever you look, beware of speculation, anecdote, and outright quackery. Stick with science (Offit, 2013). For up-to-date information on diagnosis and treatment, I recommend the American Academy of Pediatrics (aap.org) and the American Academy of Child and Adolescent Psychiatry (aacap.org).

Potential Complicating Factors

Some children with ADHD are easier to treat than others. Success requires patient, methodical experimentation—and often, trying more than one medicine. There are no guarantees. However, with uncomplicated ADHD, about 80 percent of trials are successful. Those are pretty good odds. If your child's ADHD is more complicated, then the success rate is roughly 50 percent. Still not bad.

Factors increasing the chance of side effects or decreasing the likelihood of a positive response include:

- *Younger (preschool) age.* Younger children are more sensitive to side effects. However, this should not preclude treatment in preschoolers (March, 2011). Children who fail a trial at a young age may experience a positive response, with fewer side effects, when they're older.
- *Predominantly inattentive-type ADHD.* Some children just have a short attention span, without hyperactivity and impulsivity. The lower response rate for these quietly distractible children is partly due to commonly coexisting problems with anxiety and learning disabilities. If poor focus is mostly secondary to anxiety or learning disabilities, then ADHD medication won't work. Also, subtle responses to medication are not well-captured by standard ADHD scales, which focus on more obvious symptoms such as hyperactivity and impulsivity.
- *Sluggish Cognitive Tempo.* Recently, Barkley (2018b) has been highlighting "another type of attention disorder" that does not involve distractibility, impulsivity or hyperactivity per se. Although "Sluggish Cognitive Tempo" (SCT) is

an accurate description, Barkley prefers the less pejorative sounding term, "Concentration Deficit Disorder" (CDD). These are slow-moving and slow-thinking children whose challenges probably derive from over-inhibition and anxiety more than under-inhibition and ADHD.

- *Autism, intellectual disability, Fragile X, Fetal Alcohol Syndrome, and other neurogenetic conditions.* In general, the more complicated the central nervous system, the more sensitivity to medication side effects. Also, such a child's ADHD symptoms might be at least partially secondary to their other developmental differences. Successful treatment of ADHD in these neurologically sensitive children may take more expertise, creativity, and luck, but is still worth a careful try. Treatment of ADHD and coexisting conditions will be the subject of Excursion 3.
- *Mood disorders including anxiety, depression, severe irritability, and bipolar illness.* Sometimes, ADHD symptoms are secondary to mood disorders. In cases where mood disorder and ADHD coexist, ADHD medications may work better if mood disorders are treated first. Again, stay tuned for Excursion 3.
- *Problems with eating, sleeping, tics, or other pre-existing medical issues.* Success with ADHD medication may depend upon effective treatment of these commonly associated conditions. Many children are predisposed to these specific side effects, which ADHD medication may amplify. We will cover side effect management later in this chapter.

Although sometimes challenging, these and other complicating factors should not keep parents and doctors from conducting a careful trial. Such associated conditions sometimes get better or at least easier to manage. And when ADHD makes it harder to work through associated challenges, ADHD medication might be even more important, because there may be more to gain.

Affordability and Availability

A large percentage of children with ADHD don't get proper assessment or treatment because it's simply too expensive. If you don't have adequate insurance coverage and can't afford private treatment, what can you do?

For assessment, start with your pediatrician and your local

public school. Your pediatrician can at least ask some basic screening questions, observe your child, and provide a standardized parent/teacher rating scale. For a more in-depth assessment, ask the school (in writing) for an education management team meeting. If the team agrees that your child is struggling and "not available for learning," the school psychologist can do an evaluation. A basic evaluation should include parent, child, and teacher interviews, plus rating scales and classroom observation. If indicated, the school psychologist may perform a more comprehensive assessment of executive functions, associated learning disabilities, and psychosocial problems. If ADHD is diagnosed, the school cannot prescribe medication, but it is required to provide accommodations and interventions under either a 504 plan or an Individualized Education Program. It's good to identify one strong ally in the school—the teacher, counselor, or principal—who can advocate for your child and help you through this process.

Also, for assessment, check your insurance plan for participating child-adolescent psychologists and neuropsychologists. Most pediatric hospitals and university centers employ these experts and participate with many insurance companies. There might be a long wait, but it never hurts to get on the list. If you live in a city with a university-based hospital, medical school, or research center, check to see if they're running any ADHD studies—at least then it's free, or sometimes participants may even be paid. Some universities offer reduced-fee assessments in their training clinics. All ADHD studies include some type of assessment, and some include treatment. CHADD's website has a "Find a Study" page.

If your pediatrician is comfortable prescribing medication, consider a carefully controlled trial. Ask teachers to do baseline and follow-up rating scales. If your pediatrician is not comfortable or the trial proves complicated, check your insurance plan about child psychiatrists, developmental-behavioral pediatricians, or child neurologists who would be covered. If none are available, you or your pediatrician could ask if they ever provide care pro bono or at least on a sliding scale.

Sometimes, a pediatrician is not comfortable with initial assessment and treatment—but if an expert gets things started, would be happy to take over. The expert could remain available to consult with the pediatrician as needed. Across the country, many child and adolescent psychiatrists offer free consultation to pediatricians who just need a bit of professional support; see the National Network of Child Psychiatry Access Programs (NNCPAP).

You can cut the cost of medication by going with generic, or ask your doctor to help you find a drug company that offers discount coupons. Some drug companies even provide medication for free to families in financial need. Also, try websites such as GoodRx to research low prices on different medications.

For behavioral and emotional support, check out CHADD, NAMI, Parent Effectiveness Training, and other free or pay-what-you-can parent groups, such as ParentChildJourney.com.

To find good doctors and other important resources, consult other parents whose children have similar issues. Many cities have wonderful parent list-servs.

Deciding to Do a Medication Trial

Although a substantial body of scientific research supports medication for ADHD, every child is different, and there are many different kinds of ADHD medication. How do you know if medication is right for *your* child? And which medicine? What dose? The only way to answer these important questions is with a carefully controlled trial.

Deciding to do a trial does not require a commitment to continue treatment. It's just a trial. And a stimulant trial is easy, because these medicines work right away. If you give stimulant medication in the morning, you will see effects the very same day. If there are significant side effects, then the medication should be stopped. Rest assured, during the trial period, these side effects are usually gone the day after stopping the medication. With low dosing, careful tuning, and good communication, a medication trial can be done very safely.

- Worst scenario: There are mild side effects and you stop the medication.
- Best scenario: You are able to safely and effectively treat your child's ADHD.

Medication should be continued only if a trial results in significant benefits and no significant side effects. Nothing to lose. Everything to gain.

How to Talk with Your Child About Starting ADHD Medication

Slowly but surely, the stigma attached to ADHD and other neurodevelopmental differences is fading. An ADHD diagnosis should not be treated as some shameful family secret. This does not mean that you need to tell everyone you meet, or become a neurodiversity rights advocate. (Not that I wouldn't welcome the company!)

I recommend sharing about your child's ADHD and medication with carefully selected others who need to know: trusted family, close friends, school personnel, doctors, and others who might be involved in your child's care. If they are informed about the source of your child's difficulties and educated about ADHD, they can often provide valuable support. Most important, open communication sends your child a powerfully positive message: "It's okay to have ADHD and take medicine. We've all got something."

Don't Avoid

Most parents have anxiety about putting their child on medication for ADHD. They might be concerned about side effects, or that their child will feel stigmatized. Or they might go ahead with a trial but opt to keep their child in the dark, hiding the medicine in food or drink or saying the medicine is a "vitamin"—all to avoid talking directly with their child about ADHD.

Although these worries and avoidance strategies are understandable, parents should not lie to their children. What if, some mornings, the child doesn't feel like drinking his or her secretly laced "juice"? And what about when the child eventually grows up?

Think of the Medication Trial as a Teaching Opportunity

The medication trial is an opportunity to teach your child self-awareness, self-care, and self-acceptance. In a developmentally appropriate and individualized manner, children can participate in their own treatment trial. Don't underestimate your child's readiness to be part of this important process. It's an opportunity to demystify neurodevelopmental difference, destigmatize challenges, and teach your child how to self-advocate. The trial can help your child learn to reflect upon his or her self-control, and become educated about the nature of ADHD.

Customize Your Communication

Communication with your child should be age-appropriate and individualized. The right approach will allow you to communicate with each other, clearly and effectively. Right from the start, your child needs language for self-understanding, self-acceptance, and self-advocacy—and what works for children often works for parents too.

- *Simple description.* For many children, straightforward description works best. For example: "You know how sometimes it's hard to stop and think?" Or, to "stay calm," "focus," or, "pay attention." Use whatever words—or describe whatever situation—that will be most meaningful to your child. "Lots of people—kids and adults—have the same problem. It's called ADHD. Doctors have medicines for all kinds of things."
- *Similes.* For some children, similes work best. Here are some examples.
  - ADHD can be described as brakes that don't always work right. "It's kind of like you've got a great bike, the brakes just need some fixing."
  - ADHD can be thought of as a sleepy orchestra conductor or airplane pilot. "Great orchestra. Great airplane. We just need a way to wake up the conductor/pilot."
  - ADHD can be thought of as an unresponsive TV set: "It's like your pause button doesn't always work."
  - ADHD can be seen as a snow globe or a fog. "It's hard to see clearly and focus on what is right in front of you. Medication can make all the snow go to the bottom, or all the fog clear."
  - ADHD can be thought of as a type of blurred vision. "Having a brain that needs medicine is a lot like having eyes that need glasses—to help you focus."
- *Use your child's own words.* Whenever possible, use terms and images suggested by your child. For example, many children say they don't have a problem with "attention" or "hyperactivity" but they do have a big problem with "concentrating,"

"getting distracted," or feeling like "I've got ants in my pants." As long as it's accurate and helpful, go with language that's most meaningful to your child.

- *Avoid negative language.* If a child uses inaccurate or self-denigrating language, substitute more appropriate and accurate alternatives. Don't allow your child to describe him or herself as "lazy," "crazy," "stupid," or "messed-up." Teach your child to move away from these pessimistic generalizations. Normalize relative strengths and weaknesses. Especially for older children and teenagers, encourage a more nuanced and positive self-understanding:
  - "Everybody's got some things that are easy and some things that are hard."
  - "There's a lot more to you than just your ADHD."
  - "ADHD is not a problem with knowing what to do. It's really a problem with doing what you know."
  - "It really shouldn't be called Attention Deficit Disorder. You can pay attention sometimes. It's just hard to pay attention all the time."
  - "ADHD doesn't have to control you. You can control it!"
- *Fictional characters and real-life role models.* Perhaps your child is familiar with a lovable cartoon character with features of ADHD. For example, Winnie the Pooh's bouncy friend Tigger. Or *Finding Nemo*'s distractible Dory. Share stories of family, friends, and famous individuals who have overcome ADHD to live full and successful lives. For example, Michael Phelps (swimmer), Will Smith (actor), or James Carville (political consultant). Find an ADHD success story in your child's area of interest, through a quick Web search.
- *Neurophysiology.* Higher-level description of neurophysiology can be surprisingly helpful and effective, especially for scientifically minded children. Your child may be reassured to hear that ADHD is very well-understood.
  - Referring to anatomical pictures, children and parents can learn about the prefrontal cortex (PFC). "The PFC is the brain's 'mission control.'"
  - Together, you and your child can learn about the difference between excitatory and inhibitory nerves in the brain. Then you can see how ADHD is a disorder of

inconsistent inhibition.

- You and your child can study a picture of a synapse—the microscopic space between nerve endings—and learn about neurochemicals—dopamine and norepinephrine— that send "stop and think" signals.

- And you can learn about the different ways that ADHD medicines improve the balance and effectiveness of these neurochemical messengers. Your doctor can draw pictures and explain reuptake inhibition, increased production at the presynaptic terminal, and enhanced binding at the post-synaptic receptor.

- *Treatment trial forms.* Children can learn about ADHD by using a treatment trial form to record their own baseline and follow-up symptom ratings. Again, see the Stimulant Trial scale in this excursion or make a customized version of your own. Your child can rate target symptoms and possible side effects, using numbers: 0 = no problem, 1 = little problem, 2 = medium problem, and 3 = big problem. As an alternative, your child can use pictures of a smiley face, neutral face, and sad face; green light, yellow light, and red light; or gestures such as thumbs up, thumbs sideways, thumbs down.

Timmy, a six-year-old, is about to start a treatment trial. His doctor explains: So, Timmy. We're going to see if this medicine helps you with your focusing. Sometimes it helps a lot. Sometimes a little. Sometimes it doesn't work at all. But it's safe to try. If the medicine works, great. If it doesn't, we might try something else. It's kind of like shopping for shoes. Before you get a new pair of shoes, you need to try them on and see if they're a good fit. So, we might try some different medicines to see what's right for you.

Exercise Judgment and Caution

Although I am a strong proponent of open communication with children, there is such a thing as too much information. After you and your doctor present the reasons for trying some medicine, follow your child's lead about how much he or she wants to talk. Some kids have lots of questions. Some just say "Okay." Some don't talk much at first but have more questions later, especially if medication helps them stay better focused for these conversations. If your child asks questions, keep your answers short and to the point. Don't elaborate beyond the question he or she is asking. If you're not sure how to answer a question, you can say, "That's a very good question. Let's write it down and ask your doctor at our next visit." If it's urgent, you can write your doctor an email or make a phone call together.

Be careful not to let your own anxiety propel you to provide too much reassurance or too much concern. Young children do not need to know about all possible side effects. During a medication trial, try not to ask your child about the medicine every day; keep life as normal as possible. Weekly check-ins should be sufficient. Keep it short and sweet: "Hey, since you've been taking the medicine, do you notice anything different? Do you think it's helping? Anything you don't like about it?"

Avoid making promises. If a medication trial fails, you don't want your child to feel like their case is especially severe or that they are beyond help. And there's no such thing as miracle medicine. Your child should know, "Your ADHD medicine should make it easier for you to stop, think, and focus. But you will still need to work hard."

How to Do a Medication Trial

Doing a medication trial is not rocket science. You just have to observe carefully, know what you're looking for, be patient, and establish a good system of communication with your doctor and your child's teachers. Here's how.

Before you read through this section, take a quick peak ahead at the Stimulant Trial scales in the section below, "Running the Stimulant Trial." It will help you visualize the trial process.

A warning: In the following pages, I provide detailed suggestions regarding medication management. Again, all decisions about medication should be made after a thorough assessment, in close consultation with your prescriber. Don't just get a prescription and do this on your own!

Choosing Observers

A medication trial should not depend upon the observations of just one person. Good scientific method means that different people get the same results doing the same experiment. In ADHD medication trials, this can be complicated. Different observers are with your child at different times, in different activities, and in different settings. Plus, across a variety of tasks, your child's attention and self-control depend upon his or her level of interest, motivation, and skill. Furthermore, ratings are colored by different observers' own subjectivity and their relationship with the child. For all these reasons, different observers usually report different ratings—and that's okay. What we're looking for is some agreement about the *degree of change from baseline*. We will trust the results of the trial if there is enough consensus about the effects of the medication.

Like a cup of coffee, the effects of these medications come and go. For many children, a single morning dose of stimulant medication will be in effect only during the school day, and will wear off in the afternoon. Some children burn through their medication faster, others slower. Either way, teachers may be in a better position than parents to observe medication effects during the school day. Also, morning teachers may be observing when the medication is at a peak, while afternoon teachers may get a different view. Parent observations may be more meaningful on weekends or vacations. It's important for each observer to indicate *when* they are observing (weekdays or weekends; mornings, afternoons, or evenings) and under what circumstances.

Given this variability, I recommend involving parents and *at least* one teacher. Parents may want to include other family members, child care providers, teachers, school staff, therapists, instructors, or coaches. The most important thing is to choose individuals who will be the most objective, reliable, and experienced; enough to capture differences across settings, but not so many that collecting data becomes an administrative quagmire. Generally, two to three observers works just fine.

Parents often consider not telling teachers or other observers about the medication trial. Teachers may be biased, either for or against ADHD medication. And it is true that good scientific method often requires "blinding" observers to key variables. Researchers sometimes use placebos to "double-blind" both the subjects and the researchers themselves.

In most stimulant treatment trials, this degree of caution is not necessary. On the contrary, there are good reasons for transparency and full disclosure. First, we are looking for obvious impact, not subtleties. Second, telling teachers and other observers about the medication trial usually results in more detailed and higher-quality data. We need teachers and other observers to report on all target symptoms and all possible side effects, noting degrees of change from baseline. Third, for safety and informed assessment, teachers and school nurses need to know if a child is taking medication and have information about possible side effects. Fourth, we want to know what observers think, so they should be able to provide context and interpretative comments. Fifth, by including teachers in the trial, parents and doctors build trust with the school team and promote a collaborative relationship. Finally, the treatment trial is an opportunity for teachers to learn more about ADHD and see their students in a new light.

To minimize observer bias, ensure good data, and promote positive teamwork, parents might want to "half-blind" the teachers or other observers: in other words, to let the teacher know about the trial but not about specific variables.

Timmy's parents wrote teacher Mrs. Jones an email and followed up with a phone call. "We are going to be doing a trial to see if medication might help Timmy with his ADHD. We really need—and appreciate—your help. Our doctor recommended telling you about the trial but 'half-blinding' you. This means, during the trial, we won't tell you what medicine we are using or when we change the dose. That way, you can just call it like you see it. And you won't be the only observer. The doctor will be pooling and reviewing all the data—yours and ours. We'll let you know the results when the trial is done. Please get in touch with any questions. Thanks so much for your help!"

Stimulants and Non-stimulants

Currently, there are two categories of well-studied, FDA-approved ADHD medications: stimulants and non-stimulants. Stimulants usually work better than nonstimulants, but are more likely to cause side effects. Because side effects are reversible, we usually start with stimulants. However, as discussed above, nonstimulants might be appropriate first-line medications for children who have a lower chance of success with stimulants; namely, preschoolers, children with predominantly inattentive-type ADHD, or those with coexisting neurodevelopmental, mood, or medical disorders. We'll take a good look at the non-stimulants further below. But first, the stimulants.

Choosing a Stimulant Medication

See the accompanying table for a list of currently available stimulants. No doubt this list will need updating after this book goes to publication; you can always get an updated list by going to **www.parentchildjourney.com/resources**. Medications are listed by their generic name (first letter lowercased) with brand names in caps (first letter capitalized). If no generic version is yet available, only the brand name is given. I also provide strength in milligrams and my own ratings of "splitability"—as further explained below, how difficult it is to split the dose.

Stimulants for Treatment of ADHD

Name of medication	how supplied; mg strengths	"Split-ability"*
Short-acting/immediate-release stimulants (3–5 hours)		
methylphenidates		
methylphenidate (Ritalin)	tabs: 5, 10, 20	2+
Methylin	chewtabs: 2.5, 5, 10 solution: 5, 10/5ml	2+ 3+
dexmethylphenidate (Focalin)	tabs: 2.5, 5, 10	1+
amphetamines		
dextroamphetamine	tabs: 5, 10	1+
dextroamphetamine (Procentra)	liquid: 5/5ml	2+
amphetamine-dextroam-phetamine (Adderall)	tabs: 5, 7.5, 10, 12.5, 15, 20, 30	2+
dextroamphetamine (Zenzedi)	tabs: 2.5, 5, 7.5, 10, 15, 20, 30	2+
Long-acting/extended-release stimulants (6–12 hours)		
methylphenidates		
methylphenidate OROS-ER (Concerta)	tabs: 18, 27, 36, 54, and (Relexxii) 72	0
methylphenidate ER	tabs: 10, 20	1+
methylphenidate CD	caps: 10, 20, 30, 40, 50, 60	1+
methylphenidate (Ritalin LA)	caps: 10, 20, 30, 40	1+
Quillivant XR	liquid: 25/5ml	3+
Quillichew ER	tabs: 20, 30, 40	2+

Aptensio XR	caps: 10, 15, 20, 30, 40, 50, 60	0
Daytrana	patch: 10, 15, 20, 30	1+
dexmethylphenidate (Focalin) XR	caps: 5, 10, 15, 20, 25, 30, 35, 40	1+
Cotempla XR	oral disintegrating tab: 8.6, 17.3, 25.9	0
Jornay PM**	caps: 20, 40, 60, 80, 100	0
Adhansia XR	caps: 25, 35, 45, 55, 70, 85	1+
amphetamines		
dextroamphetamine ER	caps: 5, 10, 15	1+
amphetamine-dextroam- phetamine (Adderall) XR	caps: 5, 10, 15, 20, 25, 30	1+
Evekeo	tabs: 5, 10	2+
lisdexamphetamine (Vyvanse)	caps/chewables: 10, 20, 30, 40, 50, 60, 70	1+
Dyanavel XR	liquid: 2.5/ml liquid	3+
Mydayis	caps: 12.5, 25, 37.5, 50	0
Adenzys XR	suspension 1.25/ml; disin- tegrating tab: 3.1, 6.3, 9.4, 12.5, 15.7, 18.8	3+/0

*"Split-ability"
  0: cannot be split (ruins the extended-release delivery system, dropping the whole load immediately)
  1+:tabs or caps not designed for splitting but okay (for caps, pinch, twist, and carefully tap out half the beads)
  2+:scored tabs designed for splitting
  3+:liquids measurable down to 0.1 mls (depending upon the dose, get a 1.0 ml or 3.0 ml syringe)
**Jornay brand extended-release methylphenidate is taken at night, delays release of medication until the following morning then lasts through the day.

Methylphenidates and Dextroamphetamines

As you can see on the list above, there are two sub-families of stimulants:

1. Methylphenidates
2. Dextroamphetamines

In general, one type of stimulant is not better than another. However, these medications differ in terms of effectiveness, side effects, duration of action, form, and cost. Choice of medication depends upon these individual differences and practical considerations.

Differences in Effectiveness and Side Effects

Within each of these stimulant sub-groups, there are many different products with similar mechanisms of action. You can use the same treatment trial scales for all, because they all have the same possible benefits and side effects. There are no studies that demonstrate superiority of one stimulant over another, but there are subtle differences in how they work. Different stimulants affect dopamine and norepinephrine systems in slightly different ways. Consequently, for your child, one stimulant may work better than another. So how to choose?

There is currently no way to predict which medicine will work best for each child. Your doctor may ask if you or other family members have taken ADHD medicine, to gauge family history of good or bad luck with specific products. Other doctors will recommend drawing your child's blood or swabbing cells from the inside of the mouth for genetic testing, since genetic differences may be relevant to medication response. Unfortunately, at the time of this writing, such "pharmacogenetic" or "personalized" medicine is not a reliable guide to selection of ADHD medication. Likewise, though brain scans (functional MRI) and brain wave tests (EEG) show intriguing differences between children with and without ADHD, such brain mapping can be very misleading regarding treatment.

Given the rapid advances in genetic technology, it's safe to assume that the reliability and cost of ADHD sub-typing will become more favorable, making it easier to choose. But no test will ever replace careful assessment of real-life impact.

If we can only choose the most effective ADHD medicine for each child *after* a trial, how do we choose which medicine to try in the first place? Let's turn to some very practical considerations: duration of action, child preference, and cost.

Differences in Duration of Action

Stimulants come in short-acting and long-acting forms. Short-acting stimulants are relatively quick to kick in (10–15 minutes) and quick to kick out (3–4 hours). A variety of clever delivery systems have been devised to turn short-acting medicines into long-acting medicines: beads, patches, prodrugs, osmotic pumps, and more. Long-acting stimulants may take longer to kick-in (30–60 minutes) but they can last longer (6–12 hours). Duration does not just depend upon differences between medicines. Two different children might metabolize the same medication at very different rates. Again, in theory, pharmacogenomic testing can tell us something about a child's metabolism of different medications (Hamilton, 2015). But nothing is more reliable or useful than real-life observation.

Some parents and prescribers opt to start a trial with short-acting medication, to see what happens for just a half-day. If short-acting medication works, you can always shift over to a comparable dose of the same medication in its long-acting form. It is also fine to start with long-acting medication. That way, you can gather observations over the course of a fuller day. After finding a long-acting medication that works, short-acting medication could be added on to extend coverage if necessary. (See below for a complete discussion of uneven coverage or "trough-filling.") Whatever you start with, you and your prescriber will be able to get a feel for your child's unique metabolism. This experience will guide tune-ups going forward.

Differences in Child Preference and Ease of Administration

Another important consideration in choosing a medication is your child's preference. Sometimes what makes or breaks a trial is a child's willingness and ability to take a medication. Fortunately, most of these medicines come in many different forms:

- Tablets to swallow, crush, dissolve, or chew.
- Capsules with beads to swallow whole or open and sprinkle into any soft food.
- Capsules with powder to swallow whole or dissolve in a drink.
- Liquids to drink.
- Patches to place on the skin. Patches are placed on the upper buttock or lower back each morning, removed and discarded each late afternoon or early evening. Though handy for children who can't take any kind of medicine by mouth, patches sometimes cause an itchy rash (contact dermatitis). Some children might pick at or remove their patch. Although patches usually stay on in the swimming pool, tub, or shower, sometimes they fall off. At the time of this writing, methylphenidate is the only stimulant that comes as a patch.

(Clonidine is a non-stimulant that comes as a patch but I do not recommend it because its absorption through the skin is unreliable.)

Whenever possible, present a menu of medication forms and simply ask your child to choose (Adesman, 2015). It's important to give children a degree of control over the process; we can respect a child's wishes without compromising care. It is worth emphasizing that ease of administration is tightly tied to a child's willingness, comfort, and ability.

There are pros and cons to each form of medication.

- *Route of administration.* If a child can swallow a tablet or capsule, that simplifies administration—just pop it in and swallow it whole. Other forms avoid problems with swallowing but require a bit more preparation, such as dissolving, sprinkling, and measuring. Patches, despite the drawbacks described above, are handy for children who won't take anything by mouth.

- *"Split-ability."* The physical design of some medicines facilitates micro-tuning of the dose. Other medicines can only be given according to set doses. High "split-ability" is especially important for children who are very sensitive to differences in dose. If one dose is too little (no benefits) but another dose is too big (side effects), then something in between might be just right. Many children who seem to fail a trial are on the right medication but the dose is not fine-tuned enough. You can rank ADHD medications from most split-able (3+) to least split-able (0). Generally speaking, what you gain in split-ability, you lose in ease of preparation and administration.

  - *3+ split-ability. Liquids.* If very low dosing or super-fine-tuning is required, you can't beat liquids. With a 1.0- or 3.0-ml syringe, you can adjust the dose down to tenths of a milliliter. Such flexible, precise, and incremental dosing may be especially important in younger or more "side-effect-sensitive" children.

  - *2+ split-ability. Scored tablets.* Cross-hatched tablets are designed for splitting in half or even quarters. Although not quite as split-able as liquids, this degree of split-ability is usually good enough. With the exception of Quillichew extended-release tabs, most 2+ split-able tabs are only available as short-acting stimulants.

- *1+ split-ability. Capsules (containing either beads or powder) and patches.* Some long-acting medications were not designed to be split. However, with some simple math, a steady hand, and a careful eye, in-between doses can be estimated with sufficient precision.
  - Most extended-release capsules contain two distinct populations of beads. Half the beads are designed for immediate release; the other half, for delayed release, many hours later. Randomly dividing the contents of the capsule will result in good-enough distribution of immediate and delayed-release beads. You just don't want your child to chew the beads. That would deliver the "whole mother lode"—both immediate and delayed-release doses—all at once. To "split" the contents of a beaded capsule:
    - At eye level, hold the bottom half of the capsule upright, between the thumb and index finger of your non-dominant hand.
    - Using the thumb and index finger of your dominant hand, gently pinch and twist off the top half off the cap.
    - Then tap, tap, tap out your best estimate of half the contents into a spoon of soft food. You can use yogurt, applesauce, chocolate syrup, honey, pudding—whatever your child likes. Or you can just dump the whole capsule onto a sheet of paper and divide the contents in half that way. Or, if your child can swallow a cap, recap what's left in the bottom half and have your child take that.
  - Vyvanse is an extended-release capsule with powder instead of beads. You can tap out half of the powder, just like the beads, or dissolve it in a few ounces of a beverage. Immediately after some very rigorous stirring, pour out a specific fraction of the total amount for your child to drink. Have your child wash it down with a larger amount of plain liquid. Or, better if possible, recap the remainder and have your child swallow that. (Vyvanse also comes in a chewable tab but it is not very split-able.)
  - For an additional fee, a compounding pharmacist can custom-make caps containing off-size doses. For example, if a medication comes in 5 mg and 10 mg caps but

your child's best dose is 7.5 mg, then a compounding pharmacist could carefully measure out half of a 15 mg cap and make two specially labeled 7.5 mg caps.

- Patches deliver a dose of medicine that is in direct proportion to the skin surface area it covers. In other words, 20 mg patches are simply twice as big as 10 mg patches. So, if you want to deliver ¾ of the patch dose, just measure carefully and cut off ¼ of the patch. As of this writing, methylphenidate (Daytrana) is the only stimulant that comes in a patch.

- *0 split-ability. Long-acting tablets.* Methylphenidate-er (Concerta) should not be split. This would release a whole day's worth of medication all at once. For the same reason and as discussed further below, do not split the non-stimulants guanfacine-er (Intuniv) or clonidine-er (Kapvay). Oral disintegrating tablets like Adenzys and Cotempla are not designed for splitting either.

Differences in Cost

Your choice of medication will also be influenced by cost. Some medications are quite cheap, while others are incredibly expensive. With just a few exceptions, it's okay to use generic medication, which usually costs much less. Insurance companies cover some medicines more than others, and coverage varies from one insurance company to another.

When just starting out, go online and get the list of medications that are "in formulary" for your insurance company. If you try those and they don't work, you and your doctor can claim a special medical exception. With proper documentation and/or a phone call from your doctor, the insurance companies should approve coverage of medically necessary products—even if they are out of formulary.

Websites for newer products often advertise cost-saving coupons, and some drug companies will provide medication for free or at reduced cost if there is financial necessity.

Running the Stimulant Trial

Choosing a Starting Dose

Until your doctor knows your child's general dosing range, it's always best to start with a very low dose and work up gradually.

For younger children, your doctor might recommend liquid medication starting with just 0.2 milliliters. Split-able capsules or tabs can be halved or even quartered. Ignore standard recommendations based on weight—the right dose for your child depends more on liver enzyme systems, not whole-body weight. Some people just have a high internal metabolism and burn through these medications more quickly. Others are slow metabolizers. Some very little kids need very big doses. Some very big kids and adults need very little doses. The medication trial determines the right dose for each person. We just start low and go up until we find the best dose for each medication tried.

Is there a test that can help find the right medicine and the right dose for individual children? The short answer: not yet. As discussed above, the new science of pharmacogenomics is exciting but not yet ready for routine clinical practice. Using blood samples or mouth swabs, special genetic tests can be done to determine if an individual is more likely to be a slow or rapid metabolizer. Your doctor could get lab reports that list medications in bold, authoritative-looking, color-coded columns: red (don't use), yellow (proceed with caution), and green (go for it). But just because we can do a test does not mean that we should. In current practice, such "personalized prescribing" rarely affects outcome. Such testing might be helpful in special situations, when drug trials do not go well. However, experienced clinicians start with very low doses and go up by very small increments anyway. At least for now, such genetic testing is not a reliable guide to medication dosing or selection—and it is very expensive. Prescribers should continue to rely on their knowledge of different medication effects and carefully controlled trials.

Stimulant Treatment Trial Scales

On the next pages, check out the ADHD treatment trial form for stimulant medication. On the top half of the page, there is a list of typical target symptoms that we hope will get better with medication. On the bottom half of the page, there is a list of common side effects that could get worse with medication.

This sample treatment trial form contains the most common target symptoms and possible side effects for young children. It can be modified. With your doctor's help, you can add or subtract from the list of target symptoms. Different children at different ages will have different outcome measures. Generally speaking, younger children may have more outward and obvious displays of hyperactivity and impulsivity. Adolescents and adults may have more inward and subtle symptoms of distractibility, executive dysfunction, and performance inconsistency. Also, it may be appropriate to customize the list of possible side effects. Some children may be prone to less common side effects not listed here. If you want to monitor anything that's not on the list, just add it on.

Copies are available for free at ParentChildJourney.com, on the "Resources" page.

Daniel G. Shapiro, M.D.
Developmental and Behavioral Pediatrics

Stimulant Medication Trial

Child's name: _____ Grade: _____ Year: _____

Person completing this form: _____

Relation to child: _____

When were your observations usually made? (circle): mornings / afternoons / evenings / weekdays / weekends

Dear Parents, Teachers, and Student.

Thank you very much for your help. It is so important to conduct this medication trial in a careful and controlled fashion. Please complete the table below. Record observations for the days indicated. If you were not with the child, leave that day's column blank. Your comments in narrative form are also very helpful. If there were side effects, at what time did you usually notice this? Do medicine benefits seem to kick in too late or wear off too early?

Please contact me if you have any questions or concerns. Thank you.

How often did you notice the following? 0 = not at all, 1 = just a little, 2 = often, 3 = very often

	Dose									
Target Symptoms	Date									
Restless, squirmy, fidgety, "on-the-go"										
Demands must be met immediately										
Distractibility/attention problem										
Problems with peer relations										
Misses important details										
Excitable, impulsive										
Fails to finish things										
Problems controlling behavior										
Easily frustrated										
Difficulty learning										
Disorganization/time mismanagement										
Forgetful, loses things										
Possible Side Effects										
Poor appetite										
Sleep problems										
Irritability, sadness										
Anxiety, OCD										
Social withdrawal, flattened affect										
Hyperfocus, stuck, daydreams										
Tics/nervous habits										
Headaches, stomachaches, nausea										
Dizziness, drowsiness										

Baseline Ratings

Before beginning the medication trial, observers should go to the top of the first column, put a zero in the dose box (for "no medicine"), and fill in the date box. Ratings should reflect the child's baseline symptoms, off medication. Then, working all the way down the first column, observers should rate each of the target symptoms *and* each of the possible side effects as follows: 0 = no problem, 1 = little problem, 2 = medium problem, and 3 = big problem.

- *Target symptoms (baseline).* From the start, it's crucial that we know where we are and what we're targeting. Just because your child has some difficulty with self-control does not necessarily mean it's a problem in terms of day-to-day functioning. These numbers should reflect the child's real-life impairment, *before* medication. The baseline ratings should indicate how big a deal this is. To justify a medication trial, baseline ratings usually include some 2s and 3s.
- *Possible side effects (baseline).* A successful trial also depends upon avoiding significant side effects. Before beginning the trial, make sure that all observers document baseline ratings for possible side effects. This important step is often neglected. Understandably, observers might assume that they don't need to rate possible side effects *before* the medication trial begins. But just because these symptoms are possible side effects does not mean that they are all zeroes before medication, nor does it not mean that they will only get worse. Medication does not always cause side effects. In fact, any of these possible side effect symptoms can get better with medication. We monitor carefully just to be sure nothing gets worse.

Data Collection and Communication

Throughout the trial, each observer should use their own sheet to record baseline and follow-up ratings. That way, the prescriber can make direct comparisons: day-by-day, dose-by-dose, column-by-column. Parents and the prescriber should see the pooled data. However, to avoid bias, other observers should not be able to see each other's ratings. Once again, it is *not* important for different observers to agree on baseline ratings. In fact, that's rare. We just want some consensus between raters about changes from baseline. Are symptoms getting better, worse, or staying the same?

It's crucial to set up an easy and efficient system to share and pool these ratings. There are many options. Observers can scan or digitally photograph their trial forms, then attach and send by secure email. Observers can enter their ratings directly onto a shared online document, such as (password-protected) Google docs or Excel spreadsheets. In addition to the numerical ratings on the trial form, observers should add comments and thoughts about how the trial seems to be going. With each report to the prescriber, parents should be sure to offer their own ideas, feelings, and suggestions about what to do next.

Choosing an Observation Interval

How long should you observe your child at one dose before drawing conclusions and considering adjustments? Different phases of stimulant trials have different goals and different observation intervals.

Phase One of a stimulant medication trial should tell you whether the chosen medication works, and roughly what dose seems best. Usually, we only need a few days of observation to determine the effects of a medicine at each dose. With all stimulants, there is no need to wait for weeks or even days for a cumulative effect. When observing for possible benefits and side effects at a given dose, what you see that day is probably what you're going to get the next. For Phase One of stimulant trials, I recommend having all observers complete the medication trial form every day, and pool their ratings for review twice a week.

Phase Two of a stimulant trial begins when you have arrived at a pretty good medicine but want to see if you can make it even better. This means fine-tuning the size of the dose and the timing of administration. Once you know what works, it's important to experiment with additional minor adjustments to maximize benefits, minimize side effects, and optimize coverage. For this kind of fine-tuning, I recommend longer observation intervals; anywhere from weekly to monthly. It takes more time to pick up on subtleties and not overreact to normal day-to-day variations. Remember, life happens. Not every shift in your child's behavior is about the medication. The passage of time allows you to reliably distinguish coincidental blips from persistent patterns.

How to Proceed

After obtaining baseline ratings from all observers, start Phase One of the trial with a very low dose of medication, as specified by your prescriber: the "starting dose." At each observation interval, parents should collect follow-up ratings from all observers. Parents and the prescriber can touch base by email or a quick phone conversation. Together, analyze ratings for target symptoms and possible side effects, paying careful attention to changes from baseline for both benefits and risks.

Conducting a Stimulant Trial

Complete baseline ratings off medication for both target symptoms and possible side effects.

Start with: _____. (name and strength of medication)

1. Looking good. If ...
   a. benefits are *optimal* (2s and 3s for target symptoms all come down to 0s and 1s) and
   b. side effects are *in*significant (numbers for possible side effects do not go up),

   then stay with that dose and observe longer.

2. Too low. If ...
   a. benefits are *less than optimal* (2s and 3s for target symptoms do not come down all the way to 0s and 1s) and
   b. side effects are *in*significant (numbers for possible side effects do not go up), *then* you can increase by an amount equal to the starting dose.

3. No good. If ...
   a. benefits are *less than optimal* (2s and 3s for target symptoms do not come down to 0s and 1s) and
   b. side effects are *significant* (numbers for possible side effects go up), *then* stop. Or at least talk with your prescriber. Going up more would only make side effects worse. Going down would not result in any benefits.

4. Mixed results. If ...
   a. benefits are *optimal* (2s and 3s for target symptoms come down to 0s and 1s) but
   b. side effects are *significant* (numbers for possible side effects go up), *then* decrease by an amount equal to half the starting dose. See if this allows you to lose the side effects but still keep benefits. Some medicines allow for this degree of micro-turning; others may not. Again, talk with your doctor.

Interpreting Results

Just like letter grades, or results of each at-bat in a baseball game (home run, triple, double, base hit, or strike)—bear with me if you're not a baseball fan—there are several possible outcomes for each medication trial:

A. *Optimal response (home run).* The trial would be considered a *complete success* if target symptoms all come down to 0s and 1s and side effect ratings stay down at baseline. Phase

One of the trial ends successfully. You're ready to move on to Phase Two: further fine-tuning, to maximize benefits across the entire day, while still keeping side effects at bay.

- A-plus. *Optimal response plus bonus reduction in other symptoms (home run with a runner—or runners—on base).* Remember, just because a symptom is a possible side effect does not mean that it has to get worse with medication. If you're lucky, target symptoms might get better *and* some possible side effect ratings might get better too! For example, in some children you might see improvements in sleep, eating, anxiety, and emotional impulsivity. So, in addition to the run scored for effectively treating ADHD symptoms, call it a two-run homer if, in addition, a possible side effect rating goes down, a three-run homer if two side effects improve, and a grand-slam if three (or more) side effects get better. Sometimes you get that lucky.

- A-minus. *Optimal response except for manageable side effects.* We should not settle for a medicine that provides optimal benefits but still causes side effects. But sometimes, even after you've tried a reasonable number of alternatives, that's the best you can do. On balance, if side effects are mild and manageable, you might conclude that the medicine is still much better than nothing. We have some pretty good strategies for minimizing some common side effects. See below for a complete discussion of managing insomnia, appetite suppression, tics, undesirable changes in mood, and other possible side effects.

B. *Partial response (single, double, or even triple).* During the trial, you might get up to a dose that results in a substantial reduction of ADHD target symptoms and no side effects, but still be short of an optimal response: not all 0s and 1s. There's clearly room for improvement. So, you try tuning the dose a bit more, to see if you can get a more optimal response. Sometimes, this extra tweak works well. Other times, the slightly higher dose causes side effects. In that case, you should retreat to the previous (suboptimal but maximum tolerated) dose. The trial could still be considered a modest success if the maximum tolerated dose moves baseline 2s and 3s down to 1s and 2s. Sometimes, 25–50 percent improvement is worth holding on to. Or at least, you might compare the results of this medication trial against what other medications can do. Not a home run, but still safe on base.

- B-minus. *Partial response except for manageable side effects.* Sometimes the best you can do is less than optimal, both in terms of benefits and side effects. But the improvement in target symptoms is still better than baseline, and side effects are manageable. Again, don't settle for this if you have not tried other medications. But don't let the perfect be the enemy of the good. On balance, your child might still be substantially better off.

F. *Failed trial (strike one).* If side effect numbers go up before target symptom numbers come down, then the trial is a failure. We stop and consider trying something else. Notice, when it comes to grading medication trials there are no Cs and Ds; just As, Bs, and Fs. In my opinion, when deciding about using psychotropic medications in children, we should not settle for mediocre results. The standard for continuing long-term treatment should be very high. So, strike one—you're not out. There are other options to try. But you should not continue a medication that's insufficiently safe or effective.

Not all primary care pediatricians have the time, inclination, or expertise to perform adequate medication trials. A busy primary care provider may refer families to a child psychiatrist or developmental-behavioral pediatrician.

Choosing a Non-Stimulant Medication

Before discussing overall strategy and side effect management, let's turn our attention to non-stimulants, the second class of FDA-approved medications for treatment of ADHD. There are some important differences between non-stimulants and stimulants. But when it comes to running a trial, the general principles are the same.

Alpha-agonists and Noradrenergics

Currently, there are two types of non-stimulants for treating ADHD:

1. Alpha-agonists (such as guanfacine and clonidine)
2. Noradrenergics (such as atomoxetine and bupropion)

Non-Stimulants for ADHD

Name of medication	how supplied; mg strengths	"Split-ability"*
atomoxetine (Strattera)	caps: 10, 18, 25, 40, 60, 80, 100	0
bupropion (Wellbutrin)	reg tabs: 75, 100; SR tabs: 100, 150, 200; XL tabs 150, 300	0
clonidine		
short-acting (Catapres)	tabs: 0.1, 0.2, 0.3	2+
extended release (Kapvay)	tabs: 0.1	0
guanfacine		
short-acting (Tenex)	tabs: 1, 2 or liquid 1/ml**	2+/3+
extended-release (Intuniv)	tabs: 1, 2, 3, 4	0

*See the note on *"Split-ability" on page 31.
**Tenex (short-acting guanfacine) can be made into a liquid by a compounding pharmacist.

Alpha-agonists. The alpha-agonists, guanfacine and clonidine, were originally used in the treatment of high blood pressure. Subsequently, they were also found to work for ADHD and tic disorders. Overall, alpha-agonists don't work as well as stimulants; they tend to work better for hyperactivity and impulsivity than they do for distractibility. Sometimes, alpha-agonists are used alone when stimulants cause unavoidable side effects. More often, alpha-agonists are used as an add-on medication when stimulants alone yield just a partial response. Alpha-agonists are especially useful when ADHD and tics coexist. Alpha-agonists are also handy at the end of the day, when ADHD still needs to be treated but late doses of stimulant medication cause too much appetite suppression at dinner or insomnia at bedtime. More on this below.

Although less effective as stand-alone medication, alpha-agonists are less likely than stimulants to cause significant side effects. When side effects do occur, they tend to be milder. Unlike stimulants, these medications do not cause appetite suppression, tics, or anxiety. Nor do alpha-agonists create trouble falling asleep at the beginning of the night—in fact, they can help with sleep initiation. However, in a minority of children, alpha-agonists can cause rebound night-waking. This night-waking can happen in the middle of the night or very early morning, when the medication wears off.

More common side effects include daytime sleepiness, dizziness, irritability, and low blood pressure. Your prescriber should check your child's blood pressure at baseline and at routine follow-up visits. In general, blood pressure reductions are not serious. We just don't want to continue or increase the dose if your child is feeling persistently draggy.

Alpha-agonists are different than stimulants in several important ways:

1. Alpha-agonists take time to gradually start working. Usually, you begin to see what a dose is going to do after about three to five days, but you might not see the peak cumulative effect for weeks.

2. Just like alpha-agonists usually take longer than stimulants to start working, they might also take longer to clear your child's body if stopped. Although side effects go away, it may take a few days. To minimize any rebound, your doctor might advise tapering the dose instead of stopping suddenly, especially if the dose was high or the duration of treatment was long.

3. Although we usually recommend regular use, stimulants work just the same if you take them some days but not others. But alpha-agonists don't work well if they aren't given on a regular basis. They need to build up and stay in your child's system.

Guanfacine and clonidine both come in short-acting and long-acting forms:

- guanfacine as short-acting Tenex and long-acting Intuniv
- clonidine as short-acting Catapres and long-acting Kapvay

With the help of a compounding pharmacist, as mentioned, short-acting guanfacine is the only alpha-agonist that can be formulated as a liquid. You might be able to give short-acting alpha-agonists just twice per day and long-acting forms once per day. But even moderately rapid metabolizers might need to take short-acting alpha-agonists three to four times per day or long-acting forms twice daily.

Noradrenergics. The noradrenergic non-stimulants, atomoxetine (Strattera) and bupropion (Wellbutrin), were originally designed as antidepressants. Atomoxetine was not effective for depression or anxiety but it worked better for ADHD and got FDA approval. On the other hand, bupropion was FDA-approved for treatment of depression and anxiety but not for ADHD. Atomoxetine is often selected as a second-line treatment for ADHD, especially when there is coexisting mild anxiety. Similarly, bupropion is a reasonable choice in the treatment of anxiety or depression, especially if there is mild coexisting ADHD.

Noradrenergics require more patience. Like other anti-depressants and unlike stimulants, they work only if taken on a regular basis. It takes longer for them to start working. You start by gradually increasing the dose. This means longer observation intervals.

But if these medications work, there are some real advantages. The long duration of action can mean just once-daily dosing to sustain an even 24-hour blood level—avoiding the peaks and valleys of coverage caused by many other ADHD medications. At worst, some rapid metabolizers might require twice-daily administration.

Running the Non-Stimulant Trial

On the non-stimulant medication trial form, some of the target symptoms and possible side effects are different than for stimulants. For practical purposes, I've lumped alpha-agonists and noradrenergics together. But the most common side effects of atomoxetine are irritability, nausea, headaches, and drowsiness. The most common side effects of bupropion are irritability, dry mouth, nausea, headache, and dizziness.

Non-Stimulant Medication Trial

Child's name: _____ Grade: _____ Year: _____
Person completing this form: _____
Relation to child: _____
When were your observations usually made? (circle): mornings / afternoons / evenings / weekdays / weekends

---

Dear Parents, Teachers, and Student.

Thank you very much for your help. It is so important to conduct this medication trial in a careful and controlled fashion. Please complete the table below. Record observations once each week. Your comments in narrative form are also very helpful. Please contact me if you have any questions or concerns. Thank you.

Non-Stimulant Trial Scales

How often did you notice the following? 0 = not at all, 1 = just a little, 2 = often, 3 = very often

	Dose									
Target Symptoms	Date									
Restless, squirmy, fidgety, "on-the-go"										
Demands must be met immediately										
Distractibility/attention problem										
Problems with peer relations										
Misses important details										
Impulsive, blurts out										
Fails to initiate, sustain, finish tasks										
Problems controlling behavior										
Easily frustrated										
Difficulty learning										
Disorganization/time mismanagement										
Tics										
Possible Side Effects										
Poor appetite										
Nausea/stomachaches										
Irritability/sadness										
Social withdrawal										
Headaches										
Dizziness										
Drowsiness										
Anxiety/nightmares										
Stares off/daydreams										

How to Proceed

Non-stimulant trials are run much the same as stimulant trials. As always, consult your prescriber each step of the way.

Conducting a Non-Stimulant Trial with Guanfacine or Clonidine

1. Complete baseline ratings off medication for both target symptoms and possible side effects.
2. Start with: _____. (name and strength of medication)
3. Observe for seven days or until you are sure of the medication effects at each dose.
   a. If benefits are *optimal* and side effects are *in*significant, then stay with that dose.
   b. If benefits are *less than optimal* and side effects are *in*significant, then increase by one tab.
   c. If benefits are *less than optimal* and side effects are *significant,* then stop.

Conducting a Non-Stimulant Trial with Atomoxetine or Bupropion

1. Complete baseline ratings off medication for both target symptoms and possible side effects.
2. Start with: _____. (name and strength of medication)
3. If there are no side effects, increase as directed to the initial target dose: _____.
4. If there are side effects, do not increase. Contact your prescriber.
5. After two weeks on the initial target dose:
   a. If benefits are *optimal* and side effects are *in*significant, then stay with that dose.
   b. If benefits are *less than optimal* and side effects are *in*significant, then increase as directed to a maximum dose of: _____.
   c. If benefits are *less than optimal* and side effects are *significant,* then stop.

Overall Strategy: The Whole Ball Game

Some children respond beautifully to the first medication tried. It's great when that happens—everyone feels good about the decision to treat. But very often, the first medication tried is not a home run. It's important to remember: This is just the beginning of an important and necessary process of trial and error. Finding the best medicine usually requires persistence, patience, and meticulous attention.

A failed treatment trial might test everyone's belief in the project. You might have second thoughts about your decision to try medication in the first place, or even doubt the diagnosis or the prescriber's competence. But one failed trial does not mean you're on the wrong path or that you won't be able to find something that helps. You don't want to deny your child a treatment that might truly change his or her life.

Try to go into this process determined to let it play out. Patience usually pays off. If you don't hit a home run on the first swing—even if you swing and miss—don't give up. You can always take a break if you want to. But one swing, one batter, even one inning is not the whole ball game.

Before you enter this process, it's good to know about possible outcomes and alternatives. Here's a way to think about an overall approach to medication trials.

Stimulants: "First Batter"

If the first stimulant trial fails, consider trying a second or a third. Remember, there are two stimulant subgroups: dextroamphetamines and methylphenidates. Plus, *dex*methylphenidate (Focalin) is different enough from other methylphenidates that it's also worth a try.

Sometimes, it's reasonable to try more than three stimulants. For example, you might think that one of them worked pretty well but a different form could deliver the medication more gradually. Other times, it's reasonable to stop trying stimulants after just two or even one failed trial(s). Maybe your child has a very high sensitivity to side effects, especially if there is a coexisting mood disorder, autism, tics, or another neurodevelopmental disorder. In retrospect, you and your prescriber might wish that you had started with a *non*-stimulant first. But for many children with ADHD, before concluding that stimulants don't work, it may be worth trying three: a dextroamphetamine, a methylphenidate, and dexmethylphenidate. Not necessarily in that order. If none provides a complete or even partial response, then three strikes, you're out. Next batter.

Non-Stimulants, Alone or in Combination with Stimulants: "Second and Third Batters"

If stimulant trials fail, then you should try a non-stimulant. Although non-stimulants do not usually take the place of stimulants, they often serve as a useful back-up or supplement. Non-stimulants should be considered when stimulant side effects cannot be avoided. Combining stimulants with non-stimulants may work better and more safely than using a stimulant or non-stimulant medication alone (McCracken et al., 2015). As discussed further below, non-stimulants may prove very useful in extending medication coverage or in treating coexisting conditions. A few reminders:

- Non-stimulant trials require even more time and patience than stimulants.
- Remember, there are four different non-stimulants: two alpha-agonists (guanfacine and clonidine) and two noradrenergics (atomoxetine and bupropion).
  - Consider using alpha-agonists as a second-line ADHD medication for children who are younger, have predominantly hyperactive-impulsive-type ADHD, and/or have seizures, autism, genetic syndromes, or tic disorders.
  - You might opt for noradrenergics for older children and adolescents who have coexisting depression or anxiety.

How to Tell if You Need One Medication or Two

If stimulant trials result in a partial response, then consider layering on a non-stimulant. If the addition of a non-stimulant improves control, then you might want to see if the non-stimulant works well enough on its own. Record new baseline ratings on the treatment trial form for combined stimulant and non-stimulant. Then stop the stimulant and get follow-up ratings on the non-stimulant alone. There are a few possible outcomes:

- If the combination of stimulant and non-stimulant worked better than either one alone, then restart the stimulant and continue giving them together.
- If the non-stimulant alone worked nearly as well as the combination, then stay off the stimulant and continue with just the non-stimulant.

When Medication Fails

Sometimes, a medication trial is an immediate and total success. Other times, it takes a few trials and considerable fine-tuning to get things right. Hopefully, with some good luck and careful management, you'll be able to shift out of "treatment initiation mode" and coast along in "long-term maintenance mode." At the end of this chapter, we discuss long-term management.

But what if you're still having trouble getting the ADHD symptoms under control? What if you and your doctor have done the best you can with stimulants and non-stimulants and you can't find a medication (or combination of medications) that works well enough? Unfortunately, some children are harder to help than others. In the sections that follow, we will take a deep look at the most common causes of treatment failure.

1. *Medication side effects.* The most common cause of treatment failure is when medication side effects kick in before benefits. For example, a child might become irritable at low doses of medication, making it impossible to give a therapeutic dose.

2. *Uneven medication coverage.* Another common cause of apparent treatment failure is when medication works but there are gaps in coverage. This is not really treatment failure; we just need to fill those gaps. See below for a full discussion about "trough-filling."

3. *Coexisting conditions.* Another cause of treatment failure is coexisting conditions. Symptoms of ADHD may persist despite medication because there are other important contributing factors—coexisting mood disorders, learning disabilities, family stresses, and more—that ADHD medication does not address. Beyond ADHD medication, many children need a comprehensive management plan.

Dealing with Frustration

Entering a medication trial, it's understandable for parents, doctors, and children to hope for a miracle. And sometimes, you get lucky. But more realistically, the initial treatment trials might prove complicated. You might have to try several medications. There might be side effects to manage, treatment gaps to fill, and coexisting conditions to address. Ironically, successful treatment of ADHD often depends upon well-sustained focus and meticulous attention to detail.

This trial and error process can prove especially difficult if doctors do a poor a job of anticipating possible outcomes, making themselves available, and communicating clearly. Complicated medication trials can also be more difficult if parents are struggling with their own anxiety, depression, ADHD, or executive dysfunction issues. From the very beginning, it helps to put all of these issues on the table, so that prescribers, parents, and children can work together in an open, honest, and mutually supportive fashion.

You should not continue medications that are not working. But you do not want to give up too easily either. Usually, persistence pays off.

Managing Side Effects

The most common cause of medication treatment failure is the appearance of serious side effects. For some children, side effects can kick in at doses below the therapeutic range. This can make it hard to reach an optimal response.

Realistic Expectations and Trade-Offs

As discussed previously, some children are more prone to side effects than others. At baseline, before any medication is given, most children with ADHD do *not* have all 0s on the list of possible side effects. Pretrial 1s, 2s, and 3s may be the possible side effects to which your child is most prone. Although these symptoms do not always get worse with medication—sometimes they actually get better—ADHD medication can certainly amplify pre-existing tendencies. Some side effects may emerge without any previous history at all.

Whether side effects represent amplification of a known predisposition or emergence of a new problem, prompt discontinuation of medication will always get your child back to baseline. Even so, you have a dilemma: Do you have your child live with side effects to reach optimal ADHD treatment? Or live with undertreated ADHD to avoid side effects? Usually, the answer is some kind of compromise.

Sometimes, we have to settle for just partial treatment of ADHD and minimization of side effects. Did any medication (or combination of medications) look promising? Which of your trials produced the best result? Maybe there was a trial that resulted in "A-" or even "B-" results. Review your data. Pick the best medication you've tried. If the side effects can be managed, maybe you can salvage the project and help your child achieve a meaningful degree of symptom control.

Common Patterns

Side effects present in different ways. Most are relatively obvious and immediate; they appear early in the treatment trial, as blood levels of medication rise and fall. Other side effects may be more subtle, gradual, and ddelayed; they might be ignored, dismissed, or misattributed. But these stealth side effects are never invisible. You just need to keep your antennae up. Some side effects are noticed by parents, teachers, or doctors. Others are only reported by the child. Therefore, as discussed in more detail below, active surveillance by multiple observers is necessary—and we continue to monitor on a regular basis, for as long as your child is taking medication.

The natural course of side effects varies from child to child. Over time, some side effects lessen or even disappear. Others stay the same or get worse. Some side effects do not require a change in treatment. They can be ignored, monitored, or accommodated. Other side effects require active treatment. Let your prescriber know if you have any concerns. In many cases, failure to identify, report, and manage side effects might result in the unnecessary discontinuation of ADHD treatment. An individualized approach to side effect management is crucial in the successful treatment of ADHD.

Again, you might be worrying: "What if I put my child—and myself—through all of this and still can't find good enough medication? What if side effects can't be avoided?" I will address this possibility head-on, below.

Observer Bias

Not all side effects are created equal. To objectively assess the severity and significance of different side effects, you will need help from your prescriber. It's important to be objective. Beware two potential types of observer bias: overly hopeful and fearful.

- *Overly hopeful observer bias.* Parents and other members of your team might approach the trial with a sense of urgency. They are very eager to find effective ADHD treatment. The threat of treatment failure looms large. They desperately want the medication to work. Subconsciously, they might minimize or even deny the true impact of a side effect.
- *Overly fearful observer bias.* On the other hand, some parents and other observers might be especially worried about

medication causing harm. They might have felt reluctant about trying medication at all. Some people even feel coerced. Naturally, for these folks, the severity of side effects might be exaggerated.

These biases can be found in parents, children, teachers, therapists, and even the prescribing doctor! To avoid minimizing or catastrophizing, all trial participants should try to be as objective as possible. We don't want to make mountains out of molehills or molehills out of mountains. Such over- or under-estimations can sabotage successful management.

Monitor, Accommodate, or Treat

Any significant side effects are unacceptable, but not all side effects require discontinuation of medication. Depending upon the severity of the side effect, there are three possible levels of response:

1. *Monitor.* As described above, with very careful trials, most side effects can be avoided or at least rendered insignificant. They don't really bother the child and don't interfere with daily activities. For example, if there is slight appetite suppression at lunchtime but daily calorie intake is adequate and growth rate remains normal, then it's probably okay to ignore and monitor. Talking too much about such a minor symptom might make some children unnecessarily anxious about eating or resistant to taking their ADHD medication. Mishandling of minor side effects can lead to tension or even power struggles between parents, children, and others.

2. *Accommodate.* Some side effects cannot be ignored but don't require direct treatment. Relatively simple adjustments can be made to bypass these side effects, render them harmless, and avoid any significant problems. For example, a moderate degree of appetite suppression may be okay if there is only a minor deceleration in rate of weight gain. Accommodations might include the addition of carefully timed meals during medication troughs plus one high-calorie "power shake" per day. See more about managing appetite suppression below.

3. *Treat.* Some side effects cannot be ignored or accommodated. Active treatment is necessary. With treatment, many side effects can be eliminated or at least minimized. Of course, before treating side effects, make sure that you have

done everything you can to find the best medication and the best dose. If you have found a medication that works well but side effects cannot be ignored or accommodated, you may not need to give up on treatment altogether. For example, if there is appetite suppression and weight loss despite attempts to supplement calories, then prescription of a safe appetite-boosting medicine might salvage the project. Treating the side effects of one medication with yet another medication is not ideal, but may be preferable to total abandonment of ADHD treatment.

Keeping these generalizations in mind, let's get down to the details.

Specific Management Strategies for the Most Common Side Effects

There are many ways to minimize the impact of side effects. Let's review management of some common problems.

1. *Nutrition and growth:* appetite suppression, poor weight gain
2. *Sleep:* insomnia, trouble falling asleep or staying asleep, nightmares
3. *Attention:* stares off, daydreams, hyperfocusing, perseveration
4. *Mood:* irritability, sadness, anxiety, OCD
5. *Personal-social:* flattened affect, loss of creativity or sparkle, social withdrawal
6. *Involuntary motor behaviors:* tics (motor or vocal), picking, pulling, twirling, chewing, nervous habits
7. *Physical symptoms:* headaches, stomachaches, nausea, dizziness, drowsiness

Nutrition and Growth Side Effects

Effective doses of stimulant medication commonly cause appetite suppression—sometimes just a little, other times a lot. Atomoxetine, a non-stimulant, can also cause some appetite suppression. Alpha-agonists, guanfacine and clonidine, do not usually have any impact on eating or growth.

But just because appetite suppression is a common side effect of ADHD treatment, this does not mean that poor nutrition and growth are inevitable. If it is a problem, there are usually effective ways to prevent any serious long-term effects.

For some children with poor self-control, less impulsive eating may be a welcome fringe benefit of ADHD treatment. On the other hand, some older children and adolescents concerned about their body image might deliberately seek stimulant medication or request higher than necessary doses in pursuit of unhealthy weight loss. Also, some parents like the idea of a thinner child a bit too much.

On an hour-by-hour basis, appetite suppression from ADHD medication can cause inconsistent blood sugar. Periods of hypoglycemia can cause irritability, low energy and—ironically—impaired attention.

Long-term inadequate calorie consumption can have a small but measurable impact on final adult height (Swanson et al., 2015). To the best of our knowledge, ADHD medications do not affect growth through the endocrine (hormone) system or by any other internal biochemical mechanisms. Quite simply, if your child does not eat, he or she won't grow. Most parents can tell if their child is not eating as much as before medication, and regular weight checks will reliably pick up on any significant problems.

Any child taking ADHD medication should have their weight and height documented at baseline and rechecked on the same scale. At first, I recommend checking every one to two months, then every three to four months. If appetite suppression causes a significant and persistent deceleration in the rate of weight gain, that's not okay. The degree of deceleration over time should determine the level of concern.

Ignore/Monitor

Most often, if ADHD medications are properly tuned, significant appetite suppression can be avoided. You might notice a minor change in eating habits, but if there's no real impact on mood, attention, nutrition, or growth, it's no big deal. You and your doctor should just keep up with routine monitoring. Focus on keeping eating relaxed and natural. We certainly don't want to create an eating disorder.

Accommodate

Sometimes, an effective dose of ADHD medication causes moderate appetite suppression or growth deceleration. We don't need to sound any alarms, but we certainly don't want to ignore the issue either.

- *Increase calories.* In cases of mild to moderate appetite suppression, you might be able to side-step trouble by simply increasing calories. Go with dense foods: cream cheese, other cheeses, peanut butter, tahini, whole-grain bread, dates, raisins, bananas, mango, pecans, other nuts, guacamole, granola, milk shakes, olive oil, salad dressing, mayonnaise, quinoa, and other pasta. In addition to higher-calorie meals, you can supplement with high-protein/high-calorie drinks ("power shakes") or snack bars. Consultation with a pediatric nutritionist might be helpful.

- *Eat at the "trough."* Another way to minimize the impact of appetite suppression is by carefully timing the medication doses and meals. Medication blood levels rise and fall, creating peaks and valleys of appetite suppression. We call the lowest blood level the "trough." You can usually arrange the eating and dosing schedule so that mealtimes happen when medication blood levels are at their lowest. Typically, if a child is on long-acting stimulant, peak blood levels occur around lunch, making that the worst meal of the day. Likewise, if a child takes an after-school dose of medication, a second wave of appetite suppression may occur at dinner. You can compensate for these "lost" calories by timing a hearty breakfast before the morning medication has a chance to kick in. Schedule a larger, healthy snack after school and before bedtime, when morning and afternoon medications are wearing off. This means at least five meals per day: breakfast, lunch, afterschool snack, dinner, and before-bed snack. In this way, more frequent and better-timed offerings can add up to good-enough calorie consumption over the course of 24 hours, even if lunch and dinner are compromised.

- *Beware "drug holidays."* Commonly, parents and doctors do not treat the ADHD on weekends or vacations. Afternoon medication might also be withheld, to allow for less appetite suppression at dinner time. However, this approach often results in undertreatment of ADHD. For most children, ADHD is not just a school-day problem—it also causes problems in the late afternoon, on weekends, and over vacation. If you can help it, don't put your child at a disadvantage during these times. In carefully selected cases, there may be a place for drug holidays or strategic undertreatment. However, if your child seems to need a drug holiday, it may be that he or she is on the wrong medicine, or there may be other ways to manage the side effect. Don't give up on the ultimate goal: no significant side effects *and* optimal treatment of ADHD.

Treat

If you are doing your best to supplement calories and adjust the timing of meals but weight gain is still inadequate, there are some medical options.

- *Different med.* Again, if you haven't already, consider trying a different stimulant medication. They all suppress appetite somewhat, but another one might be better.
- *Go short.* You could try shifting off long-acting medication to a short-acting product. With careful timing, this can allow medication blood levels to dip every three to four hours, creating more opportunities to "eat at the trough." Meals could be timed for when one dose wears off and before the next kicks in.
- *Lighter dose.* You can try a slightly lighter dose. If this spares the appetite but compromises ADHD control, you can touch up with a non-stimulant.
- *Appetite stimulants.* If all else fails, we have some safe appetite-stimulating medications that could be layered on top. Before giving up on adequate ADHD treatment altogether, an appetite-boosting medication might be worth a try.
  - Cyproheptadine (brand name Periactin) is an old anti-histamine. For years, it has been used to increase appetite in young children with a variety of medical problems. It is very safe, and in my experience, works in 75+ percent of cases. It can cause drowsiness or irritability, but usually doesn't. Cyproheptadine comes in liquid or tablet form. The doses should be adjusted on an individual basis. Most children do well with one or two doses per day, usually before breakfast and dinner. However, it seems to have a smooth, cumulative effect—so if it's inconvenient, you don't have to dose right before meals.
  - Mirtazapine (brand name Remeron) has a somewhat weaker and less predictable impact on appetite. However, many children get a good boost. Given at night, this medication also helps with sleep onset and sleep maintenance.

Plus, it's an anti-anxiety/anti-depression medication too, so comes in handy for mild but coexisting poor appetite, insomnia, and anxiety. With just evening dosing, the appetite stimulant and anti-anxiety effects carry over through the day, and sleepiness usually wears off by morning. If there's too much morning or daytime sleepiness, you can decrease the dose and/or give it earlier in the evening. Other possible side effects are generally mild and reversible, including possible changes in bowel or bladder function (bedwetting), dizziness, or even daytime overactivation.

- Neuroleptics such as risperidone should never be used *just* to stimulate appetite. However, if a child needs treatment for a coexisting problem with a severe mood disorder or psychosis—such as disruptive mood dysregulation disorder, bipolar illness, or schizophrenia—then these powerful medications could provide a fringe appetite-stimulating benefit.

Sleep Side Effects

It's well known that stimulant medications can cause trouble falling asleep—but so can untreated ADHD. It's awfully hard to settle down for bed just when your medication is wearing off, when hyperactivity, impulsivity, and distractibility may be on the rebound. As discussed more below, some children with ADHD actually sleep better on stimulant medication, even when the dose is given late. Insomnia can be caused by too much medication, too little medication, or both—which is why it's always important to compare sleep habits on medication to sleep habits before treatment.

Ignore/Monitor

Sometimes, ADHD medication pushes overall time asleep back just a little bit—maybe a half-hour or so. This is no big deal, as it doesn't usually affect daytime functioning.

Accommodate

If ADHD medication causes moderate insomnia, you still may be able to make accommodations. Make sure that you're doing the best you can regarding routine "sleep hygiene." Let's review some essentials.

- *Structure daily routines.* Meals should be scheduled and restricted to the kitchen table; in between, the kitchen is closed. Schedule regular exercise. Schedule time for homework. Daytime naps should be eliminated or at least limited. Establishing a regular schedule does not mean ignoring your child's natural rhythms. But if you and your child agree to structure these daytime and early evening activities, it becomes easier to structure sleep as well.
- *Agree on a regular sleep time.* For children with poor self-regulation, it is more important to set a regular sleep time. You just want to establish some sort of predictability, rhythm, and pattern, so your child's sleep clock can get regulated. Avoid large discrepancies between weekday and weekend bedtimes. Otherwise, it's like dealing with international jet-lag every Monday morning.
- *Agree on a regular sleep place.* From an early age, your child should be conditioned to associate sleep with a specific place. For some, a family bed may be the norm. However, if possible, nightly opportunity to sleep in one's own bed helps develop self-settling. Regular sleeping shouldn't be allowed in cars, on sofas, or in other people's beds.
- *Sleep places are for sleeping.* The bed should not be used for activities that are strongly associated with staying awake: TV, cell phones, laptops, or food.
- *Dialing down.* Gradually, dial down physical, intellectual, emotional, interpersonal, and play activities. The sensory environment should be modified so that noise, light, and electronic stimulation gradually sets with the sun. This does not mean speaking in whispers or eliminating all normal background noise; just make sure the environment is not overstimulating. Specifically, there should be no electronics or highly physical play for a half-hour or even an hour before bedtime. Save emotionally loaded conversations for the next day or earlier in the evening. For bedtime-resistant children, sequence evening activities from non-preferred to preferred. For example, brushing teeth and pajamas (unpleasant) could come before parent-child time, such as reading or listening to music (pleasant). The more regular, ritualized, rhythmic, and routine, the better. And of course, no caffeine.
- *Self-calming activities.* Children can choose and practice any

number of self-calming strategies:
- Listening to (relaxing) music
- Reading (relaxing) books, magazines, poetry
- Writing
- Drawing
- Meditating and using other mindfulness techniques
  - Practicing self-hypnosis
  - Breathing awareness: in/out, belly up/down, imagined balloon inflated/deflated
  - Progressive muscle relaxation: contracting (three seconds) then relaxing (five to ten seconds) muscle groups from toes to head
- Lavender-scented pillow
- Calming mental imagery (favorite place)
- *Self-calming scripts.* Children can be taught to talk themselves through their insomnia. There are many helpful sleep script apps and websites, such as **www.innerhealthstudio.com**. Here are some examples of sleep scripts:
  - "It's normal to have a little trouble falling asleep or waking up in the middle of the night."
  - "It's no big deal if I'm a little tired tomorrow."
  - "I'm going to be the boss of my worries and not let my worries be the boss of me."
  - "I can use my relaxation strategies."

Children are all different. Customize these sleep hygiene practices, and whenever possible, involve your child directly in their own sleep problem-solving.

Treat

A full discussion of managing sleep problems is beyond the scope of this book (Ferber, 2006; Durand, 2013). But let's cover a few basics here. First, rule out other contributing factors. Second, see if you can individualize your approach. Third, consider medication.

Rule out other possible contributing factors. Sometimes, it's not all about the ADHD. Your pediatrician should perform a screening history and physical exam to rule out other possible factors. Referral to specialists can be made as necessary:
- ENT: If there is noisy or irregular breathing, an ear, nose, and throat doctor can evaluate for upper airway obstruction.

Treatment may include removal of tonsils and/or adenoids.

- Dentist: A common source of pain and irritability is the teeth. Many children have undiagnosed cavities or abscesses.
- Allergist: If there is chronic congestion, cough, wheeze, or itch, an allergist may be able to help identify the cause. Treatment may include environmental control, medication, and or desensitization.
- Gastroenterologist: With unexplained irritability or abdominal distress, especially at night or associated with meals, a gastroenterologist may be consulted for the possibility of acid reflux. Treatment includes restrictions on night eating, elevation of the head during sleep, and antacids.
- Neurologist: If there are abrupt and unexplained changes in mood, behavior, or learning, or an observed seizure, a neurologist should be consulted for possible epilepsy; perhaps including a 24-hour sleep EEG. Treatment is with anticonvulsant medication.
- Psychiatrist, Psychologist, or Clinical Social Worker: If there is anxiety, irritability, or depression, a child psychiatrist, clinical psychologist, or social worker can assess. Treatment is cognitive-behavioral therapy and/or medication.
- Developmental-Behavioral Pediatrician, Neurologist, Neuropsychologist, Occupational Therapist, Speech-Language Pathologist, or Physiatrist: If a parent or teacher suspects developmental delays or disabilities, early evaluation can guide early intervention. Treatment includes individualized accommodations and therapies.
- Laboratory: Blood sample or sleep laboratory investigation is not usually necessary, but may be indicated for mysterious night waking or excessive daytime sleepiness.

Cognitive-Behavioral Therapy (CBT). When it comes to understanding pediatric sleep problems, modification of parent-child interactions is almost always a necessary part of the solution. Parents need to give their children just-right opportunities to learn self-settling, and to avoid unintentionally reinforcing sleep-resistance. CBT approaches to anxiety-driven insomnia will be discussed in detail in the next section of this book, Excursion 2. Readers needing more detailed discussion of behavioral strategies should consult their pediatrician, a behavioral sleep specialist, or one of the many other excellent books available (Owens & Mindell, 2005).

Medication. Medication should be reserved for more significant sleep problems. However, if you are practicing good sleep hygiene and behavioral strategies, medication doesn't have to be a last resort. Sometimes sleep problems are so severe that we need to treat with medication right away and get things quickly under control. It makes no sense to just give a child medication for daytime inattention and not treat a serious source of exhaustion. Sleep is essential for attention, self-control, learning, behavior, social functioning, mood, stress-reduction, and overall health.

- *Non-prescription medications for insomnia.* Before resorting to prescription medications, consider two good old over-the-counter standbys:
  - *Diphenhydramine (Benadryl).* This readily available antihistamine works for most children. It can be given on a regular basis, in standard doses, a half-hour to an hour before bedtime. Diphenhydramine can be used safely for months but it should not be used continuously for years. Beware: some children with underlying neurological disorders, rather than becoming calm and sleepy, become more aroused and even agitated. Note: Diphenhydramine should not be used in some children with epilepsy as it can lower their seizure threshold. Check with your neurologist.
  - *Melatonin.* If there are underlying neurological issues, melatonin is usually a better choice than diphenhydramine. Melatonin is also safe and effective in typically developing children. It is a naturally occurring hormone that regulates sleep cycles in all mammals. Spend a little extra to get a good-quality brand. Melatonin supplements work for sleep problems in about 50 percent of children. There are two different modes of action:
    1. *Relatively immediate sedative effect.* Given in somewhat higher doses, melatonin can cause drowsiness within a half-hour to an hour. If you want to take advantage of this sedative effect, try 3-6 mg (maximum 9 mg) before bedtime. For this effect, don't give a dose that's too small or too early.
    2. *Delayed reset of the sleep cycle.* In lower doses, melatonin does not cause as much immediate sedation but it may more effectively reset the natural sleep clock. This

chronobiologic effect takes much longer to kick in. For this potentially more durable sleep cycle reset, try just 0.5 mg–1 mg (maximum 3 mg), four to six hours before bedtime. For this effect, don't give a dose that's too heavy or too late.

- *Prescription medications for insomnia.* There is a trick to using prescription medications for insomnia. First, see if you can identify an underlying or associated condition that is driving the problem—or at least along for the ride. The most common suspects are coexisting anxiety and mood instability. Usually, there is a sufficiently sedating medication that also treats your child's primary or associated issues.
  - *For ADHD-associated insomnia.* If your child has difficulty falling asleep—at least in part—due to motor restlessness, impulsivity, or distractibility, then treating ADHD symptoms in the evening is more likely to fix the insomnia.
    - *Non-stimulants:* Unlike stimulants, alpha-agonists can cause sedation. Therefore, these medications can be given late in the day to extend ADHD treatment while helping with sleep onset. One note of caution: even long-acting forms of alpha-agonists can wear off too soon and cause rebound waking in the middle of the night.
      - Clonidine: Of the alpha-agonists, clonidine is more sedating than guanfacine. If your child needs relatively immediate sedation, you can go with clonidine a half-hour before bedtime.
      - Guanfacine: If you need to cover ADHD symptoms in the late afternoon or early evening, you can go with guanfacine or atomoxetine. In this situation, an extra dose of stimulant medication might keep your child up even later and clonidine might zonk your child out too early.
      - Atomoxetine: Like alpha-agonists, atomoxetine does not usually cause insomnia. If it is given at dinner time, atomoxetine can counter ADHD-driven problems with both sleep onset and sleep maintenance. But atomoxetine tends to be the least sedating of these three non-stimulants. Unlike alpha-agonists, middle of the night rebound-waking is not usually a

65

problem with atomoxetine.

- *Stimulants.* Stimulants are well-known to cause insomnia—but not always. For many children, stimulants have no effect on sleep whatsoever. Some children with ADHD actually sleep better with a late dose of short-acting stimulant. The timing may be crucial. Sometimes, an evening dose of stimulant works for a few hours before bedtime and helps regulate a child heading into bedtime. Other times, stimulants wear off right at bedtime and amplify trouble settling down. To avoid this rebound and take advantage of peak ADHD control, some children actually do better if an evening dose of stimulant is given 15–30 minutes before bedtime. However, this strategy certainly can backfire. If you're going to try an evening dose of stimulant, give it a first go on a Friday or Saturday night when there are no special activities planned for the next day. You might find it works great. Or you might be up with your wide-eyed child all night long!
- *For anxiety or depression-associated insomnia.* If your child has insomnia and coexisting problems with worry, sadness, or irritability, then sleep might be most responsive to medications for anxiety or depression. In these cases, it makes sense to choose an anti-anxiety or anti-depressant medication that also causes some sedation.
  - *Selective serotonin reuptake inhibitors.* Prozac, Lexapro, Zoloft, and other selective serotonin reuptake inhibitors are generally the best and safest medications we have for treating anxiety and depression. Trazodone is a serotonin medication that usually causes sleepiness. However, their effect on sleep varies from one individual to another. If they cause overactivation, you can give the dose in the morning. If they cause some sedation, you can shift the dose to evening. If they help sleep, it's often because the insomnia was really driven by anxiety. Generally, SSRIs should be prescribed only if anxiety causes daytime problems, not just nighttime insomnia.
  - *Tricyclics.* Amitriptyline is an older antidepressant/anti-anxiety medication that can be given one to two hours before bedtime. Compared to the newer SSRIs, it

is not used as much anymore, in part because it causes more side effects including too much sleepiness. But with nighttime administration, this can be a plus for some people.

- *Tetracyclic.* Mirtazapine (brand name Remeron) can help with insomnia. As discussed previously, it can be especially handy if insomnia is associated with anxiety and poor daytime appetite.

- *Benzodiazepines.* Benzodiazepine medications, such as valium and clonazepam, are very effective, especially if insomnia is associated with anxiety. However, especially in pediatrics, "benzos" are only appropriate for very limited use: to aid with episodic panic attacks, recovery from surgery, or severe stress. Because of their addictive potential, this family of medications should not be used on a regular basis.

- *For mood instability–associated insomnia.* Children with severe emotional ups and downs commonly have trouble regulating their sleep.

  - *Neuroleptics* (such as risperidone and quetiapine) and *mood stabilizers* (such as valproic acid, oxycarbamazepine, and lamotrigine) are all powerful medicines that should be prescribed only if there is a serious mood disorder.

  - *Gabapentin*, sometimes used to treat nerve pain and other conditions, has also been tried as a mood stabilizer. Its main side effect is sleepiness. Therefore, in some children with insomnia and mild mood instability, gabapentin might be just the thing.

- *Prescription sedatives.* There is a long and growing list of medications for treatment of adult insomnia, such as Ambien. However, they should not be prescribed for young people.

Attention Side Effects

Sometimes, ADHD medication can backfire and make inattention worse, especially in kids with coexisting anxiety, autism, rigidity, or "Sluggish Cognitive Tempo." Medication can amplify any predisposition to slow down, get stuck, or perseverate. All of this is discussed in much greater detail in the following chapter on coexisting ADHD, anxiety, and autism, but let's preview the main issues here.

With stimulant medication, attention can go from Teflon to Gorilla Glue. Instead of focusing on too many things to the exclusion of one, some medicated children get stuck on one thing to the exclusion of others. Stimulant medication can bring out obsessive-compulsive symptoms.

It's hard to get inside a child's head. But if you just ask the right questions, some children can help sort this out. For example:

> "When you're having trouble paying attention to the teacher, are you thinking about one thing … then another thing … then another thing … then another thing? Or, is your mind just stuck on one thing?"

Some children say, "I'm not thinking anything." Or they just don't know. In this case, try checking for subtle behavioral cues, such as patterns of eye movement. The key—as always—is to compare pre- and post-treatment observations.

Keep in mind, this plays out in different ways, across different activities and in different settings. Your child might be too focused for some tasks and not focused enough for others. Despite this complexity, we can usually tell whether there's too much medication or too little—or simply change the dose to see if the child's attention gets better or worse.

Ignore/Monitor

Depending upon the setting and activity, a degree of "stick-to-it-ness" can be a blessing—that's what we're hoping for when we treat ADHD. Extra focus usually works well in school, for homework, and for other activities that might be difficult but necessary. If the hyperfocus is mild and doesn't interfere with necessary activities, then we can simply take note and monitor.

Accommodate

If ADHD medication causes a moderate degree of hyperfocusing, accommodations might suffice. The dose of stimulant could be adjusted; for example, you could try using a slightly higher dose in academic settings and a lower dose for other times. If this dose adjustment avoids perseveration but sacrifices ADHD control, you can try behavioral and environmental accommodations for undertreated ADHD—more structure, more prompting, more feedback, more positive reinforcement.

Or you might decide to keep optimal ADHD control and accommodate the hyperfocusing. For example, you could allow your child more prolonged and deep engagement, cutting back on shifts between activities or topics. You could also support your child's transitions with choice-giving, warnings, visual schedules, or timers.

Treat

Sometimes, medication-induced perseveration is just too impairing. If you haven't already, try a lower stimulant dose, different stimulants, and/or augmentation with different non-stimulants. Otherwise, there is no direct pharmacological antidote, and you might have to undertreat the ADHD. Although this represents medication failure, there are more intensive non-pharmacological supports that can still make a big difference (Shapiro, 2016).

Mood Side Effects

ADHD commonly *causes* problems with mood regulation. In many cases, persistent negative mood and emotional impulsivity may be symptoms of *under*treatment, and optimal ADHD medication can help. But ADHD medication can also backfire, causing increased irritability, anxiety, or depression (Pozzi et al., 2018). These are perhaps the most commonly missed medication side effects—and the most consequential. They may appear early during the initial treatment trial, but can also come on more gradually and subtly, only becoming apparent over time. Mood can also change with the medication blood level, either as the medication reaches a peak or when it's coming down, during troughs.

ADHD medication can make little things feel like big things, increasing edginess or anxiety. For others, emotional distress may actually stem from improved focus. In other words, medication can make one "stuck on a feeling."

In a way, untreated ADHD can prevent ruminating or obsessing. Treatment of ADHD may make it harder to just let things roll off your back. ADHD medication can cause excessive caution, fears, phobias, nightmares, rituals, or compulsions—even paralysis. Such side effects are more common with stimulants than non-stimulants, and some kids are much more predisposed than others, especially those who already had challenges around inflexibility, irritability, anxiety, panic, OCD, or autism.

But don't let these possible tendencies scare you off. If medication has a negative effect on mood, you can reduce the dose or stop the medication. And remember, mood regulation in ADHD usually gets better on medication. For many children, that's one of the reasons to treat.

Ignore/Monitor

Parents or teachers will notice if ADHD medication significantly affects mood. If it's mild, brief, and inconsequential—for example, as medication is kicking in at the beginning of the day or kicking out after school—no big deal. Take note and monitor. If the medication is otherwise safe and effective, there may be no need to change treatment or accommodate.

Accommodate

If there are moderate effects on mood that coincide with peaks or troughs in blood level, such predictable fluctuations can be managed through simple anticipation. It may be possible to schedule low-stress/low-demand activities during these times. For example, a child with 20 minutes of mild rebound irritability on arrival home from school can be allowed time to just relax and unwind before homework, chores, or other demands. If a child becomes predictably withdrawn or anxious as morning medication is kicking in, he or she can be given time to just hang out and acclimate at the classroom periphery before the teacher requires them to participate. Adults can just let some time pass until the mood re-equilibrates, like waiting out a brief rain.

Sometimes, a child's negative mood is clearly tied to appetite suppression and low blood sugar. If this is a pattern, schedule a regular snack. This not only heads-off the "hangry" mood, it avoids "rewarding" negative mood with food.

Treat

For some children, ADHD medication can have more serious effects on mood. These negative effects are reversible if noticed but potentially serious if ignored or misdiagnosed. When such side effects are persistent, distressing, or impairing, then—at very least—the dose should be adjusted. If a lower dose results in either loss of ADHD control or failure to normalize mood, then the medication should be discontinued. In these cases, optimal ADHD control is not worth the cost.

But do not abandon ship too hastily. Remember, many children have coexisting mood disorders, perhaps amplified but not caused by ADHD medication. Sometimes, the anxiety, depression, severe mood dysregulation, or bipolar illness has to be treated first. Then you can circle back to treat the ADHD more safely and effectively. Many children need multiple medications to treat coexisting disorders. However, do not use a secondary medication to treat mood or attention side effects that were not present before treatment and are truly *caused* by the ADHD medication.

Personal-Social Side Effects

Too much stimulant medication is not "stimulating" at all. In fact, over-treatment causes over-inhibition: flattened affect, less sparkle, loss of creativity, and social withdrawal. Some kids say they don't like the way their medication makes them act with their friends—too quiet or serious, not as funny or as fun to be with. They may want to spend more time alone.

These complaints should be taken seriously. Such negative effects of ADHD medication are unacceptable. But rest assured, these untoward effects on personality and social behavior are dose-related and reversible.

Ignore/Monitor

If personal-social side effects are so subtle that parents are the only ones who notice, it may be insignificant and ignorable. Sometimes, this type of side effect softens or fades away as the child acclimates. If the side effect is mild and becoming less noticeable, just monitor for weekly and monthly trends. And remember, not all changes in personality and social behavior are undesirable. Many serious artists and athletes find that ADHD treatment allows them to perform at their full potential.

Accommodate

Undesirable personal-social side effects may cause a little bit of a problem in some settings. For example, in school, a child might feel that the benefits of being more serious in class far outweigh the social downside. However, outside of school, the same child could feel too subdued hanging with friends and playing sports. In these cases, it might work to give a full dose of medication

71

for school and a lighter dose—or even no medication at all—in non-academic settings.

This kind of customized dosing requires excellent observation skills, accurate communication, and a careful analysis of risks versus benefits. Appropriate weight should be attached to the impact of medication side effects and untreated ADHD across settings.

Treat

It bears repeating: these personality side effects, like all others, can be softened or even eliminated by trying different medications and adjusting the dose. However, if unavoidable, there is no treatment for the negative side effects on personality and social behavior. The prescriber may just have to change the medicine.

Tics and Other Involuntary Movement Side Effects

In some predisposed children, stimulant medication can cause a variety of involuntary and repetitive behaviors—but they can usually be managed without compromising ADHD treatment. Of course, many children have tics pre-medication. Simple motor and vocal tics are common in school-age children. Fidgetiness and motor restlessness may be part of the ADHD package and improve with medication. Other types of movements and vocalizations may be completely unrelated to ADHD and unaffected by ADHD medication. Usually, a pediatrician can sort this out. However, consultation with a neurologist or developmental-behavioral pediatrician is sometimes necessary.

Involuntary movements and vocalizations can range in severity, and in type (Robertson et al., 2017). There may be motor tics, such as blinking, eye-gazing, or nose wrinkling; twitches or jerks of any muscle group, such as the neck or shoulders; vocal tics, most commonly grunting, snorting, throat-clearing, or coughing. Tics can even take the form of whooping, and some children have verbal tics that cause them to say non-normative words or phrases.

Besides tics, stimulants can bring out other repetitive motor behaviors. These habits, compulsions, or nervous mannerisms may be triggered or driven by anxiety. Children may pull on or pick at their hair, eyelashes, eyebrows, fingernails, skin, or nostrils. They might target various other body parts or articles of clothing. As discussed below, alpha-agonists may be useful in the treatment of tics.

Ignore/Monitor

Involuntary repetitive behaviors may bother adult observers more than affected children. If the symptoms are mild and inconsequential, ignoring is the best bet. These types of involuntary behaviors may wax, wane, and shape-shift for a while, but, whether on stimulant medication or not, they usually fade over time. Try not to react. Parents and other well-meaning adults should take care to avoid unintentionally making a child feel bad, or reinforcing the behavior, by giving it too much attention. Just monitor and let your doctor know if there is a clear trend for the worse.

Accommodate

If a child might feel stigmatized, accommodation is appropriate. Many of these repetitive behaviors are distracting, off-putting, or annoying to others. It may be appropriate to educate teachers, friends, or classmates so it doesn't become a bigger deal. For example, a classmate might ask, "Why do you keep doing that with your head?" The child could be coached to answer, "That's just my tic," or, "That's just something my muscles do. I can't help it." For some involuntary behaviors, it may be appropriate to use baseball caps, fidgets, Band-Aids, or doodling to block the habit, occupy the hands, and minimize the issue.

Treat

Sometimes, medication-induced repetitive behaviors are too distracting, disruptive, painful, or self-injurious to be ignored or accommodated. Understandably, parents and children might want to abandon ADHD medication altogether. However, remember that untreated ADHD is still a significant problem. In these cases, as with all medication side effects, your prescriber should consider a dose adjustment or another medication (Egolf & Coffey, 2014). In particular, try alpha-agonists (guanfacine or clonidine), which treat tics *and* ADHD. Usually, lower stimulant doses and/or alpha-agonists can salvage ADHD treatment and keep these side effects at bay. With discontinuation of stimulants, tics and other involuntary repetitive behaviors may take longer to settle down than other medication side effects; sometimes weeks instead of days.

Rarely, adequate treatment of ADHD requires treatment of severe yet unavoidable tics. For these special situations, more powerful medications—namely, neuroleptics such as risperidone and aripiprazole—may be tried if all else has failed.

There are some non-pharmacological options. Habit Reversal Training (HRT) or Comprehensive Behavioral Intervention for Tics (CBIT) involve teaching self-awareness and practicing self-control. When the child becomes aware of the urge to do the behavior, they substitute a more acceptable behavior. Rewards can be helpful if a child is self-motivated. The expertise of the therapist is another key to success.

In most cases, the combination of education, accommodation, medication adjustment, and behavioral strategies can allow continued treatment of ADHD and adequate control of secondary repetitive behaviors.

Physical Symptom Side Effects

In a minority of patients, medication for ADHD can cause unpleasant physical symptoms. Headaches, stomachaches, nausea, dizziness or drowsiness can occur as the blood level of medication is ascending, peaking or descending; respectively called onset, plateau, and offset (or rebound) effects. Physical symptoms are likely medication side effects if their onset corresponds with a new medication or a dose increase.

It may help to keep a symptom diary, to track trends and patterns. For example, a child who gets headaches each afternoon may be having a rebound side effect, but it could also be school-related tension or stress headaches. To tell the difference, try not giving the medication on a school day and see if the headaches still occur, or if they occur at the same time when you give medication on weekends or vacation days. To see if the headaches might be due to hypoglycemia following appetite suppression at lunch, try giving a preemptive snack.

For any physical symptoms, talk to your prescriber about other ways of nailing down the source. Usually, careful observation and history is all you need, but sometimes a complete physical exam, lab tests, or radiographic imaging are necessary. Don't assume that all physical symptoms are due to your child's medication. Bottom line: contact your pediatrician if there are persistent, unusual, or severe symptoms.

Ignore/Monitor

Physical symptoms should always be taken seriously and monitored carefully, but this doesn't mean sounding the alarms. Mild symptoms that pass quickly might be due to medication peaks and valleys. Nothing needs to be done if they don't bother your child. Often, they gradually diminish, especially if parents—and doctors!—do not overreact. You child might just need some time to acclimatize.

Accommodate

If the side effects temporarily interfere with normal activities or cause your child discomfort, it may be best to lower demands on them until things get back to normal—for example, waiting on homework until headaches pass.

Treat

If side effects cause significant disruption or distress, then it may be appropriate to treat. Acetaminophen or ibuprofen can be taken for headaches. Antacids can be used for upper intestinal tract discomfort. However, if physical symptoms are more regular, frequent, or severe, your prescriber should probably reduce the dose or find another medication.

Managing Uneven Medication Coverage

One cause of presumed medication "failure" is uneven medication coverage. ADHD medication might work great for a portion of the day, but there may be significant symptoms before the dose kicks in, after it kicks out, or with fluctuations during the day. Here we'll explore strategies for getting medication to show up to work earlier, stay later, and not take any midday breaks.

With each dose of medication, blood levels rise and fall, in and out of the therapeutic range. A "peak" is when the medication is at its highest blood level. A "trough" is when medication is at its lowest blood level. These daily peaks and troughs yield uneven control. Like rising and falling tides, they wax and wane. During medication troughs, parents observe, "It's like he (or she) isn't even taking the stuff!" But treatment troughs can be filled so that medication delivers more even help.

Trough-Filling Failure (TFF)

Many children do just fine with a single dose of long-acting medication. But for many others, failure to identify and fill troughs in medication coverage can cause all sorts of problems. At home, medication is not usually on board in time to help with the morning routine. After school, medication may wear off before homework or tutoring. Undertreated ADHD may also compromise extracurricular, leisure, social, and family activities.

There are safety issues too. For teenagers, failure to cover ADHD after school and into the evening can result in serious problems with distracted driving and impulsive misadventures. Undertreated ADHD can also cause sleep problems.

"Trough-blindness" is when parents, teachers, prescribers, and children don't make the connection between low medication blood levels and poor ADHD control. They may abandon treatment that just needs some tuning. Moreover, trough-filling failure represents a missed opportunity to maintain optimal ADHD control across all important tasks, activities, and settings.

Tiffs from TFFs

Trough-filling failures can lead to all kinds of misunderstandings. TFFs can cause tiffs!

- TFFs and parents. Medication troughs—in the early morning, late afternoon, and evening—can lead parents to blame each other or themselves. Why does Timmy do better at school with his teachers or with my co-parent (for midday activities) than with me (at the beginning and end of the day)?
- TFFs and teachers. Uneven school-day coverage can lead teachers to blame each other or themselves. Why does Timmy do so well with Ms. Smith in the morning but so poorly with me in the afternoon? Trough-blind parents or principals might also make wrong assumptions about the competence of individual teachers.
- TFFs and children. Medication troughs can lead adults to draw incorrect conclusions about a child's potential. Worst of all, uneven medication coverage can make relatively mild skill deficits seem like insurmountable disabilities to kids themselves. This could lead to an inappropriately pessimistic self-image.

Trough-Tracking

Phase one of a stimulant trial is about determining the best medication and the best dose. Phase two is about fine-tuning the medication to maximize benefits and minimize side effects. This optimization should include active investigation for possible treatment troughs. Observers should help each other answer the following questions:

- What time is the dose taken?
- How long does it take to kick in?
- How long does it take to kick out?
- What is the time between kick in and kick out—that is, the duration of action?

For some children, kick-in, kick-out, and duration of action are unclear. If in doubt, assume that regularly occurring peaks and troughs in self-control or performance are probably due to changes in medication blood level. Draw a daily coverage curve to show peaks and troughs for different times of day, tasks, and activities.

Daily Coverage Curve

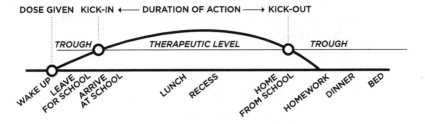

On the Daily Coverage Curve above, notice that Timmy has a therapeutic level of medicine by the time he gets to school. It lasts throughout the school day. His teachers report excellent ADHD control. But for Timmy's parents, every morning is a disaster—he won't get dressed, sit for breakfast, brush his teeth, or get his backpack. After school, he seems to be itching for a fight with his sister, and good luck trying to get him to do his homework. He won't stay at the dinner table, get ready for bed, or wind down for sleep.

It's Trough-Filling Time!

For the sake of this discussion, let's assume that everyone has done the best they can with non-pharmacological management of ADHD, but educational, behavioral, and emotional supports are not enough. To fill treatment troughs, better medication coverage is necessary.

Early-Morning Troughs

- *"Short-long."* Short-acting medicines kick in faster than long-acting medicines; usually just 10–15 minutes versus 30–60 minutes or longer. The most common solution to early-morning troughs is simply giving short-acting stimulant immediately upon waking. Wait 15 minutes or so before starting the morning routine. If necessary, move breakfast earlier in the routine to minimize appetite suppression. Wait to give the long-acting stimulant until just before your child leaves the house. This gives the short-acting stimulant some time to start kicking out before the long-acting stimulant starts kicking in. If there's not enough time between waking up and going to school to avoid too much overlap between doses, then the long-acting stimulant can perhaps be administered at a more optimal time by the nurse at school. This "short-long" strategy might also extend duration of coverage, filling an afternoon trough and avoiding the need to give an after-school dose.

Short-Long

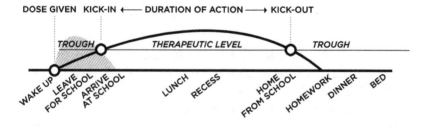

- *Nighttime non-stimulants.* Although not usually as effective, non-stimulant ADHD medications can work well enough and can have a much longer duration. Sometimes an evening dose of atomoxetine (Strattera), guanfacine-ER (Intuniv), or clonidine-ER (Kapvay) can last through the night and carry over until morning. Your child may wake up with enough medicine on board to get the day off to a better start. With a little luck, evening non-stimulants can fill an end-of-day trough and help with sleep initiation too.

Nighttime Non-Stimulant

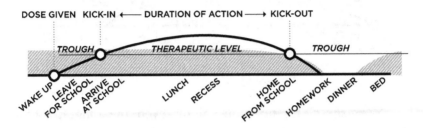

- *New delayed-release stimulant.* Marketed under the brand name Jornay PM, a potential game-changer was released in 2019. This new controlled-release medication, taken in the evening (as indicated by the X in the illustration below), is designed to provide therapeutic levels beginning in the early morning and lasting through the day.

New Nighttime Delayed-Release Stimulant

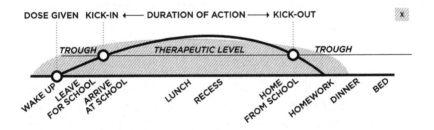

Afternoon, After-School, and Early-Evening Troughs

- *"Longer long."* Some long-acting medications last longer than others. Some newer stimulants have more extended duration of action—and more marathon medications are surely forthcoming. Sometimes, changing to a longer-acting morning stimulant gets you where you need to go. Consult an expert who is up-to-date regarding new medications and their differences in staying power.

Longer Long

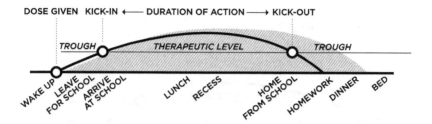

- *"Long-short."* It's not unusual for even the longest-acting medications to kick out on arrival home from school. A well-timed boost of short-acting medicine can provide an additional three or four hours of therapeutic blood level, to get through homework, chores, or other after-school activities.

Long-Short

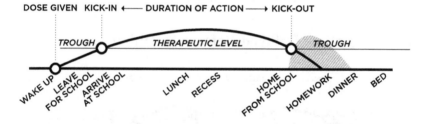

- *"Long-long."* If your child is a rapid metabolizer, the morning dose of long-acting stimulant plus an afternoon dose of short-acting stimulant may not add up to sufficient duration of coverage. The long-acting dose in the morning may not last through the school day, or the short-acting dose after school may not last through homework/bedtime routine. Either way, you might want to try long-acting medication twice each day. Let's say the 7:30 a.m. dose kicks in by 8:30 a.m. but starts to kick out around 1:30 p.m. That means a one-hour kick-in time and a six-hour duration of action. Knowing that, a second 12:30 p.m. dose of long-acting stimulant would kick-in by 1:30 p.m. and last until about 7:30 p.m. This is handy if your child is home for lunch, or there is someone at school who can administer it—especially if the child has important after-school activities but cannot take medication, perhaps because you are at work and there's no one else to safely take care of administration.

Long-Long

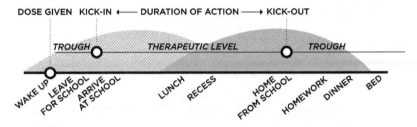

- *Non-stimulant.* Let's say you try either the long-short or long-long strategies above and achieve longer duration, but the second dose of stimulant causes too much appetite suppression or insomnia. With luck, non-stimulant medication can work well enough and avoid these side effects. If you find (during phase one of a trial) that a non-stimulant works, then you can experiment with the best timing to optimize coverage.

A.M. or P.M. Non-Stimulant

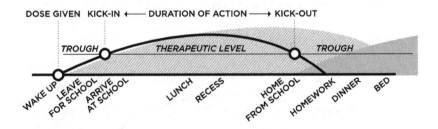

Bedtime Trough

- *"Before-bed short."* Stimulant medication can cause insomnia, but so can undertreated ADHD. Problems settling to sleep might be due to a bedtime trough of distractibility, hyperactivity, and impulsivity, amplified by medication kick-out. This rebound insomnia represents a temporary stimulant deficit, not a stimulant excess. A bedtime dose of short-act-ing stimulant *might* be the answer. In one controlled study of children with ADHD and insomnia, a pre-bedtime dose of short-acting simulant made insomnia worse in about a third of kids, no different in another third, but substantially better in the last one-third. Just give this a first try on a Friday or Saturday night when no important activities are planned for the next day!

Before-Bed Short

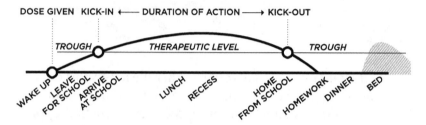

- *P.M. non-stimulant.* Of the non-stimulants, clonidine is usually the most sedating. The dose given for ADHD-driven insomnia is a bit higher and closer to bedtime than the dose given for wake-time treatment. If too much seda-tion is a problem, try a lower dose, give it later, or try one of the other non-stimulants. Optimal timing is crucial. Eve-ning guanfacine or clonidine can wear off in the wee hours of the morning and cause rebound night-waking.

P.M. Non-Stimulant

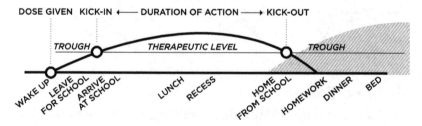

As with all treatment for ADHD, trough-filling strategies should only be done on a trial basis and with carefully individualized out-come measures. Make sure to obtain baseline and follow-up rat-ings from people who observe your child during the trough time.

To Fill or Not to Fill?

Some children need good ADHD coverage from the time they wake up to the time they fall asleep. Some even need coverage while they sleep. To fill all troughs, a combination of strategies may be appropriate.

But sometimes troughs are desirable and we should deliberately leave them unfilled—or even create them—to minimize undesirable side effects. For example, some children might do better with low blood levels at mealtimes, to lessen appetite suppression, or at sleep times, to avoid insomnia. Some children and adolescents may want to be free of medication effects for activities where lack of inhibition may be desirable: theatre, music, or other creative arts. Treatment troughs may also be left unfilled for athletics or certain social situations. In this way, trough management can be both effective and respectful of individual needs.

Managing Coexisting Conditions

Although ADHD medication is usually effective, there are no guarantees. In a minority of cases, nothing seems to work. Sometimes this is because the treatment trial was not done properly. Given the complexity and unpredictability of this process, it's understandable if parents or doctors get a little sloppy or give up prematurely. Other times, the child is just too sensitive to medication side effects.

But what if you and your team gave ADHD medication a good shot? All reasonable options were carefully tried but the results were disappointing. There was no medication, alone or in combination, that yielded complete or even partial response. Attempts to manage side effects and fill gaps in medication coverage were unsuccessful.

Coexisting Conditions as a Cause of ADHD Treatment Failure

ADHD treatment failure is often due to the presence of coexisting conditions. After all, ADHD is not the only thing that causes hyperactivity, impulsivity, and distractibility, and ADHD rarely travels alone. The best ADHD medication in the world will not eliminate symptoms caused—even partially—by other conditions. This does not usually mean that the ADHD diagnosis was wrong, but it often does mean that ADHD isn't the whole story. ADHD is much harder to control and overcome if any of the following are also present:

- Mood disorder: anxiety, depression, bipolar illness
- Neurodevelopmental disorder: autism, tics, neuromuscular disorder, learning disability, intellectual disability
- Medical problems: specific diseases, gastrointestinal and eating disorders, sleep disorders, seizures, substance abuse
- Parent/family factors: marital issues, sibling mental or physical illness, financial stresses
- Environmental factors: poor school fit, social isolation or conflict, exposure to violence, trauma, poverty

When these and other problems complicate ADHD treatment, you have to treat the coexisting conditions too. This can get complicated. Treating these associated problems might be more difficult than treating the ADHD. Beyond simple medication management for ADHD, this kind of complexity usually requires a combination of interventions. Comprehensive care means additional expertise, time, and money.

A complete overview of comprehensive assessment and intervention is beyond the scope of this book. But that's what my first book is all about. In *Parent Child Journey: An Individualized Approach to Raising Your Challenging Child,* the last chapter or "tenth mile" is devoted to care coordination for children with complicated profiles.

Consult your pediatrician regarding referrals to subspecialists as needed. In this book, I will do my best to explore specific strategies and principles for treating just a few of the conditions most commonly associated with ADHD, especially anxiety and autism. The take-home message here: if ADHD treatment is not working, look beyond the ADHD.

Medication Management of Coexisting Conditions

Sometimes, treatment of coexisting conditions means other types of medication. For example, some children with anxiety or depression might need to take an SSRI. Others with bipolar illness or severe mood dysregulation might need mood stabilizers or neuroleptics. When a decision is made to use medication for treatment of conditions other than ADHD, attention to detail is just as important. Many of the principles are the same whether you are treating ADHD, anxiety, or other mood disorders. For free, you can go to parentchildjourney.com, click on "Resources," and scroll down to "Helping Your Child with Medication." There you will find medication trial scales for the following:

- Mood stabilizers
- Neuroleptics
- Non-stimulants
- Serotonergics
- Stimulants

Of course, all medication decisions should be made in close communication with your prescriber—hopefully, someone with experience treating these disorders in children.

Psychosocial Treatment of Coexisting Conditions

Treatment of coexisting conditions often requires non-pharmacological management, such as psychotherapy, behavioral therapy, educational care, or social work. On a broader level, there may be important political and cultural factors. All the ADHD medication in the world doesn't fix racism, poverty, and other forms of discrimination. As discussed later in this book, many children with emerging differences in sexuality and gender identity face extraordinary societal barriers.

Long-Term Care

During the initial phases of ADHD diagnosis and treatment, parents are usually much more focused than their child. There are frequent visits with the doctor and lots of back-and-forth communication. But then, things change. You find a medication that works. All the energy devoted to early ADHD care wanes. Early anxieties about diagnosis and medication give way to familiarity, acceptance, and routine. Focus shifts to other things. The maintenance phase begins.

Although it continues to require considerable care—problems still pop up and fires need to be put out—it becomes just one of life's many complexities. New issues arise. It may become harder and harder to pay attention to your child's inattention.

Importance of Regular Follow-Up

Despite life's complexities, regular ADHD follow-up visits are very important. I recommend at least once every season: fall, winter, spring, summer. If your ADHD prescriber is your pediatrician, one of these could be the yearly check-up. Of course, if special problems arise, the frequency of visits should increase.

Maintenance visits are necessary for five reasons:
1. Monitoring for undertreatment of ADHD
2. Active surveillance for side effects
3. Monitoring for associated conditions
4. Guidance about upcoming developmental hurdles
5. Gradually shifting responsibility for care from parent to growing child

With these goals in mind, each visit should include the following:

- *Discussion of parent and child concerns.* You and your child might want to prepare a list of questions before the visit.
- *Review of feedback from teachers and other professionals.* Feedback questionnaires, distributed and completed in advance, can be very helpful. See the appendix for a copy of my Teacher Questionnaire or chadis.com for an excellent online screening system. Both include Vanderbilt Rating Scales, plus other important screening questions. The prescriber can schedule a brief teacher or school team conference call before or after the child's follow-up visit, as needed.
- *Review of medication effectiveness and side effects.* Before the visit, you and your child can also complete rating scales, using the original treatment trial form. This makes it easy to compare current and previous ratings. At the visit, you can combine your observations with those of teachers and other professionals, and discuss it all with your prescriber.
- *Measurement of weight, height, and body mass index (BMI).* These should be plotted on a growth chart and compared against previous points. In addition, the *blood pressure and pulse* should be checked at each visit.
- *Screen for coexisting issues.* A systematic review of physical and mental health, academic performance, extracurricular activities, behavioral issues, peer relations, home life, and environmental stresses.
- *Highlight successes and nurture relative strengths.* This

means asking about the child's accomplishments, efforts, and interests.

- *Keep building the doctor-patient relationship.* At the beginning and end of the visit, the doctor should take a few minutes to play with the child, or otherwise reinforce rapport and trust.

Monitoring for Undertreatment of ADHD

"Everything's fine. No problems. We just need a refill and we'll be on our way." All too often, this is the report—but everything is not always fine. Some issues are revealed only on closer inspection. Without active surveillance, undertreatment may fall through the cracks.

The right questions need to be asked. With deeper assessment, it often becomes clear that ADHD symptoms are not under sufficient control. Undertreatment can cause important problems at school, at home, or with friends. Sometimes, medication that was working well seems to lose effectiveness, because of growth or changing life circumstances.

Make sure to talk about the adequacy of treatment across different times, tasks, and people. Remember to distinguish coverage during medication peaks from troughs. Is there inadequate treatment even when medication is fully on board, only when medication levels are low, or during both peaks and troughs? Is medication coverage adequate for some tasks and settings but not for others?

Active Surveillance for Side Effects

Some side effects are revealed only in the context of the follow-up visit. There may be subtle but significant decelerations in weight gain. Often, parents and children come to ADHD visits certain that the weight gain has been fine and are surprised to learn otherwise. Or they might have serious concerns about appetite suppression and poor growth, then stare in disbelief when the numbers prove reassuring. This discrepancy between assumption and measurement never ceases to amaze me. But the scale and the growth chart never lie.

Occasionally, there may be low blood pressure from alpha-agonists. Very rarely, there may be high blood pressure or fast heart rate from stimulants. Sometimes, doctors pick up on medication-induced tics that parents and children might not have noticed or assumed were caused by something else. For example, many people mistake cough or eye-blinking tics for allergies.

Often, the follow-up visit gives parents and children the opportunity to step outside of their busy lives and think about other possible side effects that might be otherwise overlooked. The impact of changes in mood, anxiety, or sleep problems might be minimized. The connection between medication and many such symptoms may be missed altogether or undermanaged.

Monitoring for Associated Conditions

ADHD follow-up visits give prescribers the opportunity to screen for commonly associated conditions. Some problems may be secondary to ADHD; others might be coexisting. Over the years, new developmental phases and increasing expectations bring out new issues and new concerns. Some might be obvious, but other very important issues might not. Prescribers should create a safe place to ask about anxiety, depression, teasing, bullying, abuse, sexuality, gender identity, and substance use. An old medical school adage applies: "If you don't look, you don't find."

Anticipatory Guidance

Children and adolescents with ADHD should receive the same kind of anticipatory guidance as anyone else (American Academy of Pediatrics, 2019). They just need more of it, because ADHD usually makes everything more complicated and challenging. As a supplement to primary medical care, regular medication follow-up visits provide extra opportunities to discuss a whole range of important developmental issues. To name a few:

- growth and nutrition
- sleep
- exercise
- family relations
- screen and social media use
- drug, tobacco, and alcohol use
- driving and other safety issues
- social success and stress
- conflict resolution
- puberty and sexuality
- academic success
- life after high school

Gradually Shifting Responsibility from Parent to Growing Child

Although parents are key to successful care, the child or adolescent is the patient. The ADHD follow-up visit should strengthen the doctor-patient relationship and teach the patient self-advocacy. From the very first visit, children should be made to feel that they are crucial participants in their own care. They should be taught about the nature of ADHD and how medication works; practice monitoring target symptoms and possible side effects; learn safe strategies for self-management of medication; and feel their voice is heard.

Early on, taking medication should be a shared responsibility between parent and child. This means parent-supervised practice using schedules, reminder systems, and pill boxes. Adolescents should be taught how to use their own devices to set up reminders, and should manage their own refills. Before going off to college or entering the workforce, they should learn about medication abuse for performance enhancement and illegal sale for profit (Wilens et al., 2008).

Beyond medication management, these visits represent wonderful opportunities for your child to learn more about developmental differences, self-awareness, and self-regulation. Over the years, doctor-patient discussions become broader, deeper, and more nuanced. Gradually, a greater percentage of the visit should be spent without the parent in the room. Doctor and patient should discuss the complexities of disability. Children and adolescents can be taught to objectively evaluate their own treatment resistance, denial, ambivalence, and self-acceptance. They can learn that ADHD is an explanation but not an excuse, a hurdle but not a roadblock. Adolescents may struggle to resolve normal developmental conflicts pertaining to interdependence and self-responsibility. It helps to have a sounding board.

A strong doctor-patient relationship translates into improved ability to seek help and a greater degree of self-reliance. ADHD visits can teach children how to access the health care system and form a trusting relationship with their doctor. Moreover, the child should come to see their doctor as a caring ally, a steady presence in times of trouble and triumph. During the last few years of high school, the follow-up visits should focus on a smooth and gradual transfer of care from the pediatric provider to an adult doc. One hopes that these regular visits forge relationships that are valued and remembered fondly by the emerging adult and the aging doc alike.

Discontinuation Trials

Much has been written about starting medication for ADHD. But much less attention has been paid to the important issue of when to stop ADHD treatment and how. Sometimes, the only way to move forward with ADHD medication … is to stop.

Why Stop?

There are two good reasons to consider a discontinuation trial: 1) to see if medication is still needed, and 2) to see if medication is causing a side effect. Discontinuation trials don't have to focus on just positive or negative effects. Stopping medication can shed light on how it affects both target symptoms and side effects simultaneously.

Discontinuation Trials to See if Medication Is Still Needed

At the beginning of treatment for ADHD, parents and children often wonder, "How long will it be necessary to take medicine?" In general, the more severe the ADHD symptoms and the younger the age of onset, the more hardwired the ADHD and the longer the need for treatment (Roy et al., 2016). However, we don't have any reliable way to predict how long someone will need to continue taking their medicine (Hechtman et al., 2016).

Factors vary from one individual to another. Up to 30 years of age, brains continue to mature; some more than others. Inhibitory centers in the prefrontal cortex become better connected with the rest of the brain, but the resulting improvement in overall function differs between individuals. Children also diverge in how well they learn and practice effective compensatory strategies.

To what degree one can outgrow the need for medicine depends upon a wide-ranging and ever-changing set of issues. Factors include: learning disabilities, mood disorders, autism spectrum disorders, and other coexisting conditions; contrasting trajectories in personality development; plus, differences in family, peer group, community, cultural, and life experiences.

The road travelled certainly makes a difference. The transition from childhood to adulthood will allow your child more opportunities in natural areas of strength and interest. However, not everyone has the good fortune to find a life path that taxes their ADHD less. In reality, some adult circumstances, jobs, and relationships demand progressively more self-control. Some ADHD lies dormant or well-compensated throughout childhood. Trouble might not become apparent until one faces the challenges of adult life.

With all these variables and all this unpredictability, the only way to really tell whether an individual can successfully come off their ADHD medication is to do a carefully controlled discontinuation trial. Discontinuation trials can also help answer a related set of questions about treatment effectiveness. For example, if your child has been taking ADHD medicine for a while, how can you tell if it's still working? How much difference is it still making? Stop and see.

Discontinuation Trials to See if Medication Is Causing a Side Effect

Another less obvious reason to do a discontinuation trial is to sort out whether some suspicious symptoms are side effects of medication, coincidental, or perhaps due to frequent ADHD traveling companions: irritability, anxiety, social withdrawal, poor eating or sleeping, tics, or obsessive-compulsive behaviors. Any of these symptoms can be *either* a medication side effect or a coexisting condition.

Often, side effects are so obviously secondary to medication that a discontinuation trial is not necessary. There may be no confusion if symptoms came on just when medication was started, if symptoms come and go as medicine blood levels rise and fall, and if there are no other explanations. In these clear-cut cases, if the side effect is significant, just stop the medication or at least lower the dose. But sometimes, it's really not so clear. Some side effects can sneak up so gradually that their connection to medication requires a high level of suspicion, careful surveillance, and expert analysis. Further complicating matters, children change. New problems can develop that are totally unrelated to medication. Just because your child did not have a symptom prior to medication does not mean the medication caused it. On the other hand, just because your child had similar symptoms prior to treatment does not mean that medication could not have amplified them.

Accidental Discontinuation Trials

People do discontinuation trials all the time—unintentionally. A dose is forgotten. A bottle isn't packed. A prescription isn't refilled. If a child could consistently remember to take their own ADHD medicine, one might question the diagnosis! Given the genetics of ADHD and executive dysfunction, parents may face similar challenges with daily administration.

I say, use these unplanned disruptions in treatment as opportunities: 1) to review systems for reliable administration and 2) to gather accidental discontinuation trial data. Did you notice any difference off medication? Was the difference positive, negative, or both? Were the changes small, medium, or large?

Sometimes, accidental discontinuation trials yield clear results. Other times, results are not clear. It is possible that a few good days off medication means the ADHD no longer requires treatment.

But before throwing your child's medication away in the trash, remember, ADHD is all about performance inconsistency, not absolute inability. Most children with ADHD can do well off of medication for limited periods of time; especially if the ADHD is relatively mild, the setting is structured, and the expectations are familiar. The need for medication may eventually resurface only when self-control is required over longer periods of time and across a wider range of settings and tasks.

And ADHD changes over the years. Just because discontinuation in the past caused more obvious symptoms does not mean that your child has completely outgrown the disorder. As children get older, predominant external symptoms of hyperactivity and impulsivity usually transform into subtler internal symptoms of distractibility and executive dysfunction. To accurately determine ongoing need for medication, you might need to reassess developmentally appropriate outcomes.

So, the results of accidental discontinuation trials should not be ignored. However, the important decision to stop medication should be made carefully, after data is collected in a more reliable and controlled manner.

Controlled Discontinuation Trials

If you aren't sure about the need for medication at school, you should run a discontinuation trial when school's in session. Your child might do well off medication on weekends or vacation, but this doesn't always mean medication is unnecessary across all settings. Avoid doing a discontinuation trial during transition times: the first several weeks of the school year, just before or just after vacation. Avoid other significant life events like important exams, family stresses, or other potentially confounding changes. You don't want to be confused about whether symptom ratings reflect the discontinuation of the medicine or just a change of circumstance.

This doesn't mean that discontinuation trials should always be done during school. Summer or weekend stops make sense if you are evaluating whether medicine is necessary outside of school or seeing about possible medication side effects. And even if it's all about school, you might want to first see how things go off medication on a weekend. Choose a Saturday when a parent is around and there are no special events. If there are no big problems, then you can more safely see what happens "au naturel" through the week.

How to Run a Discontinuation Trial

Controlled discontinuation trials are really just treatment initiation trials in reverse. First, it's useful to review the goals. What are we trying to achieve with medication? What would represent an unacceptable degree of poor ADHD control off medication? What would represent an unacceptable degree of side effect on medication?

Next, identify reliable observers; usually parents, a teacher, and your child. Have all observers complete the baseline column on a treatment trial form, rating target symptoms and possible side effects on the current dose of medication. Stimulant medication doesn't have to be tapered. You can just stop. Non-stimulants should be tapered gradually, to avoid rebound side effects.

At the end of the first week off stimulant medication, or week-by-week during a nonstimulant trial taper, all observers should complete the second column on the treatment trial form and share their follow-up ratings with the prescriber.

Interpreting and Acting on Results

A discontinuation trial to see if medication is still needed yields one of four possible results:

1. *Complete relapse.* Symptoms were well-controlled on medication, but come back off medication, and again cause significant impairment. If this medication (at this dose) caused no side effects (see below), just start it back up.

2. *Partial relapse.* Symptoms were well-controlled on medication and come back off medication but cause less impairment than before treatment. Things are worse off medication, but not as bad as before. You might decide to just restart the previous dose, or to extend the discontinuation trial to see if this degree of relapse will cause significant impairment.

3. *Partial treatment.* Symptoms were not under optimal control on medication but discontinuation causes symptoms to get worse. In retrospect, the medication wasn't perfect but it was still substantially better than nothing. If there are no side effects, instead of stopping medication, you might want to try increasing the dose.

4. *Possible remission.* Symptoms were well-controlled on medication but don't come back off medication, at least not immediately. Consider extending the discontinuation trial to see if symptoms return over a longer period of time. Complete or partial relapse can occur belatedly, as your child navigates life challenges. If there is relapse, then depending upon the degree of impairment, consider restarting medication.

Hoping to outgrow the need for medication is perfectly understandable. However, failure to get off medication doesn't mean failure to overcome ADHD. In fact, the most common cause of failure to overcome ADHD is failure to treat. The over-arching goal is not to get off medication but to relieve impairment and improve quality of life.

A discontinuation trial to see if medication is causing a side effect could yield one of four possible results:

1. *Completely reversible side effect.* If discontinuation results in complete disappearance of the possible side effect in question, then it was probably due to the medication. Your child could get off the medication and perhaps try something

else. However, if the medication was otherwise working very well to treat target symptoms, you could consider lowering the dose to see if you can lose the side effect but keep the benefits.

2. *Partially reversible side effect.* If discontinuation makes a possible side effect diminish but not entirely disappear, then it's probably a coexisting condition, in part amplified—but not entirely caused—by medication. Here, judgment must be made about whether the coexisting condition should be treated. The dose of the ADHD medication could be lowered, or it could be stopped and a different one tried, ideally one that's less likely to worsen—or might even help with—the coexisting condition.

3. *Coincidental symptom not affected by medication.* If discontinuation has no impact at all on the possible side effect in question, it was probably just a coincidental problem. The ADHD medication is not making things worse. Depending upon its severity, you might have some work to do on this other issue but there's no need to change ADHD treatment.

4. *Coincidental symptom partially treated by medication.* Sometimes discontinuation makes a presumed side effect worse instead of better! For example, on medication, many children with ADHD actually do better with eating, sleeping, and mood; especially if these problems were partially driven by hyperactivity, impulsivity, or distractibility. Here, go back on the ADHD medication, knowing that it's not causing the problem.

Uncertainty and Do-Overs

Whether you're running a discontinuation trial to assess a medication for positive or negative effects, it's not unusual to get ambiguous results. It's almost impossible to control all the variables. When you stop medication, other relevant factors—obvious or hidden—are always at play. Despite your best efforts, doubt lingers.

One day, Delores came home and told her mom that she didn't want to take her medicine anymore. She'd forgotten to take her dose that morning and got her best quiz score ever. Her mother tried to explain the difference between coincidence and causation but Tammy didn't buy it. Her mother suggested repeating the experiment in a more controlled way.

To resolve uncertainty, we can try a do-over. Good scientific method depends upon repeating the same experiment and getting the same result each time. To distinguish loose coincidence (correlation) from tight connection (cause-effect relationship): A) stop the medication, B) restart, A) stop again, and B) restart again. This kind of doubling back lowers the chance of confusion. In this way, coincidental association is less likely mistaken for cause-and-effect.

Tammy agreed to a discontinuation trial. Every other week, she did not take her medication. The teachers were told that Tammy was "trying something different," but did not know what was happening week-by-week. The results were clear: ratings of 0s and 1s on medication went up to 1s and 2s during off weeks. Tammy completed her own scales and her numbers went up too. She admitted, "Well, maybe it does make a difference after all."

Trail-End for Excursion 1

And so ends our deep dive into medication management for ADHD. As emphasized, ADHD rarely travels alone. Now, we turn our attention to non-pharmacological management of two conditions commonly associated with ADHD: anxiety, in Excursion 2, and autism, in Excursions 3 and 4.

EXCURSION 2
Go—Parallel Exposure Therapy for Anxiety

The only thing we have to fear is fear itself.
—Franklin Delano Roosevelt

Raph's beak began to hurt. He started to wonder, Maybe Turtle was right. Maybe birds can't ride unicycles.

Turtle said, "I told you so. Just stay on this log with me. That way, you won't get hurt. You can rest. If you fall asleep, you can dream about Tambalacoque fruit."

Raph was exhausted from all of his falls off the unicycle. He stretched out on the log with Turtle and fell into a deep sleep. When he woke up, his beak didn't hurt so much. But his tummy was even hungrier. He couldn't stay with Turtle on the log forever.

Cautiously, he got back on the unicycle. Turtle woke up and yelled at Raph, "You're going to fall on your beak again, you fool!"

Raph just sat there. He still wanted to ride. He knew he had to get to the mountain. But he was too afraid of falling.

Signposts for Excursion 2

This excursion is a detailed discussion of cognitive-behavioral therapy for anxiety, including:

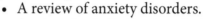

- A review of anxiety disorders.
- Anxiety in individuals, relationships, and social systems.
- How to do cognitive-behavioral therapy with individuals.
- How to do parallel exposure therapy with families and schools.
- Application of parallel exposure therapy in larger social systems and other conditions.
- What to do when CBT fails, including medication for anxiety.

Here, we will start with anxiety in the brains of individuals and then move on to anxiety in progressively larger systems.

Anxiety in Perspective

ADHD and Anxiety

ADHD and anxiety can be thought of as disorders on opposite ends of the self-control spectrum. As discussed in Excursion 1, ADHD is a problem of *too little* inhibition. In this Excursion 2, we will explore anxiety as a problem of *too much* inhibition. With ADHD, the brain brakes are too loose; with anxiety, they're too tight. People with ADHD live too much in the present. People with anxiety live too much in the past and the future.

Whether treating ADHD or anxiety, success depends upon evidence-based strategies and careful evaluation. With ADHD, as already emphasized, medication should be considered first-line treatment. With anxiety, treatment should usually begin with cognitive-behavioral therapy.

For the management of child and adolescent anxiety, there are many excellent resources already available (Zucker, 2016; Rapee, Wignall, Spence, Lyneham, & Cobham, 2008). CBT usually helps. But some children are more complicated than others. When treatment fails, it's often due to coexisting conditions and interpersonal complexities. In this excursion, I will review standard approaches to individual CBT but broaden the focus to include family, school, and even larger social systems. After all, there's more to a child than just their anxiety and there's more to anxiety than just the child. Let me explain.

There's More to the Child Than Just the Anxiety

Children with anxiety usually have other associated conditions too, which complicates therapy. Often, effective treatment of anxiety requires treatment of other intertwined neurobehavioral issues.

Emily, a kindergartner, had severe social anxiety. When she was home with her parents, Emily spoke in complete paragraphs, but in school and every other social situation, she did not speak—at all. One of Emily's pediatricians wondered about autism. Eventually, Emily saw a psychologist and received a diagnosis of selective mutism. Everything her parents read about SM fit Emily perfectly.

A combination of behavioral therapy and medication worked like a miracle. She started to talk at school, and had some successful playdates. But despite this exciting progress, there was still a big gap between Emily and other kids her age. Her rate of progress seemed to plateau. The psychologist suggested a broader assessment. Emily's parents and teachers always knew that she also had problems with motor skills. Could there be more?

A neuropsychologist did some testing. She ruled out autism but found there was more going on than just social anxiety, selective mutism, and motor skill deficits. As it turned out, Emily also had the inattentive type of ADHD and severe executive dysfunction. In addition, Emily had a reading and writing disorder. The neuropsychologist explained how this constellation of problems made it hard for Emily to keep up with her peers. All of these issues contributed to Emily's anxiety—and her anxiety made it harder for her to overcome these other challenges too.

There's More to Anxiety Than Just the Child

Children with anxiety—or any other disorder—don't exist in isolation. Each child lives in a network of relationships, with family, friends, teachers, and others. Often, to be effective, we need to move beyond treatment of the individual child to management of anxiety within larger social systems, including family, school, community, and even culture (Ross & Nisbett, 2011). If we define a problem too narrowly, our solution will be insufficiently comprehensive. Here we will outline an approach to simultaneous treatment of anxiety in children *and* parents *and* teachers *and* doctors *and* others! I call this systems approach to cognitive-behavioral therapy "parallel exposure therapy."

> *Before her diagnoses, Emily's parents had avoided birthday parties and playdates. When visiting adults asked Emily questions, Emily's parents answered on her behalf. Friends and relatives gave conflicting advice. Some said, "You've got to push her harder." Others said, "Just relax. She's just shy—a late bloomer." Still others said, "She's just an introvert."*
>
> *During recess and free-play at school, whenever teachers had tried to include her in group activities, Emily got upset and wanted to go home. So they let her play by herself. They thought it was better not to push her too hard, and hoped she would gradually warm up. Other kids tried to play with her, but when Emily didn't respond, they moved on.*
>
> *At one check-up, the pediatrician asked skeptically, "She really talks at home? Has anybody else ever heard her talk?" Emily's parents felt like they were being accused of lying, and sent him a video of Emily chattering away with her dolls at home. The pediatrician called back. He was defensive, apologetic, and confused.*
>
> *And then, on top of everything, Emily's mother's sister was diagnosed with advanced breast cancer. This stressed the whole family system even more.*

As Emily's story demonstrates, many people in her life played an important role.

Over the next two excursions, we will investigate anxiety disorders as a springboard for discussing all of this complexity. In Excursion 2, we will review anxiety disorders, with special emphasis on: 1) *coexisting conditions,* how there's more to the child than just the anxiety; and 2) *systems,* how there's more to the anxiety than just the child. Then we will discuss parallel exposure as treatment for anxiety in family systems, school systems, and other systems too. We'll wrap up Excursion 2 with some applications of parallel exposure therapy to conditions other than anxiety.

We'll go deeper into treatment of coexisting conditions in Excursion 3, especially the management of coexisting anxiety, ADHD, and autism; then, briefly, the application of these principles to the treatment of other coexisting conditions.

Against Pre-Destiny

Fortunately, there's more to anxiety than just associated problems. We can all rely on compensatory strengths. Coexisting with our irrational amygdalae, we have mighty fine cerebral cortices too. We are not just a bundle of emotions. Human beings are also the most rational and intelligent of animals. Although evolution has programmed us with fight/flight/freeze reflexes, our survival has also depended upon our unique ability to stop and use our smarts.

There is more to our upbringing than just trauma and more to our world than just terror. Even for people who have experienced the most horrible neglect, abuse, or poverty, there are tales of overcoming. And even though the modern world is full of complicated stresses and daunting challenges, one can argue that people in all countries and socioeconomic groups are objectively better off today than in the past. Over the past centuries, there is much less violence, poverty, and hardship of all kinds (Pinker, 2019).

Despite our rational capacities and the progress of civilization, people still feel stuck. Children and adults say: "It's just the way I am. Everything is so much harder and more stressful these days. There's nothing I can do about it." But must we be so pessimistic? Anxiety can yield to reason. Suffering can give way to development. Although biology and environment may predispose one, neither is carved in stone. Nietzsche defined health not as the absence of illness but the ability to overcome it. Nowhere is this more true than in the treatment of anxiety.

First, the basics.

A Review of Anxiety Disorders

When to Worry About Anxiety

Anxiety is a normal part of childhood. Anxiety is also a normal part of parenthood *and* teacherhood *and* doctorhood. For all human beings, worries come and worries go. Although too much anxiety can cause distress and impairment, too little anxiety can be a problem too. The just-right amount of anxiety is motivating ("I'd better work harder"), sensitizing ("I'm worried about my friend"), and even life-saving ("Is it safe to cross this street?"). Some of the most compassionate and moral people have effectively channeled their anxious concern for good. Perhaps it's no coincidence that many extraordinary social workers, psychologists, and other health care providers are anxious people.

Yet, some people worry more than they should. They experience too much internal tension. They avoid important situations and necessary challenges. They might even become paralyzed by fear. In many very important ways, anxiety can interfere with living life normally. If distress or impairment—to the child or the family—is severe or persistent, then it may be appropriate to diagnose an anxiety disorder and pursue treatment.

Recognizing Anxiety

Anxiety disorders have always been around but they are being recognized with increasing frequency. Estimates of incidence in childhood and adolescence range anywhere from 10 to 50 percent. Even at the low end, this makes anxiety the most common developmental disorder of young people. The good news: anxiety is a very treatable disorder. The bad news: for many reasons, most anxious children—and adults—don't get the help they need.

Although we are getting better, undertreatment is still too often due to under-recognition. This is because anxiety is often hidden. It's called an "internalizing disorder," meaning that anxiety causes more distress in the person who has it than it does to others. In contrast, ADHD (especially the impulsive-hyperactive type) is an "externalizing disorder"—it often causes more distress to others than it does to the person who has it.

Stereotypically, boys with overt ADHD often have veiled anxiety. In contrast, girls with more obvious anxiety often have relatively concealed problems with attention. Of course, there are many exceptions to these "gender-alizations." There are plenty of boys with more obvious signs of anxiety and hidden ADHD, and girls with obvious ADHD and hidden anxiety. Sometimes, anxiety is not at all internalizing. It can look very different from textbook avoidance and withdrawal. In fact, in many children, anxiety bubbles up and spills out as intermittent explosiveness or smoldering irritability. It can cause tantrums, intense defiance, anger, and aggression. The point here is to look underneath the surface. Seasoned clinicians learn not to be fooled by initial impressions. They consider the possibility of anxiety—and other coexisting conditions—no matter what the presenting symptoms.

Anxiety may be underdiagnosed simply because it goes by so many other names. If doctors don't ask the right question, they might miss the diagnosis. A doctor should not ask, "Do you have any anxiety?" The answer might be a misleading "No." However, if the doctor asks the same person the same question using different words, the answer might be "Yes!" For example, "Do you ever feel …

- nervous?"
- over-concerned?"
- homesick?"
- worried?"
- self-conscious?"
- shy?"
- oversensitive?"
- fearful?"
- scared?"
- apprehensive?"
- stressed?"

In addition, clinicians should ask questions about thoughts, not just feelings (Alvord & McGrath, 2017). Distorted or irrational thoughts are another important way to recognize anxiety. For example, "Do you ever think …

- what if something bad happens?"
- I'm going to fail?"

- I can't do it right?"
- nobody will like me?"
- I or someone I care about could die?"

Anxiety may also be missed if the anxiety trigger is avoided. No trigger, no anxiety. For example, a child with a severe fear of bees will show no fear if he or she never goes outside. Yet the bee phobia is no less real and no less impairing. The child doesn't experience the symptoms of anxiety but the anxiety is most certainly having a negative impact. To avoid distress, victims of anxiety may limit themselves to living within a very narrow comfort zone. The anxiety only kicks up when they have to venture beyond those self-protective boundaries.

Anxious children and teens may be constantly "on-guard" or "hypervigilant." When faced with novelty, their first reaction is to hesitate or withdraw. They feel threatened. They may catastrophize. They need excessive and frequent reassurance. They constantly check back with parents or teachers or friends or social media. They may react to uncertainty by adopting a broad range of compulsions or rituals. Their brains might get stuck on certain obsessions or intrusive thoughts.

Consequently, anxious children might live too much in their heads. Anxiety distorts reality. The most common cause of hallucinations in childhood—seeing or hearing things that are not there—is not schizophrenia. It's anxiety. Anxiety can make it difficult to objectively assess relative risk and tell the difference between safety and danger. Especially in today's world, anxiety doesn't just affect children.

Anxious Parents of Anxious Children

Well-meaning adults can become overly protective. Instinctively, loving parents shield their children from distress—but perhaps subconsciously, parents may be shielding themselves from distress too.

Consider the following common parent thoughts: "My child is upset. I need to protect my child from harm, both physical and emotional." Avoidance works, but only temporarily. The next trigger is just around the corner. Child anxiety and parent anxiety kick up in dynamic interplay, each amplifying the other, in a self-perpetuating anxiety-avoidance cycle. Neither parent nor child learn to face their fears. The child needs help learning to manage their anxiety. But first, adults need to learn how to manage their own anxiety too. By reassuring or avoiding too much, parents send an unhelpful message to their child: "You can't handle this yourself." They are also sending themselves a message: "I can't handle my child's distress. I can't handle letting go. I can't trust my child to learn from their own experience." Exposure that involves the parallel work of parents, children, and others in the anxiety system will allow them all to avoid avoidance, learn to face their fears, and cope (Lebowitz, Omer, Hermes, & Scahill, 2013).

However, this is not to say that nervous parents are to blame for their children's fears. True, anxious parents can make children feel anxious. But anxious children can make parents feel anxious too. Whether "worry genes" are shared or not, anxiety usually involves a complicated tangle of interacting factors, including inherited tendencies *and* environment, nature *and* nurture, seed *and* soil, chicken *and* egg, child *and* parent.

Primary and Secondary Anxiety

A child can have a primary problem with anxiety that presents as something else. Let's call this "Anxiety Causing Other Stuff." Or there can be another hidden primary condition that presents more noticeably as secondary anxiety. Let's call that "Other Stuff Causing Anxiety." Sometimes, the anxiety causation arrow points just in one direction. But more often, anxiety is both primary and secondary, existing in a circle of cause and effect, with no easily identified beginning or end. In fact, every condition listed below as a possible *consequence* of (primary) anxiety, will also be listed even further below as a possible *cause* of (secondary) anxiety. Bear with me. This will become clear as we explore the complexities of causation together.

Anxiety Causing Other Stuff

Primary Anxiety Disorders

Primary anxiety disorders usually carry a degree of genetic predisposition. Many people are just born with more sensitivity to environmental stimuli and internal sensations. This kind of heightened sensitivity, inflexibility, and over-inhibited temperament can run in families. Although a general predisposition to anxiety can be inborn, anxiety disorders come in many different flavors. Furthermore, over time, anxiety often shifts from one type to another, pertaining to the individual's current phase of life or development. For example, separation anxiety might peak at transitions to preschool, summer camp, or college. Performance anxiety increases and decreases in proportion to academic or work demands.

Diagnostic Categories

There are many types of primary anxiety disorders:

- *Separation anxiety* is a fear of separating from parents or primary caretakers, such as when going to sleep or going to school.
- *Generalized anxiety* has less specific or easily labeled triggers. Presenting symptoms also tend to be more wide-ranging and varied.
- *Specific fears and phobias* are fears of specific objects or situations, such as flying, heights, insects, blood, illness, injury, or darkness.
- *Selective mutism* is the inability to speak in specific situations and without specific people present, such as in school, away from parents.
- *Obsessive-compulsive disorders* are excessive, distorted, or "stuck" thoughts and repetitive or ritualized behaviors.
- *Perfectionism* is an excessive fear of failing or making mistakes, with unrealistically high standards and intense self-criticism.
- *Social anxiety* is a fear of social situations and interactions, including uncertainty about what to do or expect, embarrassment, or fear of negative judgments by others.
- *Situational anxiety* is a fear of new, changing, or specifically threatening circumstances.
- *Agoraphobia* is a fear of crowds or public places.
- *Acute or post-traumatic stress disorder* involves re-experiencing, distress, or avoidance after a severely traumatic event.
- *Panic disorder* is about sudden and repeated attacks of intense fear.

Secondary Physical Symptoms

Some children might be able to label and describe their own anxiety. But often, anxiety shows up in other ways. Children often experience or express their anxiety through their bodies. In other words, primary anxiety disorders often present as secondary physical symptoms. Any organ system can be affected. Dr. John

Walkup, one of the world's experts on anxiety disorders, shows how symptoms of anxiety often present along a line drawn down the body from a point between the eyebrows all the way through the belly button. Common midline symptoms of anxiety include:

- Headaches, dizziness
- Chest pain, shortness of breath, hyperventilation, heart palpitations
- Lump in the throat, swallowing difficulties, vomiting
- Eating too much or eating too little
- Abdominal pain ("stomachaches")
- Bowel/bladder urgency, frequency, or loss of control ("accidents")

Many—if not most—symptoms of anxiety have components of both mind *and* body. For example, gastroesophageal reflux (heartburn), irritable bowel syndrome (spastic colon), and asthma involve very real abnormalities in the gut and lungs. But there is an emotional piece too. In a vicious cycle, stress can bring on physical symptoms and physical symptoms can bring on stress. Psychosomatic illness means mind *and* body, not one or the other. Although it's not *all* in your head, *some* of it is. The degree of accompanying emotional distress plays a very real role in making physical symptoms better or worse.

Medical consultations may fail to consider important contributing psychological factors. Doctor after doctor may evaluate organ after organ. Test after test may lead to treatment after treatment. A wild goose chase. This anxiety-fueled doctoring only prolongs uncertainty. Unnecessary and even harmful treatments may amplify the underlying anxiety. Sometimes, the evaluation process itself makes things so much worse that the true source of difficulty becomes impossible to find.

Albert, a 12-year-old, had a long history of ADHD, executive dysfunction, and school-related anxiety. Early in the school year, he was already struggling to keep up with the increased homework load. Then, the week of his first exams, Albert fell off his bike riding to school. He skinned his knee badly, but did not hit his head. He got checked out in the emergency room— no leg fracture, no other serious injuries.

The next day, he had a bad headache and didn't feel like going to school. His parents figured one more day of recovery would be fine. But the next day, the headache was still there. They took Albert to his pediatrician, Dr. T. Despite there being no evidence of head trauma and a normal neurologic exam, Dr. T. was worried about a possible concussion. He sent Albert to a neurologist.

The neurologist did a thorough exam. Again, normal. But she recommended a brain MRI, "for peace of mind." The MRI was a stressful experience for Albert. Being in the scanner felt like being in a coffin. The MRI was normal, but there was a "nonspecific bright spot in the right dorsolateral prefrontal cortex." The neurologist tried to be reassuring. "It's probably just a coincidental artifact—nothing to worry about and nothing to do with the bike accident." But all of this only increased Albert's anxiety. His parents grew more confused and worried too. They searched the Internet and read all about concussions.

Albert had more headaches, and missed more school. His parents got a second opinion. Another neurologist concluded, "Post-concussion syndrome cannot be ruled out with 100 percent certainty. Experts disagree about the importance of brain rest following concussions."

They decided to "play it safe" and have Albert take a leave of absence from school. Gradually, his headaches improved. But he fell farther and farther behind with schoolwork. Albert seemed to be getting more and more depressed. Whenever his parents even casually mentioned returning to school, Albert's headaches returned, along with full-fledged panic attacks.

Albert's parents spoke with a friend who was a child psychiatrist. He asked, "Do you think Albert might have had this trouble even without the bike accident? Could the MRI and everything else have made things worse?" Was their doctor friend implying that Albert was faking the whole thing? Or that they had caused the problem themselves? They became defensive, furious, and confused.

Although emotional factors can be underappreciated, parents and clinicians should be aware that physical symptoms can also be falsely ascribed to psychiatric problems. This may be more common when the doctor is a white male and the patient is female or a person of color. In all cases, across gender and race, the possibility of a medical illness should be taken seriously and never dismissed out of hand as "just stress."

Secondary Neuropsychological or Behavioral Disorders

In addition to masquerading as medical problems, primary anxiety disorders can also look like other neuropsychological or behavioral disorders.

- *Attention, executive, and learning problems.* Anxiety can cause secondary problems with attention, planning, organization, and learning, which in turn can cause poor school performance. Unless anxiety is identified as the source of the trouble, adult help may be misguided. Subject-specific educational interventions may miss the emotional source of difficulty. For example, math tutoring may not directly address math anxiety. Lowering expectations and demands—a form of avoidance—may provide temporary relief but just compound the problem long-term. If ADHD is misdiagnosed when anxiety is the primary cause of inattention, then stimulant medication might only make the anxiety worse.
- *Aggressiveness, explosiveness, and depression.* Anxiety can spill over into aggressive behavior. The child's primitive fright reactions can provoke flight, freeze, or fight behaviors. Emotional flooding then causes melting down or boiling over. Instead of responding with calm and understanding, adults may react with frustration and anger. Adult admonishment or punishment misses the root of the anxious child's problem, only adding to the underlying emotional turmoil. All of this stress can exacerbate feelings of helplessness, hopelessness, and depression.
- *Sensory reactivity.* Anxiety can co-occur with sensory processing differences, either over- or underreactivity. Anxiety can affect any of the senses: hearing, vision, taste, smell, touch, movement in space, or internal bodily sensations. The anxious child might have problems eating, toileting, or bathing. Anxiety can also present as difficulty tolerating haircuts or wearing certain clothing. In these cases, if the psychological component is not appreciated, inappropriate accommodation or narrowly focused sensory therapies may not help.
- *Sleep problems.* Any primary anxiety disorder—especially separation anxiety—can cause difficulties falling asleep or

staying asleep. Parents might rush in to either comfort or reprimand. Physicians may suggest sleep studies or medication. These responses can miss—and perhaps reinforce—the underlying anxiety issue. The child needs more practice tolerating separation, not avoiding it.

Zelda was an extremely fussy baby and a strong-willed toddler. She had very rigid likes and dislikes. Her parents learned to cater to Zelda's intense preferences, to avoid her prolonged and intense tantrums. In her unstructured nursery school, Zelda did fine. The teachers let her do her own thing. If other kids didn't want to do things her way, she just played by herself.

But then she started a standard kindergarten. The transition proved difficult. For the first time, she was required to follow a class schedule. The other kids enjoyed the teacher's creative and varied curriculum. But Zelda refused to participate in these ever-changing activities. She yelled at other kids for not doing things right. She aggressively pushed her classmates to the floor if they accidentally brushed up against her. Zelda even hit the teacher for asking her to start an art project. Zelda's teacher thought she was "oppositional-defiant." Her classmates thought she was a bully. But each night at home, Zelda cried herself to sleep, trembling with fear about what the next day might bring.

Other Stuff Causing Anxiety

As outlined above, anxiety commonly causes a wide variety of symptoms. But the causation arrow can point in the other direction too—other stuff can cause anxiety. In fact, many of the same conditions that anxiety causes can also cause anxiety. Pretty much any developmental difference or skill deficit can lead to secondary emotional distress. It's normal to feel anxious when the going gets rough. When anxiety is secondary to an underlying condition, effective treatment depends upon recognizing the primary source of the anxiety, not just the anxiety itself.

- *Other mood disorders.* Children with severe mood dysregulation, depression, or bipolar illness often worry about their inability to control their emotions. They fear being possessed by their own unwanted feelings. Their emotional reactivity may cause very real impairment, embarrassment, and misunderstanding. Consequently, they may compensate by lashing out or withdrawing.

- *ADHD/executive dysfunction.* Children with an impairing degree of hyperactivity, impulsivity, or distractibility usually have associated problems with time management, planning, organization, initiating, sustaining, inhibiting, and shifting. Consequently—at home, at school, and with friends—they are plagued by chronic underperformance, often compounded by negative feedback from their environment. Success deprivation and frustration cause secondary stress and worry. In addition, children and adolescents with executive dysfunction can be challenged by things that have nothing to do with academic or social performance. The world can be very overwhelming for people who have difficulty processing information and responding flexibly.
- *Learning disability or weakness.* Children with learning difficulties struggle to please teachers and avoid the negative consequences of poor school performance. They don't want to disappoint their parents, or themselves. They feel inadequate, compared to their peers. And language processing problems can make it hard to keep pace in ordinary conversation, in play, and in other social interactions.
- *Motor deficits.* Fine motor and gross motor weaknesses can have a significant impact on a child's comfort, in school, at home, and in play. Ordinary motor demands can be extraordinarily stressful or frustrating. Many tasks that come naturally to others feel daunting to children with atypical muscle tone, poor strength, or discoordination.
- *Movement disorders.* Children with involuntary movements or vocalizations may be embarrassed by their tics, spasms, or repetitive motor behaviors; especially if other children or adults are unkind, unsympathetic, or confused. Even if other people are understanding and supportive, these children may worry about their lack of control and feel stigmatized.
- *Sensory differences.* If a child is inherently under- or overreactive to sensory stimuli, they may experience the world in ways that can be confusing, irritating, or distressing. Through hearing, vision, taste, smell, touch, movement, or bodily sensations, many children experience the world differently. These sensory differences can affect engagement, learning, socialization, or mood regulation. Directly or indirectly, anxiety is often the result.

- *Autism spectrum disorder/social skills deficits.* Many children have poor social awareness, social motivation, or social skill. For them, ordinary social situations can feel like being plunked down in a foreign country without knowing the customs or language. Social anxiety may cause poor social function but, conversely, poor social function can cause social anxiety.
- *Medical problems.* Many children with chronic medical problems have anxiety about their illness and treatments. Understandably, they experience a variety of stresses dealing with repeated symptom relapses, doctor's visits, and medical procedures. Then there is all the talk about their medical issues at home and school. They feel different and alone. Often, they don't know any other kids with the same challenges. Moreover, they feel vulnerable and uncertain about their future. Relatively mild or short-term medical problems can also trigger disproportionally serious or lasting anxiety in predisposed children.
- *Medication/drug side effect.* Anxiety can be a side effect of many drugs. Some commonly prescribed culprits are stimulant medication for ADHD, bronchodilators for asthma, and steroids for a wide range of illnesses ranging from poison ivy to asthma to brain tumors. Marijuana, alcohol, and other "recreational drugs" can provide temporary relief. However, marijuana can cause rebound anxiety, psychological dependence, or—in about 10 percent of adolescents who are regular users—true addiction. Some people who smoke or vape marijuana can have full-blown panic attacks. Also, don't forget about caffeine- or nicotine-induced edginess and jitters.
- *Environmental stresses/trauma.* Childhood anxiety rises and falls with family or community stresses. Such environmental stresses may be acute or chronic, mild, or severe. For many children, life is much too hard. Within the family, there may be illness or disability, violence or death. Many children are exposed to substance abuse. They may directly experience physical, emotional, or sexual abuse; inappropriate disciplinary measures, neglect, changes in caregivers, marital discord or divorce; food insecurity or financial hardship. Outside of the immediate family, children may have challenges with relatives, peers, bullying, social media, cultural differences, discrimination, school, safety, or upsetting

current events. Any number of environmental stresses can cause a great deal of worry.

Anxiety in Systems

So you see how anxiety can cause other stuff and other stuff can cause anxiety. In most cases, the causation arrow doesn't just point in one direction. Rather, anxiety is usually due to a complicated combination of primary and secondary factors. Once again, it's chicken-and-egg, nature-and-nurture, child-and-parent, individual-and-environment.

In many cases, determining primary and secondary factors can be very helpful. It's obviously more effective to tackle problems at their source—clear the smoke by putting out the fire. But what if there is more than one fire? What if various fires fuel each other? With anxiety, things are usually not simple. Because anxiety exists at many levels, effective treatment usually requires a broad perspective.

Let's look at the following increasingly complicated levels of assessment:

1. Adult-child dyads
2. Family systems
3. Larger social and cultural systems

Adult-Child Dyads

As mentioned, parent anxiety can sometimes "infect" a child, and child anxiety can sometimes "infect" a parent. But let's not forget: These complexities are also present across other child-adult, adult-adult, and child-child relationships. Another relative, teacher, coach, clergy, therapist, or doctor can also be a vector of cross-contagion.

Normal Worry

A certain amount of adult worry is normal. Good parents naturally wonder, "Will my children be safe and healthy? Will they be happy and successful?" Adults may be visited by "ghosts from the nursery" (Fraiberg, Adelson, & Shapiro, 1975): issues from their own childhood that affect their confidence as parents. "Perfect parent syndrome" is when parents feel extraordinary pressure or guilt about normal imperfections, in themselves or their children. Tension in the family system can become compounded if two adults share the same worry, have different worries or have different degrees of concern. And there's a lot of perfect teacher, perfect doctor, perfect other adult syndrome out there too!

"Vulnerable Child Syndrome"

Parents may have excessive worries about their children's medical problems, developmental differences, or difficult circumstances. Such worries may be shared inappropriately: unfiltered or indirectly, consciously or subconsciously, obviously or subliminally. The term "vulnerable child syndrome" refers to parents who cannot stop catastrophizing, even after their child has fully recovered from a serious illness or injury (Green & Solnit, 1964). Understandably, a history of prematurity, meningitis, or other life-threatening disease can continue to haunt the parent-child relationship. Anxiety about the distant past becomes anxiety about the near future. In these cases, a child may learn from their parents to live fearfully, as if a history of fragility represents a real and present threat.

Adult Anxiety Disorder

Adults can have their own anxiety disorders, which may predate having children, or be brought out with the stresses of childrearing. Either way, parent anxiety may lead to the imposition of unrealistic expectations and inappropriate demands—on their child and themselves. Just like children, parents and other adults can have "anxiety causing other stuff" or "other stuff causing anxiety." Consider the list of primary and secondary anxiety disorders for children—it's the same list for parents. And all these generalizations about parents can apply to other adults in your child's life.

Challenging Versus Overprotective Parents

Let's shove one overly simplistic idea in the trashcan. I call it, "The Myth of the Challenging Parent" (Majdandžić et al., 2018). In this variation on the blame-the-parent theme, childhood anxiety is caused by the "overprotective parent." In contrast, the "challenging parent" pushes their child to take risks and toughen up, engages their young child in rough-and-tumble play, and insists upon increasingly difficult goals. They encourage their child to break through perceived limitations, take the hardest classes, and show some grit. According to this myth, challenging parent behaviors protect children from developing anxiety. There certainly is validity to the idea that coddling can interfere with emotional development (Lukianoff & Haidt). But is it really this simple?

A young woman became pregnant with dizygotic (non-identical) twins. The twins shared the same womb but had very different genes. Unlike monozygotic (identical) twins who have 100 percent the same DNA, these twins were no more genetically similar than any other brother and sister. In fact, they were more different than many non-twin siblings. The biological mother had an anxiety disorder. The biological father had ADHD.

They were adopted together, soon after birth, by an adventure-seeking couple in Colorado. The adoptive parents had met and fallen in love hiking the Pacific Coast Trail. They got married at the top of Pikes Peak and honeymooned rafting down the Colorado River. They were determined to raise their adopted twins to be self-reliant, outdoors-loving risk-takers.

The girl turned out as they hoped. The first time they put the family canoe in the river, she literally jumped in, shouting, "Go, boat, go!" That became a life-long metaphor for her impulsive behavioral style.

Despite parent encouragement and twin modeling, the boy could not have been more different. That same day, he never got in the canoe. Screaming in terror, he clung to his mother. His extreme risk-avoidance and emotional reactivity continued throughout his life.

It didn't take long for these parents to see how different two twins can be. When they pushed the girl, she just wanted more. They tried pushing the boy too. They told him, "You've got to learn to face your fears." But each time they pushed, his fears only increased. Gradually, they adjusted their expectations. They learned to approach their two very different twins in very different ways.

Chicken and Egg

Just because a risk-avoidant parenting style is correlated with having more-anxious children, this doesn't mean that coddling alone causes anxiety. Parent behavior can certainly be a factor, but it's never the whole story. Infants with an overreactive behavioral style condition their parents at least as much as their parents condition them. Any parent who has raised more than one child knows how different your own parenting style is with each of your temperamentally different children. You adjust to each child more than each child adjusts to you. Or, at least, you should.

For good reason, parents of fussy infants, fearful toddlers, or easily distressed children are less likely to "challenge" their children than parents of children who are easy, adaptable, and less sensitive. Does the parent cause the child's behavior or did the child cause the parent's behavior? At least in part, the child's anxiety may be the cause—not the result—of the parent's cautious style. Knowing what we do about genetics, any correlation between a child's anxiety and a parent's overprotective behavior may be due to nature as much as nurture. If child and parent are both anxious, maybe it's because they were both born with the same anxiety genes. True, they might reinforce each other's anxiety—but the primary causation arrow might be one that runs through many preceding generations of anxious ancestors and points at both of them together.

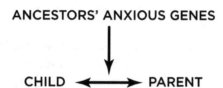

Genetics and inherited temperament matter. But biology is not destiny. By shoring up the parent-child interaction, unfavorable genetic currents can be resisted. Toward that goal, let's consider parent-child anxiety in greater detail.

Patterns of Parent-Child Anxiety: Shared, Sympathetic, and Antipathetic

Coexisting parent-child anxieties amplify each other. But there's no reason for anxious parents of anxious children to feel guilty. Everybody's human. The good news: understanding and acknowledging parent-child anxiety marks the beginning of effective management. If its full complexity is not recognized and countered, it can sabotage successful intervention.

Parallel exposure therapy targets these intertwined anxieties. To help your child overcome his or her worries, you may need some help overcoming your own anxieties too. That's okay. You're not an obstacle to your child's recovery. On the contrary, an anxious parent can be the best person in the world to help an anxious child. In helping your child, you help yourself. In helping yourself, you help your child. By helping each other, you change larger systems in which you're both embedded.

Let's take a look at three different patterns of parent-child anxiety. Please note: although we are starting this discussion by looking at simple parent-child dyads, we will eventually see how these same patterns of parallel anxiety exist across larger systems.

1. *Shared parent-child anxiety.* You and your child might be anxious about the same thing. For example, you might both be anxious about dogs, lightning, germs, medical procedures, separation, or social situations. In these cases, the same exposure can simultaneously trigger the same anxiety in both parent and child. Example: *You both see a dog. You both take a step back.*

2. *Sympathetic parent-child anxiety.* What loving parent doesn't feel anxious about their child's anxiety? Likewise, children can worry about their parent's anxiety. Parents don't want their children to suffer; children don't want their parents to suffer either. Here, the anxiety trigger is the other person's anxiety. Example: *Elizabeth is worried about her grades in school. Her father, Joe, is worried about getting a pay raise at work. Elizabeth is worried about her Dad. Joe is worried about his daughter.*

3. *Antipathetic parent-child anxiety.* Life is stressful. Parents have their own issues. Plus, parenting an anxious child can be tough. It's understandable if parents sometimes feel frustrated or even resentful. Likewise, children may be uncomfortable, confused, or anxious when their parents seem emotionally unresponsive or out of control. Example: *Instead of sympathetic concern, imagine Elizabeth and Joe each resenting the other's anxiety. Elizabeth might think,* Dad's always so stressed about work. What about me? *Joe might think,* Elizabeth is always so stressed about school. She doesn't have a clue what I deal with every day!

In sections that follow, we'll be going into more detail about management. But let's digress for a moment to preview coping with shared, sympathetic, and antipathetic anxiety.

Coping with Shared and Sympathetic Parent-Child Anxiety

Parents and children with shared or sympathetic anxiety instinctively shield each other from distress. This works in the short-term but only makes anxiety worse in the long-term. In parallel, parents and children may deny each other opportunities to learn coping and resilience. Together, they sweep their anxiety under the rug. As a result, they undermine each other's self-confidence. Parent and child can become entangled in a vicious cycle of mutual avoidance.

For example, a child might get anxious about schoolwork, athletic performance, or peer interaction. The parent is also anxious about the child's ability to succeed. The parent helps too much or shields the child from these normal challenges. This protection inadvertently sends the message that the parent doesn't believe the child can do it (Chansky, 2004). Possible failure is avoided— but so is possible success. Neither parent nor child learns how to overcome their shared fear of falling short.

Parents and children with shared or sympathetic anxiety should attend to and reinforce bravery, not anxiety. The emphasis should be on nurturing a "can-do" versus a "can't-do" attitude. They can communicate to each other a belief in each other's ability to overcome anxiety rather than reinforcing each other's passivity and pessimism—adopting a philosophy of empowerment, for themselves and for each other. In this way, anxiety gives way to quiet courage for both children and parents.

Coping with Antipathetic Parent-Child Anxiety

Parents and children with antipathetic anxiety struggle with a different set of challenges. Whether it's a parent dealing with an anxious child or a child dealing with an anxious parent, it's human to react with a complicated range of negative thoughts and feelings.

- *What's wrong with my child (my parent)? What's wrong with me?*
- *Will my child (my parent) be able to handle this? I don't know how to handle this.*
- *What have I done wrong as a parent (as a child)?*
- *I don't like feeling like my child (my parent) is out of control.*
- *What will others think of me as a parent (as a child)? Am I being judged by my spouse or partner, family, friends, or*

co-workers? (Am I being judged by my parent, siblings, friends, classmates, teachers, or others?)

- *What will it mean for my life if my child (my parent) never becomes independent (reliable) or has long-term psychiatric problems?*
- *How am I going to deal with my child's (my parent's) anxiety and also deal with my own stresses at home, with work, marriage, and other relationships (at school, with teachers, and with friends)?*
- *I don't have the time or energy or skills or emotional makeup to deal with this!*
- *I feel so alone in all of this. Sometimes, I'm overwhelmed. I understand that my child (my parent) has problems. But what about me?*

Antipathetic parents and children, through no fault of their own, may lack understanding, know-how, or both. They may fail to see the anxiety underlying each other's behavior. They may be blind to the emotional basis of their own reaction. Either way, if parents don't know what causes a child's behavior or what to do about it, they usually default to exerting control, either verbally, emotionally, or physically. They may scold or punish, making children feel more confused and more anxious. Likewise, if children don't know what causes their parent's behavior, they may shut down, lash out, or regress in other ways.

> *Tammy is a six-year-old girl. At a burger place, her father gets a refill from the soda machine. Tammy starts crying and screaming. She's thinking, It's illegal. My daddy's going to get arrested and end up in jail and then I won't ever see him again. Her father is thinking, This is ridiculous. Tammy is making a scene. I can't deal with her nonsense right now. Sometimes she can be such a pain.*

Antipathetic parents need to understand why their children act the way they do—and they also need to have insight into the source of their own thoughts, feelings, and behaviors. Then, when a child is anxious, parents can react with empathy toward their child and compassion toward themselves.

Over time, children need to learn the same kind of empathy and self-awareness. They need to learn that their parents are human too. What better way for a child to learn charity and self-acceptance than to see this empathy and self-awareness modeled by their parent?

Mixed Parent-Child Anxieties

Shared, sympathetic, and antipathetic anxiety are not mutually exclusive. They can all be triggered simultaneously. For example, a child gets anxious about separation from his or her parent. This can happen at any age; on going to bed, school, camp, or college. The parent's anxiety may contain strands of all three parent-child anxiety patterns:

1. *Shared anxiety.* The parent shares the child's fear of separation. *I feel anxious about separating from you too.*
2. *Sympathetic anxiety.* The parent understands and feels genuine concern about the child's distress. *I feel anxious about you feeling anxious.*
3. *Antipathetic anxiety.* The parent may also feel worried, frustrated, or confused about the child's inability to function independently. *I feel anxious because you shouldn't be feeling anxious.*

Each of these anxieties can amplify the others. Shared and sympathetic anxiety drive the parent into rescue mode. Separation is avoided and there is temporary relief, but neither parent nor child learn to cope. Consequently, antipathetic anxiety kicks in. The parent becomes more frustrated and resentful, and flips into a "tough love" approach. The child feels more confused and helpless. The parent-child dynamic becomes more stressed.

> *Jackie, a 10-year-old, didn't want to go to summer day camp. She didn't know what to expect. None of her friends would be there. She just wanted to stay home and watch TV. Her mother, Elise, remembered having similar fears about going to camp when she was young. (Shared anxiety.) And every time Jackie cried about going, Elise felt sorry for her. (Sympathetic anxiety.) Jackie's mother decided not to push the issue. They would figure something else out. But when school ended, Jackie didn't have anything to do. She got bored watching TV. Elise had to work, and felt increasingly angry and resentful. She found herself yelling at Jackie, "Why can't you just go to camp like other NORMAL kids?! If you're going to be so immature about it, no more TV for you, young lady. You're going to have a long list of chores to do each and every day."*

(Antipathetic anxiety.) Jackie was distraught.

How to address all of this complexity? Well, before we can start effective management, we have to understand a few more layers. Moving beyond the anxiety that exists in individuals or between parent and child, let's take a look at how anxiety happens in family systems.

Family Systems

Different Types of Relationships

Family systems theory is all about the hidden impact of complex relationships. Not just within families but across generations, we can discover intricate webs of interpersonal history. Between any three individuals, there are varying degrees of attachment and intensity; siblings, parents, grandparents, aunts, uncles, and others all have unique relationships with one another. Some relationships are very close. Others not.

Family systems theorists use all sorts of terms to describe the broad array of interpersonal gaps and junctions. Relationships can be "fused," "conflicted," "detached," "estranged," "cut-off," "indifferent," "abusive," "harmonious," "hostile," "controlling," and "distrustful." The type of relationship between two family members inevitably affects their relationships with every other family member, setting up important relationship triangles. Anxiety is often a key factor.

Triangulation

Let's explore a classic triangle. Parent A might be overly responsive and controlling. This might make Parent B dependent, helpless, and depressed. The child with the least amount of emotional separation from Parent A might respond anxiously to the tension between the parents. According to this view, the child's anxiety is a symptom of marital stress; at least in part, the child's anxiety is caused by a problem within the family system. Consequently, it's not the child who needs fixing. It's the family.

But the focus stays narrow. The parent naturally attends to the child's symptoms and ignores these other more complicated and hidden family relationships. In fact, the child's anxiety draws more attention away from the parents' relationship with each other. In this example, the child's anxiety is the smoke but the parents' marriage is the fire. Fanning the air only fuels the burn.

Or, triangulated parents and/or other care providers might struggle with how to manage a child's separation anxiety. One parent might be anxious about the child. Another parent might be worried (sympathetic) or stressed (antipathetic) about their spouse's anxiety. This difference in the parents' reactions to the child further stresses their relationship with each other. Both parents fear talking about their marriage with each other. It's easier to just focus on the kid. If one parent (or care provider) is tough and the other is soft, the child will be confused. To avoid their own anxiety, a child learns to appeal to the "softer" parent. This increases the stress between parents even more. Unrecognized, such a triangle of dysfunction can go on and on. Ironically, the child avoids anxiety about temporary separation from a parent as the parents avoid their own fear of permanent separation from each other. Everything gets swept under the rug. A cascade of anxious avoidance takes on a life of its own, escalating and disabling the whole family.

	Anxious child	Anxious parent A	Anxious parent B
Anxiety trigger	separation	child anxiety	spouse anxiety
Avoidance behavior	cling to parent	cling to child	increase distance from both

When evaluation and management of anxiety is narrowly focused on individuals, these interlocking pieces in the family puzzle are often given short shrift. Failure to acknowledge these family complexities interferes with treatment. Without a family systems perspective, a pattern of stressed relationships can even replicate across generations.

Just being aware of such dysfunctional webs can promote better communication and a healthier dynamic. By gently shining a light on the underlying problematic relationships, family systems therapy reduces the secondary symptoms of anxiety. If everyone in the family understands these triangles, they can reduce the overall tension in the family system, and stop blaming themselves and each other.

Sibling Relationships

Family systems theory doesn't limit its scope to triads of two parents and one child. Of course, many children are raised by single parents. And sibling relationships are just as important. So, let's digress a bit to highlight some complexities between brothers and sisters that are relevant to our discussion of anxiety in family systems.

In families with more than one child, parents may have difficulty meeting everyone's needs. Parent resources are easily stretched. There never seems to be enough time, money, energy, or emotional availability to go around. Some children, relative to their brothers or sisters, might feel neglected or insecure. Unequal attention doesn't just feel unfair—it can add to a child's stress and anxiety.

In any family system, there are many factors that can affect sibling relations and anxiety:

- *Sibling temperament.* As discussed in great detail in *Parent Child Journey,* we are all born with different behavioral styles. Siblings don't grow up in isolation from one another and no one can choose their brothers' and sisters' temperaments. Sometimes there is a "good fit" between siblings. Other times, siblings may have real incompatibilities. For example, one sibling might tend toward hyperactivity, distractibility, poor inhibition, inflexibility, high intensity of reaction, irregularity, and negative mood. The other sibling might be predisposed to low motor activity level, long attention span, over-inhibition, low intensity, high regularity, and positive mood. Across situations, these discordant behavioral styles can have different effects on family relationships and cause varying degrees of interpersonal stress.

- *Birth order.* Compared to their siblings, first children have different relationships with their parents. The arrival of each subsequent sibling affects the balance of parental attention, the patterns of conversation, and the dynamics of play.

- *Multiple births (twins, triplets, etc.).* In affluent countries, due to a rise in maternal age and the use of infertility treatments, there has been an increased incidence of multiple births. This increases the risk of cesarean delivery, prematurity, and some developmental disabilities. The whole family may experience more stress and strain with the quantum leap in child-to-parent ratio that multiple births can bring.

- *Spacing.* Parents often ask pediatricians about the "best spacing" between sibling births. But sibling interaction depends less on spacing than it does on the unique characteristics of parents and children. The balance of pros and cons attributable to wider or narrower sib spacing changes over the years. But the number of years between each sibling's arrival can affect the degree of rivalry and conflict.

- *Family size.* Over time, except for some specific ethnic groups, the average size of families has been decreasing, from seven in 1865, to around three and a half in 1950, to less than two now. Larger families mean less one-on-one interaction. There may be more complicated alliances and exclusions. A larger age range between youngest and oldest children means a greater variety of roles. Older siblings may function less like playmates and more like additional parents—disciplinarians, teachers, and caregivers of the youngest in the family.

- *Modern families.* Most families are no longer "traditional" (Solomon, 2013). The new majority of families are not composed of a father, a mother, and their biological children. Now, there are all kinds of families. Step-families are becoming the most common family structure in the United States. Before 18 years of age, more than half of children experience divorce and live with a step-parent. Whether step, adoptive, or foster family, these structures require adjustment to a new parent, a new home, new sibs, and a new ordinal position. Under these varying circumstances, children may experience different types of attention. In addition, they might feel uncertainty about the security of the current family structure. Some families have more than two parents. Single-parent families are also much more common than in the past. Interracial, surrogate, IVF, and LGBTQI (lesbian, gay, bisexual, transgender, questioning or queer, intersex) families may have to deal with other layers of complexity.

- *Chronic illness/special needs of siblings.* The stress in any family system increases if any children have chronic medical issues, disabilities, mental illness, or other special needs. Time, money, and energy are stretched further—often, much further—than usual. There is increased emotional strain on everyone in the family, and a greater risk of anxiety and depression. The "kids without issues" might not get as much attention as their sibling(s) with special needs. Normal resentments might be amplified or distorted. "Well" siblings might feel the weight of increased expectations. They might be required to take more care of themselves even as they are expected to take more responsibility for their sibling. They might worry about these childhood precedents becoming long-term obligations. On the flip side of such unequal relationships, the more-dependent sibling might feel guilt, depression, or resentment.

- *Death of a sibling or parent.* When tragedy strikes a family, survivors are affected in different ways. Parents may overprotect their remaining children, which can interfere with the normal development of self-reliance and resilience. In response to loss, such children may experience a wide range of difficult emotions, shifting between anger, guilt, depression, and anxiety.

- *Labels.* Siblings should be treated as unique individuals with their own styles, desires and needs. Even so, consciously or subconsciously, parents and siblings may assign each other roles within the family. Some of these labels are culturally driven. Traditional gender-norms may be automatically assumed. Boys are "supposed to be" active, athletic, and assertive. Girls are "supposed to be" quiet, pretty, and deferential. Such stereotypes may represent self-fulfilling prophecies or sources of guilt, shame, disappointment, and discrimination. A child may live down to their label or fail to live up to it. Parents and siblings may pigeonhole a child in many ways: the smart one versus the slow-learner; the gifted one versus the disabled one; the nerd versus the jock; the shy one versus the outgoing one; the responsible one versus the unmotivated or lazy one; the happy one versus the grumpy one; the easy one versus the difficult one; and so on. Certain diagnoses—even when accurate and appropriate— can become significant and lasting sources of distress and limitation.

- *Parent temperament, behavior, and history.* "Goodness of fit" between parents and children involves more than just the interplay of inborn temperaments. Parent behavior, just like child behavior, is the product of predisposition and conditioning, nature and nurture, biology and environment. From one generation to the next, a parent's own sibling history can affect how they treat their children. Your childhood follows you into your parenthood: your own family structure, birth order, role, and sibling relations, along with the relationship you had with your parents, and they had with each other.

All of these factors combine in different ways, in different families. Consequently, sibling interactions may be tense. Brothers and sisters may find themselves engaged in deep and frequent conflict. There may be rivalry for parental attention, love, and approval. Siblings may engage in non-cooperative play and unhealthy competition. They may exclude, ostracize, or ignore each other. There may be disputes over property or territory. Individual reactions can vary from passivity and withdrawal to acting out and aggression. Siblings may get in a habit of teasing, taunting, insulting, and bickering. This may escalate into recurrent bullying or violent fights. There may be inappropriate sexual interactions and abuse. Some sibling interactions lead to serious physical or emotional harm.

Parents may under- or overreact, potentially amplifying the conflict between siblings and increasing the anxiety of individual children. Antagonistic or tense sibling interactions can cause anxiety in individual children. Conversely, anxiety in individual children can cause difficulties between siblings.

Although Sid and Dave were twins, they could not have been more different. Sid was quiet and somewhat withdrawn. Dave had a more intense temperament and a constellation of developmental differences. Ultimately, Dave was given a diagnosis of Asperger-type autism. For the first years, Dave was more demanding of his parents' attention. His parents worried about his future. They took Dave from one specialist to another. He ended up in a special-education preschool and that made all the difference.

Just as Dave started to excel academically and make a few friends, Sid began to struggle. Sid attended the neighborhood public school. He didn't participate in class, and had frequent stomachaches. The doctor couldn't find anything wrong. It became clear that Sid was having difficulty recognizing letters and understanding speech sounds. Dave had taught himself to read and was already close to a second-grade level. Dave showed off his reading ability and was constantly asking Sid why he couldn't read. This didn't help Sid's mounting anxiety.

I don't mean to imply that all sibling interactions are bad—far from it. Positive interactions can be as common as moments of rivalry. We learn about relationships from our siblings. Early on, our siblings may be our most consistent and reliable playmates, our partners in social learning, and our primary inspiration for growth. Siblings give each other a uniquely familiar source of comfort and support, an opportunity for closeness and affection. Sibling relationships are often lifelong, mutual, dynamic, strong, and deep. How do you best describe the ultimate friendship? "He's like a brother." or "She's like a sister." Sometimes, siblings truly are each other's best friends. Let's not forget that the presence of a child with chronic illness or special needs can bring out the best in siblings, leading to deep and beautiful relationships.

In the context of this discussion on anxiety, the main point is this: Anxiety doesn't exist solely within individuals, or between parent and child. Rather, anxiety unfolds within larger family systems. Consequently, effective treatment of an anxious child often depends upon understanding these extra layers of complexity.

The Extended Family

There are other important relational triangles that include grandparents, aunts, uncles, cousins, step-parents, step-siblings, and others in the extended family. In addition, non-relatives—such as care providers and close friends—might function as if they are part of the family. Usually, the more regular their presence, the more important the relationship, though some extended family members exert their influence remotely. Biological parents of adopted children or even deceased relatives can be part of some surprisingly powerful triangles. Such stressors within family systems can have varying degrees of relevance to anxiety in individual children.

The Rodriguezes were a military family. Three generations back, most of the family had proudly served in the U.S. Air Force. Everyone in the family understood that service required periods of separation. When parents were on assignment, children were expected to deal with it. When the family had to pick up and relocate, anywhere around the world, it was just part of serving. But 10-year-old Mary had always had severe separation anxiety. She had lots of trouble acclimating to each new country, school, and home. Over the years, when her mother went away, Mary cried and had trouble sleeping.

Her father's parents would come and stay with them. They took turns sleeping with her at night. Mary's mother's parents scoffed and criticized them for not understanding military realities, and giving Mary's distress too much attention. But secretly, they admitted to each other a mixture of guilt and resentment. They wanted their granddaughter to need them too—but not in that "coddling way."

Aunts, uncles, and cousins all weighed in on each side of the argument. For Mary's parents, all of this strained their marriage. Mary's mother felt torn. Just before her own highly decorated grandfather died, he had told her how proud he was of her for carrying on the family tradition.

Larger Social and Cultural Systems

For brilliant expositions of system complexity, see Robert Sopolsky's (2018) *Behave: The Biology of Humans at Our Best and Worst* and Joshua Greene's (2014) *Moral Tribes*. Thankfully, implementation of parallel exposure therapy doesn't require a degree in sociology, economics, and complexity theory. But to overcome anxiety, we do need to at least consider the following potential factors.

School

There are many different types of schools: traditional public, charter, magnet, virtual or online, traditional private, religious, boarding, language immersion, Montessori, special education, Reggio Emilia, Waldorf, and more. Within each of these school types, there are different curricula, extracurricular activities, expectations, climates, student types, cliques, limitations, opportunities, and facilities. School administrators, teachers, and support staff also come with their own styles, experiences, and personalities. They all play a huge role in the lives of students and families.

Daphne's older brother had a great experience at the neighborhood Montessori. Daphne's parents were excited for her to start there too. They loved the child-led philosophy and laid-back teachers. But during the first few weeks, it became clear that

Daphne was struggling. Other children engaged deeply with the rich variety of materials and shifted naturally from one activity to another, but Daphne seemed paralyzed by so many choices. She just sat on the carpet in the middle of the room, overwhelmed. The teachers made gentle suggestions, presented puzzles and pretend play items. But Daphne just glanced before her gaze drifted and she became lost in her own thoughts.

Daphne's parents brought in a consultant, who observed and suggested more structure and positive reinforcement. The teachers said they would try but it was really inconsistent with the school philosophy.

Neighborhood and Community

Children and families are embedded within neighborhoods and communities. Just like the relationships within families, the relationships between families and communities can take different forms: close or distant, peaceful or conflicted, supportive or adversarial. At this level of analysis, there are an infinite variety of triangles.

Every community has its own vibe and degree of connectedness. Plunk the same individual in different neighborhoods and you have very different fields upon which anxiety plays out—and very different approaches regarding management.

The east side of town was famous for having produced two National Basketball Association Hall of Fame players, plus many college stars. It seemed like every kid—and every kid's parents—had "hoop dreams" of their own. Edwin's parents were both well over six feet tall. As a seventh grader, Edwin could handle the ball and shoot much better than most high school kids. Word got around.

A coach approached Edwin to play in a select league. He would be challenged, and could develop his skills to his full potential. He could play for the same high school that launched the town heroes toward college scholarships. Then, maybe, a professional career, fame and fortune. A few college scouts started showing up for his middle school games. Everybody was buzzing.

Edwin loved basketball but all this hype was getting to him. He started feeling sick to his stomach before games, even threw up a few times in the locker room. He started making careless passes and missing easy shots.

Finally, Edwin decided to quit basketball. All the stress just wasn't worth it.

Medical and Mental Health Care Systems

Health care systems can have a significant impact on the causes and treatment of anxiety. Access, affordability, and availability to services have the potential to either exacerbate or ameliorate health problems. The type of health insurance can have a profound impact on family stress and individual health. The number, location, and quality of providers in your area are also important. Sadly, health care systems and providers may be more a part of the anxiety problem than the solution.

Dr. Quito had put up with this situation long enough. Mrs. White was not complying with any of his suggestions. He wrote prescriptions but Kamisha kept showing up in the emergency room with late-night asthma attacks. The ER docs would tune her up and send her home, but she just bounced back to the ER, wheezing and struggling to breathe, again and again. Sometimes Kamisha even had to stay a few days in the hospital. And her mom couldn't stay with her. Mrs. White had to go to work. Kamisha was getting more and more frightened. Keeping up with her schoolwork was impossible. The stress was mounting.

When Mrs. White brought Kamisha in for a visit with Dr. Quito, he asked, "Are you not giving her the medicine I prescribed?" He was thinking about dismissing her from his practice. After all, Dr. Quito thought, what could he do if this mom was going to continue being so negligent?

Mrs. White looked Dr. Q in the eyes, and said, "Listen, doc. I work two jobs during the week and one on the weekend. None of them provide health insurance. Even if I had time to get to the pharmacy, I can't afford the prescriptions you write. The pharmacist says you need to give Kamisha medicine that's covered by my insurance. At least when I take Kamisha to the ER, I don't have to miss work and they give her enough medicine to last a few weeks. You're the only doctor for miles who takes Medicaid and I still have to take two busses to get here. And I've already looked for psychiatrists, but I can't find one who *takes Medicaid, has evening or weekend hours, and a waiting list less than a year long. So please, let's get real."*

Culture

Culture can be categorized according to current, past, or original geographic region; ethnicity, race, or religion; politics, gender and sexuality, economics, and consumer patterns. Cultures can be communitarian or individualistic, strict or permissive. The parent's educational background, training, and work can have a powerful impact upon children. There are cultural differences regarding recreation, arts, disability, and age. It's hard to think of a single aspect of human existence unaffected by cultural milieu.

Anxiety can exist because of discrepancies—"poor fit"—between individual differences and cultural expectations. In many cultures, emphasis on performance may come into direct conflict with normal development and emotional health. On the other hand, some cultures provide crucial support in the face of adversity. Whether cultural factors wound or heal, culture is always important. In many ways, anxiety can be seen as a problem with society, not just individuals. From a public health perspective, we must expose our culture to its own fault lines, then work to fix anxiety across them. Diagnosis and treatment must include individual children but also the wider world in which they live.

Highly individualistic cultures (such as the United States) place disproportionate value on having professional careers, making lots of money, having a specific physical appearance, and getting married to a certain type of person (Levine, 2008). Other more communitarian cultures (like China, Korea, and Japan) traditionally place high value on fitting in, loyalty, and subservience. Both individualistic and communitarian cultures can produce anxiety in individuals or smaller social systems, albeit for different reasons (Nisbett, 2004). Lastly, although much of the world has become more accepting and supportive of sexual, racial, religious, neurodiverse, and other minorities, a degree of stress and discrimination is still the norm.

In our high-stakes world of intense competition and standardized testing, childhood performance anxiety has become epidemic. "Perfect or hurried child syndrome" usually centers on academic achievement (Elkind, 2006). This bizarre normalization—even celebration—of accumulating stress now begins in nursery school, builds relentlessly through the school years, and culminates in the college application process. For example, many high schools have students taking advanced placement courses in ninth grade and calculus in tenth grade. *Washington Post* education columnist Jay Matthews rates high schools according to how many AP courses they offer. Acceptance to a "good" college is held up as the ultimate measure of a successful childhood (Stixrud & Johnson, 2019). This unhealthy gap between inappropriately high expectations and normal development smothers curiosity in the classroom, throttles flow on the athletic field, saps joy from the stage, and stifles creativity in the studio. All of this culturally based anxiety is only amplified by constant comparison on social media.

> *From a young age, Judy loved to read. Book after book, she immersed herself in the many worlds of fiction. But as she got older, there was more homework, more stress about getting good grades, and more talk about developing good study habits. As her grades slipped, Judy's parents became more worried. They warned, "You need to stop reading so much and do your schoolwork. What about your future?"*
>
> *Michael was scared to death about getting into a good college. At his large suburban high school, college was all anybody was talking about. But school was never his thing. He just didn't really care about his classes or his homework. He liked music and building stuff. There was a tech program at another school that his counselor recommended. But that would mean being away from his friends and they would think he was even more of a loser.*

As we'll discuss in Excursion 4 and Excursion 5, minority stress is a very important source of anxiety. There, we'll discuss the anxiety experienced by people in neurodevelopmental, sexual, and gender minorities, and members of racial, religious, and other minority groups.

And so you see, there's more to overcoming anxiety than just "fixing" parents and children. Complicated social factors have a powerful impact as well. Beyond genes, children, and parents, we also need to fix our anxious culture. Parallel exposure therapy targets all of these contributing factors.

Family, Social, and Cultural Systems

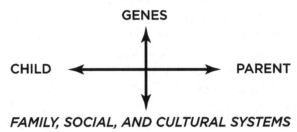

Cognitive-Behavioral Therapy and Parallel Exposure Therapy

We have just completed a detailed review of anxiety in children, emphasizing how anxious children don't exist in isolation. Each child is embedded in different types of relationships and systems.

This is not a new idea. Any good therapist looks beyond the individual and considers a range of possible contributing factors. Many wonderful books about cognitive-behavioral therapy make mention of family and cultural factors. Yet the practice of CBT for children still focuses mainly on the child. Here, by offering a new framework, I hope to shift the focus from individuals to systems.

Overview of Cognitive-Behavioral Therapy and Parallel Exposure Therapy

Cognitive-Behavioral Therapy

Cognitive-Behavioral Therapy (CBT) is based on the idea that thoughts, feelings, and behaviors are all interconnected. If a person is scared of dogs, they may think "dogs will hurt me" (thought), which leads to fear (emotion), which leads to avoiding dogs (behavior). In certain situations, anxious thoughts may be appropriate, healthy, and protective. But when those thoughts are exaggerated, unrealistic, or distorted—so that they contribute to an impairing degree of anxiety—then we need to substitute more correct and realistic thoughts. People can learn to ask themselves, "Is this thought realistic? What positive parts of the situation might I be ignoring? Just because I feel afraid, does that mean I'm in danger?" That's the "C" or cognitive part of CBT.

133

The most important component of CBT for anxiety is exposure therapy. This is the "B"—or behavioral—part. Exposure therapy means deliberate exposure to the anxiety trigger or "stimulus," so that it no longer leads to an unhealthy behavioral response. This is what is meant by *exposure/response prevention*. Conditioned responses to anxiety—such as avoidance, maladaptive thoughts, behaviors, or distress—are prevented and unlearned, and a new and healthier response is triggered instead. I will go into greater detail below but, in a nutshell, here's how it works.

When a triggering thought or situation is presented over a long enough period of time, the person gets used to it. It's like gradually acclimating to cold water in a swimming pool or a noise in a movie theater. The exposure to the stimulus must be just right—not so big that it's overwhelming, not so small that it poses no challenge at all. At first, the exposure might be indirect or direct. For example, if a child has a fear of being in crowds, the exposure process might begin by just talking about crowds, not by direct exposure to a crowd. This mental exposure is far from the goal—but it's a start. Limited exposure is still much better than complete avoidance.

Gradually, the type and intensity of exposure progresses from just thinking or talking about the anxiety trigger to looking at pictures, listening to audio recordings, watching videos, re-creating physical sensations, or using computer-based virtual reality experiences. Before each exposure, the child knows what's coming, rehearses brave self-talk, and practices specific coping strategies. A reward system can be used if a child needs external motivation. Once children can handle this type of increasingly provocative preview, they will be much more ready for incrementally greater exposures to real-life situations.

CBT Pitfalls

Often, CBT works well—but not always. Here are some reasons child-focused exposure CBT sometimes fails.

   a. *Avoidance.* The most common reason for CBT failure is avoidance of prescribed exposures. Understandably, people don't like putting themselves in situations that trigger discomfort—even when they have a very good reason to do so.
   b. *Technique.* CBT success depends upon doing just-right exposures: not too much and not too little, not too fast and not

too slow. Some therapists spend too much time talking about anxiety or practicing relaxation exercises, without moving ahead with real-life exposures. Other technique problems stem from a failure to individualize the approach and provide sufficient motivation. Some therapists focus too much on protocol and not enough on the individual child.

c. *Coexisting conditions.* To be addressed in much greater detail below, failure of anxiety therapy often stems from failure to consider other overlapping conditions: developmental differences, mood disorders, ADHD, learning disabilities, motor skills deficits, environmental stresses. As we've learned, there's often more to the child than just the anxiety.

d. *Parent factors.* As emphasized throughout this discussion, CBT for children cannot merely acknowledge the presence of parent anxiety. It must address the dynamic interplay between child and parent anxiety. It's not enough to just refer parents to their own therapists or psychiatrists, or for parents to merely sit in on their child's CBT sessions, or just supervise their child's exposure homework. Parallel exposure therapy requires parent inclusion in the *actual exposure therapy.* The child learns to face their fears while parents learn to face theirs as well.

e. *Larger system factors.* Again, we should not stop with the parent-child dyad. Anxiety is usually more complicated than that; it exists in all kinds of systems, small and large. Parallel exposure therapy is meant to target this broad range of players and variables. What about other family members? Siblings? Grandparents? What about old relationships and deceased family members, no longer with us in body but still very much a part of the family dynamic in spirit? All too often, CBT is designed as if the child or the parent-child dyad exist in a vacuum, isolated from other family, friends, teachers, coaches, other adults, neighborhood, community, and culture. Designing exposures that include the parent-child dyad *and* these larger systems isn't easy. But failure to account for these overlapping factors interferes with the therapy's effectiveness and might even undermine success altogether.

Again, as a matter of routine, well-trained CBT clinicians do exposures in various settings and with various players. For example, in treating selective mutism, a good therapist always goes into the child's school to work with the teachers and the other children there. Unfortunately, CBT is not always sufficiently broad and inclusive.

Parallel Exposure Therapy

Parallel exposure therapy emphasizes the importance of addressing all these layers of complexity; including children, parents, families, and larger systems as well.

All CBT treatment programs include some discussion of parent anxiety. Everyone acknowledges that child anxiety is "bidirectional" or "contagious," and that parent anxiety needs to be addressed when treating child anxiety. However, recommendations on how to tackle this vary widely from source to source. Some suggest that parents seek their own anxiety therapy. Some insist upon parent involvement in child CBT sessions and exposure homework. Others go even farther, designing exposures that simultaneously trigger anxiety for child and parent, plus parallel coping strategies. But in practice, CBT often doesn't provide a sufficient degree of parent inclusion in the actual exposure therapy. Here, I hope to present a more systematic approach to simultaneous exposure for everyone involved.

An anxious child, family members, teachers, classmates, and other important individuals may all be part of the same triggering situations. Each one reacts in their own way, and each person's response affects the others. Parallel exposure therapy means deliberate exposure of the child and relevant others to shared triggers. Everyone in the system unlearns anxiety-reinforcing thoughts and responses, in their own way, but together.

Throughout this discussion, instead of listing all the possible factors—the child, parents, nuclear family, extended family, neighborhood, communities, health care system—that contribute to a child's anxiety, I will use the term "anxiety system."

In this excursion, the application of parallel exposure therapy will be limited to children and any relevant adults—parents, other family members, teachers, coaches, therapists, or other care providers. In the next excursion, on autism and social change, I will broaden the application of parallel exposure therapy to include larger systems, such as neighborhoods, schools, communities, health care systems, and culture.

Practices of Cognitive-Behavioral Therapy and Parallel Exposure Therapy

Before going any further, let me emphasize that treatment of anxiety is both a well-developed science and a nuanced art. This book is meant to educate parents, teachers, and clinicians—but it's not meant to take the place of consultation with experts. Just like medication management, if exposure therapy is not done properly, it can make things worse instead of better. Some situations are simple. Others require very specialized help.

Recognize and Externalize the Anxiety

Often, children and adults need help seeing that the object of their anxiety is not so much the problem as the anxiety itself. For example, "It's not about the spiders. It's about your fear of the spiders." Help your child understand why it's important to control his or her anxiety. Ask your child to consider how their anxiety is like a trap. Encourage your child to imagine freedom from fear. In the same way, adults need to externalize their own anxiety, examine it, and come to believe in the importance of facing their anxiety head-on.

Ask your child and ask yourself:

- When anxiety messes with you, what are you thinking? How do you feel?
- What happens when you have these anxious thoughts and feelings? What do you do?
- What does your anxiety keep you from doing?
- When you're calm, what do you think? How do you feel?
- What happens when you have calm thoughts and feelings?
- What are you able to do when you're calm that you can't do when you're anxious?
- How can you take back some of the territory controlled by anxiety and make it your own? Do you want your anxiety to be in control of you or do you want to be in control of your anxiety?

Use language that is at the right developmental level for your child. The answers to these questions should motivate children, parents, and other adults to take control of their anxieties.

To further externalize anxiety, children can assign it a name, such as "Egbert" or "Worry Monster." A little humor can help. For example, "When you see the Worry Monster coming, who you gonna call? Worry Busters!"

Do Not Try to Prevent Anxiety

Anxiety is a normal emotion. Stress and fear happen. We don't always need to fix our worries or make them go away. Much of the time, all we need to do is say, "Such is life." Together, children, parents, and other individuals can learn to accept and tolerate normal degrees of distress and simply wait for difficult moments to pass, like bad weather or bumps along the road.

Usually, the harder we try to prevent anxiety by avoiding triggers, the more anxious we become. Often, it's best to follow the advice of the White Rabbit in Alice in Wonderland: "Don't just do something, stand there." Sometimes, CBT focuses too much on control and not enough on simple acceptance. Even when more severe anxiety comes ashore, we should not try to suppress it or force it away. Rather, we should learn to just "ride out the wave."

Do Not Allow Avoidance

Avoidance is the enemy. Naturally, if children anticipate discomfort, rejection, or failure, they will resist entering, joining, or trying. When facing a difficult situation, they may shut down or try to escape. Parents, teachers, and other adults may allow or even encourage this kind of avoidance. After all, it's natural to try to spare a child some pain.

In parallel, adults often rationalize their own avoidant behaviors as well. For example, one parent may declare their spouse better-equipped, their child's therapist too unrealistic, or their child's teacher too insensitive. Spouses, teachers, and therapists may turn this logic around and reflect the same accusations back upon the parent. This kind of multidirectional delegating, dodging, and blaming is really just adults avoiding their own anxieties. By blaming each other, adults don't have to confront their own fears.

In the short run, avoidance of anxiety-provoking situations certainly works. For the moment, side-stepping stress-triggers makes things easier for the child, the parent, and anyone else involved. However, avoidance is no cure. It denies children, parents, and other adults crucial opportunities to learn problem-solving, face their fears, and build confidence. Avoidance narrows the comfort zone and places an artificial limit on growth and development. As discussed in detail below, a certain amount of scaffolding and graduated exposure is crucial to overcoming anxiety. However, when it's best to take a step forward, children and adults should *not* get in the habit of taking a step backward. Grabbing too much short-term anxiety relief only works at the expense of long-term anxiety control.

Overall, Betsy did well in her fourth-grade class. But math didn't come to her as easily as other subjects. Just the thought of numbers and equations sent her into a bit of a panic. Whenever there was a new concept, she would think, "It's just too hard!" At the beginning of each new unit, Betsy found herself going to the bathroom—a lot. Or she went to the school nurse for stomachaches and spent some time lying down on her comfortable cot.

Mrs. Rubal, Betsy's teacher, saw what was happening. Mrs. Rubal prided herself on being able to work with anxious kids. She tried to talk with Betsy. But Betsy didn't like being singled out. She became more dispirited and withdrawn. Mrs. Rubal called Betsy's parents. She recommended letting Betsy do her in-class math as homework, "to take the pressure off." Betsy liked this idea and her parents reasoned, "It's better for her not to be freaking out in class." While other kids did their math problems, Betsy read a book.

A few of her classmates complained. The teacher told them to keep their comments to themselves. Betsy could tell what they were thinking. But at least she didn't have to do the math. In class, she was quieter but calmer. The trips to the bathroom and the school nurse stopped. Mrs. Rubal breathed a sigh of relief.

But then, every afternoon, right off the bus, Betsy got weepy. Her parents tried to calm her down and help. Betsy just got more upset. She would whimper, "I can't do it." Her mother got frustrated and yelled, "Just cut it out with the complaining. You can do this! You just need to try!" Betsy complained to her father, "Mommy keeps yelling at me about math." Behind closed doors, Betsy's father told his wife, "Stop being so hard on her. Don't you see that your yelling just makes things worse?" They came to an agreement: Betsy's mother would stay out of it altogether. Betsy's father would take over helping Betsy with her homework— essentially doing it for her while she watched. At least, he thought, she'll see how to do it and be able to hand something in to the teacher.

Betsy's math test scores started to slide. On the next exam, Mrs. Rubal noticed Betsy glancing at her table-mate's paper. But Betsy did poorly on the test despite cheating. Mrs. Rubal kept it to herself. Betsy was stressed enough, and she was doing well in her other subjects. Her emotional health was more important than math performance. Math just wasn't her thing.

Beware of Avoidance in Disguise

Sometimes parents and children think they are facing their anxiety when they are really just avoiding the trigger.

Ilana was deathly afraid of the dark. She always slept with her lights on. And every night, she made her parents repeat their promise not to turn the lights off. Ilana would not go to movies or other places where the lighting could not be controlled. Even with a very full moon, she did not like going outside at night. Ilana's parents did everything they could to make sure that Ilana avoided these situations. Her grandparents complained to her parents about their never letting Ilana sleep over at their house. But Ilana had an irrational notion that the lights there were somehow not as reliable or that her grandparents could not be trusted to keep them on.

So, Ilana went to a play therapist to help her face her fear. In weekly sessions, they acted out different "lights out" scenarios with toy figures. They talked about Ilana's fear. They practiced breathing exercises. The therapist told Ilana's parents that she was making great progress. But outside of the therapist's office, Ilana was no less afraid.

- *Talking versus walking.* Parents and children may feel that they are dealing with anxiety by talking about it. But just talking about anxiety is not the same as real-life exposure and coping. For example, just talking about a fear of the dark or a worry about soccer performance is not the same thing as turning off the lights or getting out on the field. The more we talk, the less we do. Prolonged question-answer sessions or excessive strategizing can give the anxious thoughts and feelings too much attention. Sometimes, weekly visits to a therapist's office only create the illusion of intervention. Talk-only therapy without exposure is like learning how to swim without ever getting in the pool.
- *Timing the talk.* If there's some talking to do, it should take

place well before or well after exposure to the anxiety-provoking situation. Talking *during* the exposure can easily turn into delay and avoidance, for both the parent and child. Take separation anxiety, for example. When it's time to say good night or good-bye, talk just prolongs or replaces separation. Preparatory talking *before* separation is different than talking *instead* of separation. When we talk instead of facing fears, we delay and avoid, which only reinforces anxiety and dependence.

- *Repetitive reassurance.* Adults who provide too much reassurance or answer the same question more than once are giving the anxiety too much attention—driven at least as much by the adult's anxiety as the child's. The child who just stands on the end of the diving board listening to shouts of encouragement is not actually diving. This is true whether the repetitive reassurance is communicated verbally or nonverbally. Consider the child who gets a long, warm hug every time they express a bit of nervousness.

- *More than words can say.* Nonverbal communication is often more powerful than verbal communication. The number of words spoken usually says more than the specific words said. Touch, body language, facial expression, and tone of voice can communicate much more about the adult's level of worry than the most carefully chosen phrases. Each touch of reassurance sends a signal of worry. Such nonverbal messaging can be more powerful than talk of bravery and courage. All the words in the world don't erase other signals of doubt and concern.

- *Relaxation or distraction "strategies" as avoidance.* Ironically, when a child or adult uses relaxation or distraction strategies, this can interfere with the actual exposure. Let's consider a child with a fear of elevators. He is taught to do his breathing, take a "mind trip" to the beach, or talk with his mom about next week's soccer game. These strategies are all designed to turn attention *away* from the fear of elevators. However, these relaxation or distraction strategies can "work" so well that the child never really gets the degree of exposure needed to become habituated. Exposure therapy works only if some anxiety is actually triggered. The fear must be faced. Most experts recommend not using relaxation or distraction during exposures. Such strategies should be used only if needed to allow the child to engage and then faded as quickly as possible. Seasoned therapists prescribe only enough relaxation and distraction to ensure a just-right exposure: not too much anxiety, but not too little.

- *Medication as avoidance.* Just like relaxation and distraction strategies, anti-anxiety medicine can work so well that the child or parent is denied the opportunity to learn strategies and experience success overcoming anxiety. Medication should be considered if a child or adult cannot function in day-to-day activities or participate in their own therapy. Seasoned prescribers use just enough medication to relieve an impairing degree of distress but not so much that there's no chance for exposure, habituation, and reversal of avoidance habits. Children who need anxiety pills still need anxiety skills.

Eve, a teenager, was not making progress with her cognitive-behavioral therapist. So her parents had her go to a psychiatrist who prescribed Prozac. Eve had a great response to this medication. Her old social anxiety magically melted away. She told her parents that she didn't want to see the therapist anymore. She was doing so well! A year passed. Then two years. Still doing great. Eve asked her parents about stopping the medication. They talked with the psychiatrist, who recommended a discontinuation trial.

The first week, on three-quarters of the previous dose, Eve's old anxieties came back—not as bad as before, but still there. The doctor told her to go back up on the Prozac dose. The anxiety disappeared again. Eve and her parents were relieved. But Eve asked, "Will I have to take this stuff for the rest of my life?" The psychiatrist recommending combining a slightly reduced dose with cognitive-behavioral therapy. Eve said no. She told the psychiatrist that she did not want to go back to the therapist. She just wanted to keep taking the medicine. Her parents agreed. Like Eve, they had not missed the hassle of CBT. It was expensive and the Prozac was working so well. Reluctantly, the psychiatrist agreed to just stick with the medicine.

Don't Give the Anxiety Too Much Attention

Even if anxious behaviors are not initially attention-seeking, they can become attention-getting. Your child cries. You respond. We all have protective reflexes, hardwired by evolution and soft-wired by experience.

Child anxiety might trigger a wide range of adult emotions. Beyond primal "fight, flight, or freeze" reactions, parents, siblings, and others may react to an anxious child with a whole smorgasbord of complicated, perfectionistic, or personalized feelings. When a child is distressed, adults may feel incompetent, frustrated, helpless, or angry. Adults may magnify or catastrophize. Of course, it's just as problematic to minimize, dismiss or invalidate a child's feelings. Either way, disproportionate or distorted responses can be counterproductive. All of this applies not just to parents but also relatives, teachers, care providers, and clinicians.

One fundamental tenet of behavior management is this: turn your attention toward behaviors you want to reinforce, withdraw your attention from behaviors you want to extinguish.

When children are anxious, adults often provide too much reassurance, too much discussion, or too much emotion. Subsequently, children learn that anxious behaviors get lots of attention. Whether the parent response is positive or negative, anxiety is running the show. Overprotective adults unintentionally model anxious thoughts and behaviors.

Instead of feeding the anxiety, adults should recognize some of their own distorted thoughts and feelings as "false alarms." Then, they can substitute more appropriate and proportionate responses. Sometimes, this might mean muting your natural response and pretending not to notice the child's anxiety. Then you can turn your attention back to the child after the anxiety passes. Better yet, you can praise the child if they demonstrate bravery.

Nurture Bravery

All too often, we give our children more attention when they are decompensating than when they are coping. Adults should make a point of catching children being brave. Give positive attention and praise whenever they take even small steps out of their comfort zone. Reward progress, no matter how incremental. Recall previous moments of healthy risk-taking and bravery. Look for evidence of courageous intent and let your child know that you noticed. Children can be helped to create a bravery photo album.

Using a cell phone, the family can collect pictures in which the child was "scared but did it anyway."

Share tales of courage. Stir your children and energize yourself with parables from history, fiction, and your own family archives. Adults should openly acknowledge their own anxiety and then recount courage in facing their own fears. Remember your own victories over fear and doubt. Let these memories inspire your child and continue to motivate you as well. By telling your own stories of hesitation and overcoming, teach your children how to muster best efforts in coping with life's inevitable challenges.

Aspire to be your child's hero. This doesn't mean possessing superpowers or being a perfect parent, teacher, or care provider. Just the opposite. Show children that real courage means facing life's everyday challenges, big or small, despite imperfection and uncertainty. When you experience self-doubt or frustration, let your child hear your compensatory optimism and can-do strategizing. As Reinhold Niebuhr taught: *Model serenity to accept the things you cannot change; courage to change the things you can; and wisdom to know the difference.* Someday, you might be just as inspired by your children as they are by you.

> *Candace loved Super Girl. She was strong and brave. Candace had trouble going to new places. But whenever she did, her parents were sure to say, "Just like Super Girl!"*

Nurture Self-Reliance

One overarching goal in the treatment of childhood anxiety is to shift responsibility for dealing with anxiety from the parent to the child—or at least, to share that responsibility. In anxiety-provoking situations, parents should inhibit their "rescue reflex." Rather than swooping in, taking over, and protecting, you should try to step back and give your child a chance to "bust" his or her own anxiety. At most, help your child participate in his or her own problem-solving or prompt your child to implement previously rehearsed self-help strategies. When your child demonstrates self-reliance, make a point of noticing.

Parents and other adults need to accept responsibility for tackling their own anxiety as well. Sometimes, adults need professional help weaning themselves from their own enablers.

Believe in Your Child's Resilience—And Yours Too

You and your child may not be as fragile as you feel. This is an especially important consideration for families that really do face extraordinary challenges. If you and your child are dealing with significant illness, disability, or environmental stresses, all the more reason to learn how to adapt and instill an optimistic spirit. This doesn't mean denial of real hardships or limitations. But it does mean opening yourselves to the possibility that you're not completely powerless. Doom and gloom prophecies can be self-fulfilling. Pessimistic thought habits can be unlearned. After all, health and success are not marked by the absence of illness or failure. Rather, health is the ability to overcome life's inevitable adversities.

Even if we can't work miracles, maybe we can make things better. When a misty-eyed adult reflects back on his or her own childhood, it's often with profound gratitude to "the one person who believed in me." Adults can teach children that kind of self-confidence. At least to a degree, children can overcome misfortune. But first, you have to believe it yourself. Anxiety is contagious. Hope is contagious too.

Recognize Irrational or Distorted Thinking

Even at a young age, children can be taught to critically examine the source of their anxious thoughts. The key question is, "Why am I so anxious?" For children and adults, anxiety management begins by understanding how anxious feelings stem from distorted, irrational, or unrealistic thoughts—"making mountains out of molehills." Although there is usually some truth to anxious thoughts, *excessive* anxiety is the result of *exaggerated* probabilities and *amplified* consequences. True, there's a remote chance of getting struck by lightning at some time in life—but the chance of getting struck by lightning is certainly so small that one need not go through life worrying about it.

The too-anxious child or adult tends to think in absolute terms rather than considering probabilities or relative risk. Anxiety disorder represents a failure to remember that most of life is lived between extremes. Anxiety comes from distorted all-*or*-none thinking:

- extremes instead of in-betweens
- 0 or 10 instead of 1 through 9

- heaven or hell instead of the real earth
- perfection or catastrophe instead of "good enough" or "somewhat disappointing"

Such binary language can shove aside more realistic and accurate descriptors, such as "*some* things, *some* places, *sometimes*."

The too-anxious child or adult lacks skepticism. They are far too certain that worst-case scenarios are going to happen. Anxious individuals habitually assume that they can read other people's minds or predict the future with unerring accuracy. In doing so, they routinely fail to consider alternate possibilities and outcomes. They have difficulty tolerating any degree of doubt. They wrongly assume that uncertainty means inevitable disaster. All of this is just as true for adults as children.

> *Mrs. Oliva was very concerned about her student Alan, who had dyslexia. He was falling farther behind his classmates. He tried to avoid reading whenever possible, and even started calling himself stupid. Mrs. Oliva feared, If I don't get Alan caught up this year and feeling better about himself, then his whole life is going to be ruined.*
>
> *Alan's mother could sense Mrs. Oliva's concern about Alan's future. She started waking up every night in a panic. She had an uncle with learning disabilities who couldn't finish school or get a job, and ended up in prison for selling cocaine. Would Alan go down the same path?*

Challenge Irrational or Unrealistic Thinking

Correcting distorted thoughts means seriously considering relative risk and objectively evaluating the actual level of danger. Gently ask:

- Is that really true? Let's examine the evidence.
- Are there other possible explanations or outcomes?
- What is the *true* risk? What would someone else think about the actual risk? Maybe we should ask someone else?
- What's most likely to happen? What's the worst thing that would really happen? How likely is that?
- Maybe we should test your hypothesis by doing an experiment?
- Maybe we can do some research or ask an expert?
- If your fear actually came true, could you handle it? What could you do to cope?

Goals can be set by contrasting current levels of anxiety with more objective levels. In other words, "Is my anxiety level out of proportion to what someone else would feel?"

In these ways, you can coach your child to substitute realistic and calming thoughts for irrational and anxious distortions. When your child is certain of disaster, you can introduce just a little bit of healthy doubt. To help children avoid catastrophizing, we can teach them how to think about problems as temporary situations, not inescapable quagmires.

After fixing distorted thinking, it's easier to control anxious feelings and physical symptoms. The goal is not to eliminate all anxiety—that would be unrealistic. And we certainly don't want to get all anxious about getting rid of anxiety! But you do want to help your child—and yourself—bring anxiety to a manageable range. Even if there is some reason for anxiety, the idea is to salvage an appropriate degree of hope and control.

Over time, using a numerical rating scale, you and your child will see a reduction in stress ratings. Learn to ask, "How anxious am I?" This question should be answered in anticipation of the exposure, after talking about the actual risk, and at various intervals during the exposure. The goal for children and adults is to see that their anxiety ratings come down. This is accomplished by thinking realistically about the anxiety trigger and repeatedly facing it.

For example, using a scale from 0–10, you could ask your child, "You say that being alone in your room is a 9. Now that you've thought about the facts and evidence, how likely is it that something bad will happen? How anxious do you feel about it now?" Your child might answer, "Maybe it's not so bad—just a 6." Hopefully, after repeated practice being alone, the irrational fears might come down further yet.

Parent Pitfalls

Anxiety is anxiety, whether we're young or old. As you gently challenge your child's irrational thoughts, take an objective look at your own. For example: *When I leave my child alone, my anxiety level is a 7. But after thinking about the risk more realistically, it's just a 4.*

Here are some examples of distorted "all-or-none" thoughts that can clutter a parent's mind, drive up unrealistic worries, and fuel parent anxiety.

- If I give up control, disaster is inevitable.
- My child's issues or differences mean she cannot have a good life.
- A few steps backward might mean freefall.
- My child will never be an independent adult.
- If I disagree with my spouse, our children will be totally messed up and our marriage will be a disaster.
- If my friends don't understand, I'll be alone.
- I don't deserve compassion. I should do better.
- It's all my fault. My genes. My parenting.
- My child misbehaves just to get me angry.

And here are some more accurate, realistic, and calming replacement thoughts:

- No child is perfect. No parent is perfect.
- I'm not responsible for my child's every success, failure, emotion, or thought.
- Even if my child has an inherited disability or predisposition, biology isn't destiny.
- Just like adults, children don't always feel motivated.
- Nobody shows constant appreciation.
- It's normal for children and parents to feel stressed and moody.
- Raising a challenging child is really hard work.
- Few adults achieve—or even want—total independence.
- Just because my child has developmental delays, that doesn't mean that he or she cannot continue to make progress.
- Maybe my previous view of success was too narrow.

Strive for an "Uncluttered Mind"

Rather than adding to a child's anxiety, parents and other adults should do their best to tamp back as much irrational mind clutter as possible. Even a little less mental commotion will make it easier for parents and other adults to respond with compassion and understanding. Sometimes, before an adult can respond with empathy, they need to pause for self-reflection. They need to give themselves the chance to practice the language of self-acceptance and the habit of staying calm amidst turmoil. With practice, anyone can become more skillful in quickly identifying their own distorted thinking, i.e., *Oops, there goes my catastrophizing again.*

Some self-reflection questions include:
- What am I dealing with in this moment?
- What am I thinking?
- What am I feeling?
- What am I carrying with me from my own past?
- What judgments am I making about myself?
- What distorted or irrational thoughts am I having?

Adults who can learn to accept themselves generally have a much easier time accepting their children. As Andrew Solomon writes in *Far from the Tree* (2013), "Parenting is no sport for perfectionists." In *Not What I Expected* (2015), Rita Eichenstein discusses different phases that parents might experience toward letting go of some idealized version of the child they wanted and accepting the child they really have.
- Denial: "Not my child!"
- Anger: shifting blame
- Bargaining: "I promise to be the best parent in the world."
- Depression: helplessness
- Acceptance: joyful and purposeful living

Not every parent experiences all these phases—and the order of the phases may vary. The key is in recognizing what phase you might be experiencing. This grants a more objective perspective. Then, with an uncluttered mind, adults can listen reflectively and nonjudgmentally, and respond with genuine understanding.

As discussed in my first book, *Parent Child Journey*, such an empathic response allows parents and other adults to:
- Stay out of power struggles
- Make a genuine effort to understand the child
- Help the child feel understood
- Validate the child's feelings
- Teach the child the language of emotion
- Gain traction with the child for collaborative problem-solving

Teaching (And Learning) Opportunities for Pediatricians

Pediatricians are uniquely situated to help parents unlearn irrational or distorted thoughts about their children. Early in life, a pediatrician can gently address a parent's thoughts when:
- their child has trouble feeding
- their child has a minor illness or injury

- their child requires vaccination, medication, or special assessment
- their child has difficulty with self-settling for sleep or other separation
- their child resists toilet-training
- their child experiences any kind of distress

Discussion of catastrophizing, all-or-none thinking, perfectionism, and other distorted cognitions can become a routine part of anticipatory pediatric care. By teaching parents about these normal mind-traps, pediatricians can counter negative and inflexible thinking throughout the family system. An ounce of prevention is worth a ton of cure.

And of course, pediatricians and other clinicians have irrational thoughts too. Even the most experienced health care providers can lose touch with their own perfectionism, fear of failure, worry about reputation, obsessive-compulsive traits, and other distorted cognitions. Caring for children and families can be stressful. Nowhere is the axiom "Physician, heal thyself" more apropos than when treating anxiety in others.

Respect the Anxiety

At first, anxious children—and adults—insist that their worries are justified. They defend their exaggerations. They claim that they *should be* as anxious as they are. But when talking with anxious children and adults, it's important not to be dismissive. Anxiety demands respect.

Anxiety can be a very tough adversary, for children and adults. It's not easy to modify one's thoughts and feelings. The emotional brain has a mind of its own. The irrational nerve networks and modules fire so much faster than the rational ones. Anxiety will not just go away on command, especially right when it's flaring and inflaming the rational brain. Do not try to address irrational misconceptions in the middle of an anxious situation. Wait for calm. Then, you can gently try to correct irrational thoughts.

Candy-coating and tough-love are equally ineffective. We should not patronize children or invalidate their feelings. Don't tell your child "Just think happy thoughts," or "Don't worry about it." Conditioned habits and instinctive reflexes can be difficult to unlearn. Overcoming anxiety takes time. Children can't just stop being scared. Parents can't just tell children to face their fears. It doesn't work to command, "Just deal with it!" Think about how hard it is for you to overcome your own anxieties. Adults can have just as much difficulty willing away their own doubts and fears. If children knew how to control their fears, they most certainly would.

Coaching Model

Now that we've covered some general principles, let's get down to specific strategies. Most children and adults need some help learning *how* to keep anxiety in check. Some do well enough just talking with friends or reading a book (Huebner, 2005). But many need substantial instruction and rehearsal. If you're going to go for professional help, make sure to find an expert. As discussed above, some therapists just talk and listen in their office but don't set up systematic exposures for real life. A coaching model works best, with explanation and demonstration followed by guided practice.

This can take time, reassurance, and patience. Don't push too hard. Set realistic goals. The approach should be individualized, empathetic, collaborative, and gradual. In the process of teaching children to manage their own anxiety, adults can learn how to help themselves. Likewise, adults who learn how to manage their own anxiety are in a better position to model and teach bravery skills to their children.

Here's how.

Parallel Exposure Therapy

Whether they realize it or not, every member of the child's anxiety network is exposed, directly or indirectly, to the same anxiety triggers. As discussed above, interpersonal anxiety may be shared, sympathetic, or antipathetic. Whatever the type of emotional domino-effect, parallel exposure therapy helps each and every player control their own response. Otherwise, anxiety and avoidance continue rippling throughout the system, impairing the progress of embedded individuals.

Devon's Story

Consider the following tale of narrowly focused individual CBT.

> *Devon had a good singing voice. From a young age, he enjoyed singing along to recordings of Broadway musicals. He loved imagining himself onstage, performing a range of roles, in the privacy of his own home. But he had always been a painfully*

shy kid. When he got old enough, his mother encouraged him to try out for the school musical. She thought, *Maybe this will help him come out of his shell.* Devon was excited. But he starting having trouble sleeping and could not concentrate in class. Anticipatory stage fright was taking its toll.

One of Devon's teachers asked him to come see her after school. She was concerned about his low score on a math test. More and more, Devon seemed lost in his thoughts. On the day of the big audition, Devon woke with a stomachache. On the way to school, he threw up. He went straight to the school nurse and told her, "I need to go home." His mother knew that this was probably anxiety. But she took him to the pediatrician just to be safe.

The doctor examined Devon's abdomen, asking, "Does it hurt here?" Devon said, "Yes." A urinalysis showed two red blood cells. *Probably nothing.* But the doctor recommended more blood tests and a follow-up visit, "Just to play it safe."

That night, Devon's father was frustrated. In the first place, he had mixed feelings about Devon doing musical theater. But he was more upset with Devon for not "toughing it out" with the audition. On top of that, he challenged Linda: "Why do you keep taking Devon to the pediatrician for every little thing?" Devon's sister chimed in: "He's just faking the whole sick thing because he's chicken!"

The next day, Devon wanted to stay home from school. Devon's mother emailed the director of the musical and explained. The director was sympathetic. She knew all about performance anxiety. She called back and said, "I really want Devon in the show." She suggested having Devon come to auditions the next day. Just to watch—no pressure. She would let him put off his tryout until the end of the week. Maybe he would gradually acclimate to the idea, see that the other kids weren't any better.

The following morning, Devon's abdominal pain was worse. He threw up again and told his mom, "I'm too sick to go." Devon's mother could see his fear building. She reassured him that there would be another show in the future. His father was relieved. Devon wasn't sure how he felt. Devon's sister said, "I knew you'd wimp out!" The pediatrician had Devon come back in to get some blood tests.

Devon went back to school. His friends got parts in the show. The weeks passed. Devon's abdominal pain went away. His grades came back up. But he became a bit more of a loner. Secretly he vowed, I'll never even think about trying out for a show again.

The key to conquering anxiety is breaking the cycle of anxiety and avoidance, not just for the child but for everyone in the anxiety system. In Devon's case, it would have helped to have a plan that included his parents, sister, teachers, musical director, and pediatrician. The musical director had tried to help him— but even if Devon had seen a therapist who developed a better plan, it would still be less likely to work without coaching all the involved players.

That's the difference between child-focused exposure therapy and parallel exposure therapy. FDR didn't say, "The only thing *you* have to fear is fear itself." Rather, "The only thing *we* have to fear is fear itself." System-wide exposure therapy is not easy. But it's much more effective than more narrowly focused interventions.

Jordanna's Story

It's time to get practical and specific. Let's consider, in greater depth, another example. First, I'll set the stage. Then, step-by-step, I'll show how parallel exposure therapy can work on the entire anxiety system.

Jordanna was having all sorts of anxiety problems. Her parents, Linda and Sanford, consulted Dr. Oh, a psychologist who specialized in cognitive-behavioral therapy for anxious children.

Before the first appointment, Dr. Oh asked Jordanna's parents and her teacher to complete some questionnaires. Dr. Oh met with Jordanna's parents, observed Jordanna's class at school, and spoke with her teacher and counselor. Then she met with Jordanna at her office. At some visits, she also met briefly with Jordanna's siblings and grandma. Through such meetings, brief phone conversations, and emails (all with parent permission), Dr. Oh made contact with key players in Jordanna's anxiety system. In this way, she learned about each person's role, personality, and level of insight. This took extra time and effort. But Dr. Oh believed in a systems approach.

Jordanna's story: *Jordanna was a seven-year-old second-grader. She attended the neighborhood public elementary school. Jordanna had always been a very sensitive and serious girl. More and more, she was having problems separating from her mother, and she had a bunch of other anxieties too. She responded to them by clinging, screaming, withdrawing, seeking reassurance, or trying to stay home. Jordanna also had some difficulties with language processing and production. She had always struggled putting her thoughts into words. In school, she was having trouble keeping up in reading and writing.*

Linda's story: *Jordanna's mother, Linda, had always struggled with anxiety. Although Linda's first child, Brianna, had been easy, Jordanna was sensitive and demanding. After a long day of work as a full-time lab technician, Linda had little left to give. She wished she didn't have to work so much, but the family needed her regular paycheck and health insurance benefits. Linda was often depressed. In response to Jordanna's mounting anxieties, Linda did her best to provide comfort and reassurance, but she often lacked the emotional energy, and leaned heavily on her own mother to help. Over time, Linda became more stressed and exhausted, and more easily frustrated by her husband, who was not much help at all.*

Sanford's story: *Jordanna's father, Sanford, was a freelance software designer. When Sanford was on a job, he worked very long hours and sometimes traveled out of town. Between jobs, he felt stressed, guilty, and ashamed that Linda made more money. When Jordanna got upset, he got frustrated and angry. Sometimes he snapped at her, "Just cut it out already!" Then he would quickly withdraw to watch TV and—even in the morning—have a few beers. He worried about his marriage and felt estranged from his family.*

Brianna's story: *When Jordanna was in second grade, her older sister, Brianna, was in fifth grade. Brianna was a star student-athlete, self-confident and self-reliant. Jordanna worshipped Brianna. They had been very close, but now Brianna was busy with school, sports, and friends. Jordanna and Brianna rode the same bus to school but Brianna sat as far away as possible. When Jordanna got upset, Brianna might make snide comments, like, "Is it time to grow up yet?"*

Frank's story: *Linda's youngest, Frank, was the "cutest baby ever born." Frank responded to Jordanna with the biggest smiles, but Jordanna seemed to think he was some kind of devil. Now, Frank was in pre-kindergarten at a different school than his older sibs. Whenever Jordanna was anxious, he felt rejected and confused. Not knowing what else to do, he tried to cheer her up by being silly. When that didn't work, he imitated her anxious symptoms, but this got Jordanna even more upset. A few times, she hit him in the shoulder—hard. Then he would go off crying to Linda, who would say, "He's just trying to cheer you up. Is that so terrible?" Loud enough for Frank to hear, Jordanna said, "Yes." But Jordanna loved her brother. She got upset when he had one of his asthma attacks.*

Grandma's story: *Linda's mother was slowing down. She was having more shortness of breath and more frequent doctor visits. Sometimes she needed to stop what she was doing to sit down and rest. Grandma loved the kids and knew that Linda and Sanford needed her help. Whenever Jordanna got upset, she gave her hugs and sweets. But she was frustrated with her son-in-law and worried about her daughter. And she wondered how much longer she'd be able to keep this up.*

Mrs. Smith's story: *Jordanna's second-grade teacher, Mrs. Smith, had a class of 28 children. She was kind and experienced, and very fond of Jordanna. She prided herself on her ability to identify and support children with differences, and frequently encouraged Jordanna. But Jordanna was seeking her reassurance more and more frequently, and Mrs. Smith worried that Jordanna was growing too dependent. She had a whole class of kids to worry about.*

Mr. Fred's story: *Jordanna's bus driver, Mr. Fred, was a 42-year-old musician who performed on weekends. He wrote songs and practiced on weeknights. He liked the kids and hummed to himself as he drove the bus. He noticed that Jordanna always looked tense and tearful getting on the bus. He thought, Nice kid, but what a bundle of nerves. Jordanna confessed to Dr. Oh that she thought Mr. Fred was cool. She liked sitting near him at the front of the bus, listening to his humming.*

Mrs. Alvarez's story: *Jordanna's Sunday-school teacher, Mrs. Alvarez, was good friends with Jordanna's grandmother. She had a traditional approach to religion and teaching, and was concerned about Jordanna's lack of interest. She tried to draw Jordanna out of her shell by asking questions, but Jordanna just said "I don't know." Exasperated, Mrs. Alvarez would call on one of the "smarter" children to "help," and announce to the class, "There's nothing more important than learning about your faith and your religion." Jordanna knew the comment was meant for her.*

Dr. G.'s story: *Jordanna's pediatrician, Dr. G., was the youngest doctor in her group practice. She saw about 25 patients each day. Well-trained and bright, Dr. G. liked the job but she felt stressed. Her hospital-based training had not prepared her for primary care pediatrics—especially mental health problems. At a routine check-up, Linda told Dr. G. about Jordanna's anxiety. After asking just a few questions, Dr. G. recommended medication. Linda frowned and told her a friend had recommended a good therapist, Dr. Oh. Inwardly, Dr. G. was a little offended that Linda didn't follow her advice, but she endorsed the referral.*

Dr. Oh's story: *Dr. Oh had years of experience and considerable success helping anxious children. She thought the pediatrician's medication suggestion was premature. But Dr. Oh knew that doing exposures at home and school was not going to be easy. Jordanna had lots of anxiety triggers. Dr. Oh's office manager told Dr. Oh that she was already taking too many sliding-scale patients, but Dr. Oh didn't have the heart to turn them away.*

Middleville community's story: *Middleville was a moderate-size city of tremendous diversity. The main employers were a growing government research facility, a small university, a large automobile manufacturing plant, and local farms that depended on seasonal migrant workers. There was a wide range of incomes, ethnicities, political affiliations, and educational backgrounds. Outside of the public school system, there wasn't much mixing between these socioeconomic groups.*

Middleville Elementary School's story: *Overall, the school system was considered very good. Jordanna's school was known for its well-trained and dedicated teachers. The curriculum was advanced, and the school prided itself on its high test scores and percentage of college-bound students. Considerable importance was attached to doing homework, getting good grades, and involvement with extracurricular activities.*

Medical and health care systems' story: *Jordanna's parents got health insurance through Linda's employer. Most of the mental health providers listed "in-plan" were adult psychologists. Dr. Oh was "out-of-plan." Linda and Sanford could submit her invoices for partial reimbursement, but were shocked to learn that reimbursement came to only 25 percent of Dr. Oh's standard fee. Dr. Oh said she could offer a sliding scale and payment plan. Even so, beyond a few visits, that would still come to more money than Linda and Sanford could afford.*

Jordanna's anxiety system was not unusual. There were many players, each with their own issues and stresses. In traditional child-centered exposure therapy, the first step is setting up a hierarchy of anxiety triggers. The child ranks each fear from mild to severe. The therapist works with the child to help her first face a relatively minor fear, before gradually moving up to tackle more challenging triggers. Sometimes this child-focused approach works, but other times things don't go as well. Dr. Oh knew that CBT had a higher chance of failing if she forgot either of these key principles:

1. *There's more to the child than just the anxiety.* Dr. Oh screened for underlying learning disabilities, ADHD, social problems, and other coexisting issues that might be contributing to the anxiety. She discovered Jordanna's mild difficulties with expressive and receptive language, which contributed to her anxiety socializing, reading, and writing. Treatment of the anxiety would have to include attention to all these issues. Dr. Oh would have to modify her approach, both in office sessions with Jordanna and in real-life exposures. Furthermore, while Jordanna shared her anxiety disorder with her mother, she shared her language problems with her father.

In working with Jordanna's parents, Dr. Oh knew that she would need to accommodate their differences as well.

2. *There's more to the anxiety than just the child.* Dr. Oh wanted to include other members of the anxiety system in the exposure therapy. Clearly, many players had a part. Even if Jordanna's exposures to separation were "just-right," triggering just enough anxiety but not too much, what about Jordanna's mother? Her father? Siblings? Grandma? Teacher? Sunday school teacher? The bus driver? What about the pediatrician and therapist? Each had an important role to play, and could either help Jordanna overcome her separation anxiety or inadvertently contribute to avoidance.

Parallel Exposure Therapy: The Mountain Hiking Party Checklist

It's time to introduce the Mountain Hiking Party Checklist. This will serve as a template for organizing Parallel Exposure Therapy.
 1. The Anxiety Triggers List
 2. Organizing Your Mountain Hiking Party
 3. The Anxiety Response (Symptoms) List
 4. The Anxiety Trigger Rating Scale
   a. Relative difficulty
   b. Relative importance
   c. Relative motivation
 5. Choosing a trail together
 6. View from the top
 7. Marking a trail
 8. The backpack

Those of you who are familiar with traditional CBT will notice that this checklist begins with the usual survey of anxiety triggers. But then, traditional child-centered exposure therapy and system-wide parallel exposure therapy part ways. The mountain hiking party metaphor captures these key differences, including everyone in the anxiety system.

Child-focused cognitive-behavioral therapists often use ladders. Each ladder represents a different anxiety trigger, and each rung on the ladder represents progressively greater levels of exposure to that anxiety trigger. The child climbs, rung by rung, toward the top of the ladder—and when they reach the top, they have mastered that fear.

The ladder metaphor can work well enough. But it has one important limitation: there's not enough room on a ladder to accommodate more than one person. In contrast, many people can hike up a mountain trail together. That's why, for parallel exposure therapy, I prefer to picture everyone in the anxiety system in a mountain hiking party. Parallel exposure therapy is broader than just one person climbing a ladder as bystanders look up.

The mountain trail metaphor is certainly not the only way to represent exposure therapy. Feel free to use other metaphors that might feel more appropriate. In addition to rungs on a ladder, you could also use a simple checklist, number system, Lego towers, or computer-generated graphics. It's important to choose a final symbol of mastery that's meaningful to you and your child. This part of the project can be as fun as it is helpful. Whatever image or metaphor you choose, you just need a way to represent a starting point, a final goal, and sub-steps in-between. Here, however, I'll continue with the mountain trail metaphor.

Out With Ladders (Child-Focused CBT)

Final goal: _____

My reward: _____

Goal #5: _____

My reward: _____

Goal #4: _____

My reward: _____

Goal #3: _____

My reward: _____

Goal #2: _____

My reward: _____

Goal #1: _____

My reward: _____

In With Mountains (Parallel Exposure Therapy)

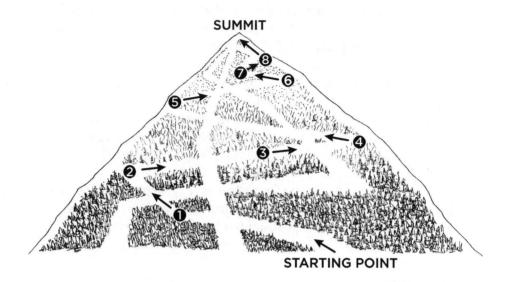

Continuing to use Jordanna's case as an example, let's work our way through the Mountain Hiking Party Checklist and see how parallel exposure therapy works in action.

The Anxiety System Triggers List

Each anxiety trigger can be represented by different mountain trails. Some trails are easy. Some are more difficult. Some might even seem impossible.

First, we simply list different anxiety triggers from the child's perspective. Write down specific situations, events, sensations, or stimuli that set off your child's anxious response. The parent(s) and the child start the list. Additional stimuli or triggers may also be suggested by family members, teachers, and others in the anxiety system. When does anxiety happen? Where? Who's around? What seems to precede spikes in worry, discomfort, or stress? Why does each stimulus cause anxiety? Again, some common anxiety triggers for children include separation from parents, public performance, making mistakes, changes in routine, social situations, crowds, robbers, storms, germs, dogs, dark, homework, tests, sports, certain physical sensations, doctor or dentist visits, elevators, insects, and other concerns about safety for themselves or others.

If you don't know what triggers your child's anxiety symptoms, try to do some detective work. Think back or keep a diary going forward. What happens right before the anxiety symptom appears? What kinds of thoughts and feelings immediately precede the symptom? Who's around? Where are you? When does the anxiety seem to strike? If you can't identify any specific trigger, maybe it's a non-specific kind of distress known as "generalized anxiety." If there is really no specific trigger, then you can just list the symptom itself and label it "trigger unknown."

At their initial meeting without Jordanna, Linda and Sanford told Dr. Oh about Jordanna's anxiety triggers. Dr. Oh started making a list.

Jordanna had always been clingy, but after the birth of her little brother, Jordanna had become more tightly attached to her mother. She had hypersensitivities to clothing, certain foods, bathing, and having her hair brushed. At the beginning of each school year, just the thought of getting on the bus made her scream in terror. Throughout the school day, Jordanna was quiet and serious. In kindergarten and first grade, her extreme anxiety had gradually softened through the year. But still, Jordanna never really wanted to go to school. She frequently sought reassurance from the teacher about how she was doing with her work and whether there would be a change in the daily schedule. She played by herself at recess. She also resisted going to birthday parties, playdates, or church. In addition, Jordanna worried whenever her dad went out of town for work, Frank had asthma attacks, Grandma seemed tired, or her parents argued with each other. All of this seemed to be getting worse.

Then Dr. Oh met with Jordanna. At first, Jordanna didn't want to join Dr. Oh in the playroom. Dr. Oh asked, "How about if your mom comes too?" Jordanna and Linda held hands and followed Dr. Oh to the playroom together. Dr. Oh hung back and just let them explore. Jordanna glanced at the piano, basketball hoop, and blocks. Then, Dr. Oh noticed Jordanna taking a longer look at the art supplies. At a previous meeting, Linda had mentioned that Jordanna liked to paint.

Dr. Oh set up a table with some watercolors and paper. With her mother by her side, Jordanna gradually became immersed in painting. Dr. Oh made her way over and took a look at Jordanna's painting. Not saying a word, Dr. Oh pulled up a chair and started her own painting.

After five minutes, Dr. Oh asked Linda to get some fresh water from the sink in the next room—a gentle way of seeing if Jordanna could tolerate a few degrees of separation from her mother. Jordanna looked a little concerned but Linda came right back and Jordanna relaxed again.

After a few more minutes, Dr. Oh excused herself from the room, "to get something." When Dr. Oh came back, she asked Linda, "Would you mind filling out this form?" Dr. Oh handed Linda paper and pen. On the paper, Dr. Oh had written, "Don't say anything to Jordanna. Just take this clipboard with you across the room. Be casual. Have a seat on the sofa and write whatever you like. Every 30 seconds, come back and look at Jordanna's drawing. When you return the fourth time, ask me if you can use the restroom. Leave the room for 30 seconds and come right back." Linda smiled knowingly and did as instructed. Jordanna needed a small amount of encouragement that she could tolerate these brief separations—and she did. A successful first visit.

At the next visit, Dr. Oh continued in the same way. Gradually and incrementally, she helped Jordanna feel more comfortable. Dr. Oh came up with more reasons for Jordanna to separate from Linda for slightly longer intervals. She also found non-threatening ways to ask Jordanna about her worries. They played with toys and puppets. They drew pictures and talked just a little. Dr. Oh knew that she could not rush winning Jordanna's trust. She also knew that Jordanna might have trouble responding to questions that were too direct or open-ended. Each time Jordanna mentioned a worry, Dr. Oh wrote it down on her worry list: a few words with a corresponding stick picture. Dr. Oh said, "Here are some worries we came up with together. Your mom added some too." Some of Mom's additions to the worry list had actually been suggested by other family members and teachers.

Anxiety Triggers

Jordanna's Triggers
going to school
schoolwork
homework
recess
birthday parties
playdates
church
Dad going out of town
Frank's asthma attacks
Grandma being tired
Mom and Dad arguing
sleep

Dr. Oh told Jordanna, "When you come to see me, I'll help you practice being the boss of your worries. Then we'll always make time for fun before you have to go."

Organizing Your Mountain Hiking Party

Now that you have a list of your child's anxiety triggers, consider:
1. *Who is in the hiking party?* Which people are around at each trigger point? What role might they play?
2. *Who is going to be the trail guide?* On the scene of the anxiety trigger, who is going to be the team leader? Who is going to take charge of implementing a plan, coordinating everybody's efforts, and monitoring progress?
3. *How will everyone in the hiking party communicate?* How will the team leader talk with everyone in the anxiety system? How will everyone involved in parallel exposure therapy share thoughts and report progress with each other?

Setting up a treatment plan that involves many people might seem daunting. But just because it's challenging doesn't mean it's impossible. So, let's get organized.

Who Is in the Hiking Party?

The therapist, child, and parents should make a list of people in the mountain hiking party; any members of the anxiety system whose active participation in the exposure therapy is key to success. The parallel exposure "hiking party" should usually include at least three people: the child plus a family member, teacher, or other involved adult.

The makeup of the hiking party will vary depending upon the anxiety trigger and the setting. Some hiking parties can be relatively small. For example, if there is a very specific home-based trigger like fear of the dark, then a parallel exposure team might be limited to just one parent and one child. For other anxiety triggers, the hiking party might be larger. Consider a child with a bug phobia who will not go outside. Then, parallel exposure therapy should cut across many settings, wherever there might be bugs. If the exposure therapy is targeting separation anxiety for sleep, the hiking party should include the child, parents, and perhaps other household members. If the targeted anxiety is about separation anxiety on arrival at school, the hiking party could include the child, a parent, other carpool parent, the bus driver, teacher, or school counselor. Separation anxiety in other settings could require yet other team members: babysitters, camp counselors, religious school teachers, grandparents, medical or mental health providers.

> At subsequent visits, Dr. Oh told Jordanna that she wanted to help with her whole list of anxieties, including problem situations at home, school, church, and with friends. She suggested Jordanna consider the roles played by her parents, siblings, grandmother, regular teacher, Sunday school teacher, pediatrician, and even the bus driver. Jordanna would not be able to conquer her fears alone. She would need other important people in her life to help. Dr. Oh and Jordanna thought about what it would take to help with her fear of going to school. They decided that the hiking party could include Jordanna, her mom, her dad, Grandma, Brianna, Frank, Mrs. Smith, Mr. Fred, and Dr. G., her pediatrician.

Some children like the idea of a team approach. They feel more supported if they know that everyone is working together. Other children don't like this "hiking party" idea at all. They want to keep their anxiety private. Sharing it might make them even more anxious. Sometimes, talking about anxiety—or just knowing that others are talking about it—needs to be added to the list of anxiety triggers. In those cases, we might need to design just-right exposures to talking openly about the anxiety itself. Although subtle, there is a difference between respecting a child's right to privacy and cloaking an anxiety problem in shame.

Anxiety about dealing with anxiety can also be a problem for parents and others in the hiking party. Parents might hope that they can just drop their child off at the therapist's office and pick them up all fixed—and may balk when asked to participate. Other adults might also become anxious or feel threatened when asked to be part of the team. Therefore, it's important to design exposures that are just right for everyone in the anxiety system. Otherwise, anxiety in even one member of the hiking party might spread to others or cause ongoing avoidance of the anxiety trigger. This failure to take everyone's responses into account could sabotage the exposure therapy.

> *Dr. Oh had won Linda and Sanford's trust. She had listened as they told their story, and had asked lots of questions. They were impressed by her thoroughness and compassion. She was realistic yet optimistic. They understood why Dr. Oh emphasized the importance of working with the whole family, the teacher, and other important people. All of this made sense. But Linda and Sanford had questions about how to make this work in real life. After all, everybody was pretty busy. But, through practical planning, strong leadership, and good communication, Dr. Oh hoped to win the others' trust too.*

Who Is Going to Be the Trail Guide?

Parallel exposure therapy requires a considerable amount of coordination, leadership, and commitment.

- *Expert therapists.* Ideally, parallel exposure therapy takes place under the guidance of a trained and experienced psychologist or social worker—not just for child-focused CBT but also for broader coordination of everyone in the hiking party. Successful exposure therapy depends upon direct support in the natural setting; home, school, playground, sports field, etc. Experts face a choice: they can leave their offices and do the field work, or they can acknowledge their limitations and delegate at least part of the leadership role to someone else who can be a more consistent presence on the scene.

- *Parents.* A parent may be well-suited to serve as trail guide. After all, parents are usually the most essential, embedded, motivated, diligent, and connected member of the anxiety system. Nobody is better positioned and more knowledgeable about their child than a mom or dad. As emphasized throughout this discussion, a parent's own anxiety doesn't disqualify them from taking a leadership role. In fact, parents who learn how to help themselves are better equipped to teach their children.
- *Others.* In many situations, neither a specialist nor a parent is best-suited to take on the leadership role. If the anxiety trigger occurs at school, a teacher or counselor might be best positioned to take control of the mission. Every member of the cohort has their own strengths, weaknesses, and life circumstances. The job of trail guide can go to any member of the hiking party who is ready, willing, and able.

One of many potential fringe benefits of parallel exposure therapy is liberation from experts. This decentralized team approach requires distribution of knowledge to everyone on the team. The trail guide is a teacher and coach, not just a leader. The goal of good therapists or leaders is to make themselves obsolete by making others more self-reliant. Everyone learns strategies for facing current and future challenges. The ultimate goal is to empower everyone in the anxiety system.

> *Dr. Oh offered to take the lead, organizing the team and helping everybody maintain good communication. Linda and Sanford expressed some concern about involving others, both inside and outside of the family. But Dr. Oh reassured them that she would not do anything without checking with them first. And it made sense to involve people who were around when and where the anxiety was happening. In fact, they would need to designate trail leaders for home and school, when Dr. Oh could not be right there.*

Often, there is a different trail guide for different trails. Ask yourself—and your child—who is best- positioned to take the lead for each anxiety trigger. Sometimes, a peer or sibling leader works great. Coaching is best done by the most capable person on the scene. For example, if your child has anxiety on the soccer field, the *soccer* coach may also be the best *anxiety* coach. In the elementary classroom, the *math* teacher may be the best *anxiety* teacher. In high school, perhaps it's the counselor. On the bus, it might be an older sibling.

Some people are simply not well-suited to lead exposures. They might be disqualified because of their own temperament, lack of self-discipline, poor motivation, weak coaching skills, or limited availability. Think strategically. Use different trail party members according to their own strengths.

Dr. Oh had learned that Mrs. Smith would not be available on Jordanna's arrival each morning. At that busy time, she had to devote her attention to the whole class. The school counselor, Mrs. Dettmer, could not make a consistent commitment either. But Dr. Oh and Linda found a very capable leader who was also very available.

At one of Jordanna's visits, Dr. Oh had met Brianna. Dr. Oh empathized with Brianna about the attention Jordanna was getting and how frustrating Jordanna's anxiety was for the whole family. As a precocious fifth grader, Brianna had a burgeoning interest in psychology.

Picking up on Brianna's interest, Dr. Oh talked with her about the principles of exposure therapy and family systems. Dr. Oh drew a family tree. Together, they made lines to represent the different kinds of relationships Jordanna had with each of her family members. Gently, Dr. Oh helped Brianna understand how her own response to Jordanna's school refusal—getting Mom or Grandma—just made Jordanna more dependent on her parents, and shifted their attention away from her and toward Jordanna.

Brianna was interested in learning about different parts of the brain. She asked surprisingly sophisticated questions about conditioned responses and family dynamics, fascinated by how all this explained her little sister's problems. Brianna's attitude shifted from irritation to revelation.

Brianna liked the way Dr. Oh treated her like an adult. When Dr. Oh asked her about leading the morning transition team, her mom added, "Now I see how all this stuff with Jordanna has cut into my time with you. No matter what you decide, how about we do a movie and popcorn every Friday night— just you and me—after Jordanna's asleep?" Although she didn't say it out loud, Brianna liked the idea of helping her sister and her family.

How Will Everyone in the Hiking Party Communicate?

In parallel exposure therapy, success depends upon sharing a plan, getting feedback, and trouble-shooting with everyone in the anxiety system. An effective communication system should be efficient so that everyone can easily share viewpoints and coordinate efforts.

To overcome communication challenges, I recommend using a secure group email system. With parent permission, everyone in the hiking party can be copied and just hit "reply all" on each communication. Other options include conference phone calls, video conferencing, or actual face-to-face team meetings. Sometimes, when communication challenges prove insurmountable, the team leader might just have to put him or herself in somebody else's shoes and make a best guess on their behalf.

Good-enough team communication doesn't require regular team meetings, therapist interaction with every member of the anxiety system, or frequent contact between all team members. It's hard enough just scheduling child-therapist appointments. Expecting an untenable level of contact across the entire anxiety system will only add to everyone's frustration and distress, even making key players skeptical about joining the hiking party. For effective recruitment and sustained engagement, a communication system has to be efficient, easy, and practical.

The Initial Team Meeting

Despite the difficulty, whenever possible it makes a huge difference if core members of the hiking party can meet—even briefly—for an initial team meeting in person. If this isn't possible for some or all, then arrangements can be made for a conference call, or better yet, a secure video conference. At very least, there can be a group email. During the initial meeting, the team leader can share the list of anxiety triggers, review the principles of exposure therapy, and ask each member to anticipate difficulties they might have with the exposure. Then the team can hammer out specific roles for each member, air concerns, and offer suggestions. The team leader can answer questions and help everyone arrive at a coordinated plan. The primary goal is for everybody to connect around a shared goal. Whatever the form of this first meeting, the trail guide should summarize and share details of the plan by secure email.

During parallel exposure therapy, regular communication is important. If needed, subsequent team meetings can be infrequent and brief. Depending upon the nature and severity of the anxiety trigger, weekly to monthly group email is usually sufficient. As we work through Jordanna's case in the following pages, you will see how group emails or other electronically shared documents allow for easy sharing of observations.

Dr. Oh started out by copying everyone in the hiking party on a group email. This included Linda, Sanford, Grandma, Brianna, Mrs. Smith, Mr. Fred, and Dr. G.

Dear Team Jordanna,

I'm a specialist in helping children with anxiety problems. As you know, Jordanna has been struggling. Her parents have given us permission to communicate with each other and work together. (Please see their signed form attached.) With your help, I'm sure that Jordanna will do well.

Over the years, I've learned that treating childhood anxiety requires a team effort. It's not enough to just talk with children about their anxiety—they need real-life experience learning how to face their fears. I'll be working with Jordanna and her parents in my office, but we would really appreciate your help implementing these strategies in Jordanna's real world. That's how she will make the best progress. Usually, a few well-timed and supportive words as Jordanna encounters some of her anxiety triggers will be sufficient. Little things can make a big difference—she just needs to get the same message from all of us.

If possible, I would like to meet with you to get your perspective and set things in motion. The principal and teacher at Middleville Elementary School have kindly agreed to let us use Jordanna's classroom, #18, right after dismissal from 3:30-4:00 PM, on Wednesday, October 17.

I realize that some of you may not be able to attend. But it would be great if most of you can. Phoning in and connecting with the group by speakerphone is also an option. Whether or not you can make this meeting, I'll be keeping us all in touch by email so that we can coordinate our efforts in helping Jordanna.

At the meeting, I will briefly outline the overall strategy. This will be a step-by-step approach.

Attached, please see our initial list of Jordanna's anxiety triggers. Let me know if you think we've missed anything.

I'm happy to answer your questions and appreciate any suggestions.

Will you be able to join us? In person or by phone?

Gratefully,

Dr. Oh

During the few weeks leading up to the initial team meeting, Dr. Oh met again with Jordanna and her parents, gathered more background history, and got a better read on Jordanna's anxiety triggers. She built rapport while continuing to educate Jordanna and her family about parallel exposure therapy.

The Anxiety Response (Symptoms) List

For children and adults, strategic anticipation is the key to overcoming anxiety. If an anxiety trigger cannot be totally foreseen, we can at least try to recognize the earliest warning signs. Rather than waiting for full-blown "fight, flight, or freeze" reactions, try to identify precursor symptoms, to nip it in the bud.

Child's Responses

Help your child make a list of anxious thoughts, feelings, physical symptoms, and behaviors. Using behavior science jargon, the symptoms would be called "the response" (R) to an anxiety trigger or "stimulus" (S).

- Anxious thoughts include obsessions, fears, pessimistic assumptions or generalizations, catastrophizing, blame shifting, and paranoia—to name a few.
- Anxious feelings might include nervousness, worry, panic, or dread.
- Physical symptoms can include muscle tension, headaches, stomachaches, "butterflies," chest tightness, heart palpitations, or skin flushing.
- Behaviors commonly include crying, aggressiveness, running off, getting stuck, hesitation, avoiding, or shutting down.

Most children and adolescents cannot make this list for themselves. They need some help. Give whatever level of support is necessary—not too much, not too little. For younger children or others who don't have sufficient verbal or cognitive skills, you might have to make the list on their behalf or show them pictures of anxiety-provoking situations and let them choose and/ or rank them.

Every child shows anxiety in their own way. You know your child well: that look in the eyes, that change in facial expression or body language, those tell-tale behaviors. Hopefully, over time your child will become more skillful at recognizing their own anxiety symptoms.

Jordanna's Anxiety Responses

Jordanna's Triggers	Jordanna's Responses
going to school	cling
schoolwork	scream
homework	quiet
recess	withdraw
birthday parties	frequently seek reassurance
playdates	stay home
church	stomachaches
Dad going out of town	
Frank's asthma attacks	
Grandma being tired	
Mom and Dad arguing	
sleep	

Parents' Responses

Whenever a child experiences anxiety, parents have their own stress reactions. Remember the three different types: shared, sympathetic, and antipathetic. Parent anxiety is commonly triggered by child anxiety, separation from child, child's misbehavior, and the child's other displays of emotion. Parents may worry about their own parenting abilities, other children, work, finances, marital issues, other adult relationship stresses, or feeling judged by family or friends.

At a meeting without Jordanna, Dr. Oh asked Jordanna's parents about their own feelings and responses to Jordanna's anxiety triggers. Every time Jordanna cried for her, Linda said she felt a complicated set of emotions. She wanted to comfort Jordanna, but it was never enough. Linda felt more depressed and helpless. Jordanna seemed to be getting more and more

171

dependent. Was there something wrong with Jordanna that the doctors were missing? Would she always be this anxious? How was she going to get through life? Linda's nerves were frayed. She felt always on edge, just waiting for Jordanna's next episode. She didn't have time for her friends. When would she ever get a break?

Sanford told Dr. Oh, "Linda is just too much of a softy. When Linda's not around, I just tell Jordanna to cut it out—and she does! But if Linda is in the house, Jordanna will just go to her." It was clear to Dr. Oh that Sanford was frustrated, even angry. Jordanna seemed to take all of Linda's attention. Feeling powerless and inadequate, Sanford resorted to having "a few" beers and watching sports on TV.

Parents' Anxiety Responses

Jordanna's Triggers	Jordanna's Responses	Linda's Responses	Sanford's Responses
going to school schoolwork homework recess birthday parties playdates church Dad going out of town Frank's asthma attacks Grandma being tired Mom and Dad arguing sleep	cling scream quiet withdraw frequently seek reassurance stay home stomachaches	comfort reassure worry get frustrated with Sanford ask Grandma for help	Get frustrated and angry with Jordanna, Linda, and Grandma yell withdraw to TV, beer worry about marriage feel estranged from family

Other Team Members' Responses

One child's anxiety usually causes secondary anxiety or other feelings in siblings, grandparents, and other members of the family system. Consider each player in the anxiety system. In each of the child's anxiety-triggering situations, how do others usually respond?

Family Members' Anxiety Responses

Jordanna's Triggers	Jordanna's Responses	Linda's Responses	Sanford's Responses

going to school
schoolwork
homework
recess
birthday parties
playdates
church
Dad going out
  of town
Frank's asthma
  attacks
Grandma being
  tired
Mom and Dad
  arguing
sleep
	cling
	scream
	quiet
	withdraw
	frequently seek
	  reassurance
	stay home
	stomachaches
		comfort
		reassure
		worry
		get frustrated
		  with Sanford
		ask Grandma
		  for help
			get frustrated
			  and angry with
			  Jordanna,
			  Linda, and
			  Grandma
			yell
			withdraw to TV,
			  beer
			worry about
			  marriage
			feel estranged
			  from family

Grandma's Responses	Brianna's Responses	Frank's Responses

get angry with
  Sanford and
  worried about
  Linda
hug
offer food and
  sweets
	ignore
	call for Mom or
	  Grandma
		try to cheer her
		  up
		suggest games
		get silly
		get attention
		  from adults
		  when Jor-
		  danna gets
		  aggressive

Non–Family Members' Anxiety Responses

Jordanna's triggers	Mrs. Smith's Responses	Mrs. Alvarez's Responses
going to school schoolwork homework recess birthday parties playdates church Dad going out of town Frank's asthma attacks Grandma being tired Mom and Dad arguing sleep	frequent reassurance problem-solving discussions	call on her to participate more call on other kids when she doesn't answer
Mr. Fred's Responses	**Dr. G's Responses**	**Dr. Oh's Responses**
distract her with singing positive attention	repeated requests to have mother call suggestion of medication expressions of frustration	positive attention for facing fears gentle but relentless pushing to make more progress

The Anxiety Trigger Rating Scale
Child's Rating of Relative Difficulty

For starters, help your child rate each anxiety trigger according to difficulty. Using a developmentally appropriate, customized "worry scale," "fear-o-meter," or "difficulty rating scale," your child should rate the relative challenge of facing each anxiety trigger on the list—reflecting not just the severity of the anxiety symptoms, but also how hard it would be to tolerate exposure to the trigger. Put this question to your child: "How difficult would it be for you to face this and handle your anxiety?" If your child can not answer for him or herself, make your best guess on their behalf.

Younger children usually need simpler and more individualized rating scales, such as:

• *Numbers.* 0 = no problem, 1 = easy, 2 = medium, 3 = hard

- *Traffic lights.* green = no problem, yellow = little problem, red = big problem
- *Thumbs.* up = no problem, sideways = little problem, down = big problem
- *Faces.* smiley = no problem, neutral = little problem, frowny or scared = big problem

For older children, adolescents, and adults, the scale can have more subtle gradations. Using the mountain climbing metaphor, I like to visualize these as trail difficulty ratings, such as one finds on a trail map.

- 1–3 = Little problem. "This will take a little effort but I'm sure I can do it." Flat, smooth, short, easy.
- 4–6 = Medium problem. "This will be hard but I think I can do it." Uphill gradient, a few rocks and minor obstacles, longer distance, requiring moderate exertion.
- 7–9 = Big problem. "This will be very hard and I'm not sure I can do it." Steep, poorly marked, rocky, many miles, requiring excellent conditioning and maximum effort over an extended period of time.
- 10 = NO WAY! "Pretty much impossible!" Vertical cliff with no toe- or hand-holds, requiring expert skills, elite athleticism, intense effort, and extraordinary endurance.

Dr. Oh asked Jordanna to rate each of her anxiety triggers according to difficulty. Jordanna was good with numbers— much better than with words. Jordanna's ratings of difficulty were as follows.

- *go to school? 5*
- *do schoolwork? 3*
- *do homework? 7*
- *play with others at recess? 2*
- *go to birthday parties? 3*
- *go on playdates? 3*
- *go to church? 2*
- *deal with Dad going out of town? 2*
- *deal with Frank's asthma attacks? 2*
- *deal with Grandma being tired? 2*
- *deal with Mom and Dad arguing? 2*

Dr. Oh knew that Jordanna was minimizing her own difficulties. Jordanna's parents would probably rate some of these triggers differently. But Dr. Oh dutifully recorded Jordanna's answers without questioning their accuracy.

Anxiety Mountain Map

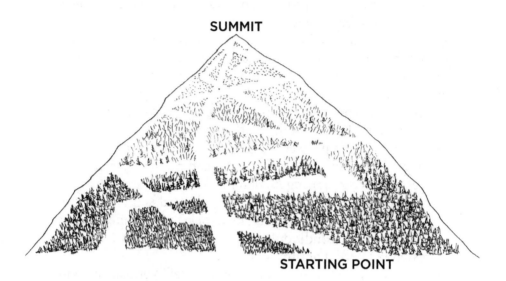

SUMMIT

STARTING POINT

System-Wide Ratings of Difficulty

After rating each worry, fear, or problem situation, rearrange the child's trigger list in order of difficulty, from hardest to easiest. You can picture each anxiety trigger as a different trail on the same mountain, or as a different mountain altogether. Either way, the most difficult triggers can be represented by the steepest and rockiest trails. The least difficult triggers can be represented by the flattest and smoothest trails. Each anxiety trigger, along with its numerical rating of relative difficulty, can be written in at the bottom of the representative trail.

After your child rates each fear, then parents, other children, and other adults should assign a difficulty rating that reflects their own degree of challenge in the same situations—including how hard it will be for everyone to deal with each other! It may be difficult or inappropriate for everyone to comment on all situations. Everyone in the anxiety system isn't directly involved with each anxiety trigger. And some private family triggers (such as Grandma's fatigue and parents arguing) should not be shared with others.

If you can ask different participants in the anxiety system to rate their own difficulty, great. If not, just try to put yourself in their shoes and make your own best guess. If you were just facing a fear on your own, it would be one number. But living as we all do—within family, school, neighborhood, community, and cultural systems—others may push your own rating of relative difficulty higher or lower: higher if a system works against you; lower if a system is supportive and works for you.

Relative Importance

After rating, arranging, and mapping the anxiety triggers in terms of difficulty, everyone in the anxiety system should also rate each anxiety trigger in terms of importance. No matter what the difficulty, how big a deal is this in the child's life? In the lives of others involved? Rate the relative importance of each anxiety triggers as follows:

0 = not at all important
1–3 = a little important
4–6 = medium important
7–10 = very important

Relative Motivation as Difficulty Versus Importance

Difficulty and importance sometimes match up; other times, they don't. For example, facing a fear of dogs might get an 8 for difficulty. But let's say there aren't many dogs in the neighborhood, and no close friends or relatives have dogs. In that case, facing a fear of dogs might only get a 3 for importance. Dog avoidance is pretty easy; the status quo is okay. Especially given the high difficulty rating, why bother? Motivation will be low.

On the other hand, if you live in a neighborhood with lots of dogs, your best friend has a dog, and your mother is a veterinarian, then the importance of learning to control your dog phobia should get a much higher number—maybe a 9! The difficulty rating may still be high, but the stakes are higher. Avoidance isn't a realistic option. Despite the difficulty of conquering this fear, it's very important. Motivation will be higher.

Note: In the discussion that follows—whether referring to difficulty, importance, or motivation—I recommend putting ratings of 5 or greater in the "high" category and ratings of 4 or less in the "low" category.

When considering difficulty versus importance, there are four possible combinations of ratings, as explained in Miller and Skolnick's classic *Motivational Interviewing*:

	Importance	➡
Difficulty	**D.** high difficulty	**B.** High difficulty
	low importance	high importance
↑	**C.** low difficulty	**A.** low difficulty
	low importance	high importance

D. Clearly, motivation will be lowest if the difficulty is high and the goal is unimportant. *Why bother? Not worth it.*

A. Motivation will be highest if the path is easy and the goal is very important. *Why not? Big gain. Little pain. Let's go for it!*

Motivation will be more complicated, mixed, and moderate for either of the remaining two combinations:

B. High difficulty but high importance. *This is going to be tough. But is it worth the price? I think so. Maybe we should give it a try.*

C. Low difficulty but low importance. *So easy. But who cares? Maybe this isn't even worth the time. But there's not much to lose. Why not just pick some low-hanging fruit?*

After assigning a motivation letter grade to each trigger, it makes sense to rank and order motivation as follows:

A. High motivation

B. Moderate motivation

C. Low motivation

D. No motivation

Choosing a Trail Together

Picking anxiety triggers for parallel exposure therapy is much like gathering hiking companions and looking at a trail map together. Choosing where to start and how to proceed depends upon everyone's ratings of relative importance, difficulty, and motivation.

Choosing Ease over Importance

Traditionally, exposure therapy targets the easiest anxiety triggers first—exposures with the lowest difficulty ratings. Even if the most strenuous hikes result in the most beautiful views, it's smart to choose a trail that you know you can finish, to learn techniques with the least challenging targets. Then, you gradually move up in difficulty. After you've "skilled up" and conquered the easiest levels, then you can tackle tougher trails. Some therapists reasonably default to this as the most surefire way to fuel confidence and increase motivation for the greater challenges that lie ahead. With this strategy, you deliberately resist the temptation to go right after the most pressing problems—saving the most difficult for last.

Choosing Importance over Ease

Often, the most difficult challenges are the most compelling. A child or adult might understand the reasons for starting low and going slow, but they might not want to waste their time or energy (or money for a therapist) on lesser goals. The difficulty of the trail is outweighed by the importance of achieving that higher summit. When calculating the odds of success, higher motivation may outweigh greater difficulty. If so, as discussed further below, we must be careful not to overwhelm and cause frustration. If importance outweighs difficulty, special care must be taken to break down the task and make it more doable.

Choosing System-Wide Versus Individual Motivation

Commonly, therapists choose to work on an anxiety trigger based only upon the child's rating of difficulty. But it's crucial to also consider others' difficulty, importance, and motivation ratings too. Parents and other adults have their own problems with anxiety, depression, ADHD, executive dysfunction, language processing—you name it. And all of the team members have different relationships with each other. Challenges implementing any part of a plan can ripple throughout the whole system. Consequently, the order of exposures (trail selection) should take everyone's ratings into account.

Of course, the larger the hiking party, the harder it is to choose a trail. And the size of an anxiety system varies with each trigger. Sometimes, it makes sense to keep things simple and choose an anxiety trigger that only requires the participation of one child and one adult. Other times, you might choose to start with an anxiety trigger *because* it involves the greatest number of people. Although more complicated, there may be good reasons to engage everyone right from the get-go.

Ultimately, real-life success depends upon real-life exposure to real-life triggers, including all the real-life players. This is reason enough to solicit everyone's active participation whenever possible—especially those who are regular cogs in the anxiety machine. Ignoring their role decreases the odds of success. For these reasons, whenever feasible, "choice of trail" should at least consider the combined ratings of all the participants.

As strongly implied throughout this discussion, a huge fringe benefit of parallel exposure therapy is *relationship repair.* In many anxiety systems, some relationships are detached; others are too enmeshed; yet others are conflicted. These relational difficulties may be a cause *and/or* an effect of anxiety in various systems. In any case, by soliciting everyone's perspective and working together on specific anxiety triggers, we create an opportunity to improve communication and rebalance relationships. In the process of helping a child conquer anxiety, it's not unusual to see improved connections between parent and child, parent and parent, parent and teacher, teacher and therapist, doctor and therapist, and so on. When we fix systems, we fix anxiety. When we fix anxiety, we fix systems.

Discrepancies in Ratings of Difficulty, Importance, and Motivation

If different individuals all rate an anxiety trigger the same, it's easy. For example, let's say you and your child are both just a little bit afraid of dogs but you both really want one. In that case, you would both agree that having a dog is of high importance and low difficulty, and give your shared fear of dogs a high motivation rating. This would simplify trail selection. Your chances of mutual success are excellent.

But what if parent and child ratings don't match up? What's easy for one of you may be hard for the other. Remember that parent and child anxiety are usually intertwined, and a parent's parallel anxiety may be of three types:

1. shared (as in the above example, in which child and parent have the same fear),
2. sympathetic (in which the parent has anxiety about their child's anxiety), or
3. antipathetic (in which the parent resents the child's anxiety).

No matter what the type of parallel anxiety, child and parent may not agree on what's the easiest and most important trail.

Continuing with the example of shared anxiety, your child might have a mild fear of dogs (rating 2) but you might have a very serious fear of dogs (rating 9). Or just the reverse: Your child's fear of dogs is high (9) but yours is low (2). On top of that discrepancy, your ratings of importance might be different too. What's very important to one is unimportant to the other. What if your child really wants a dog (9) but you really don't (1)? As is often the case, what if you really think your child needs help facing their anxiety but your child doesn't? Exposure therapy is less likely to work if we don't at least consider such discrepancies in motivation.

There's not one simple formula for resolving these differences. But the process should be mutual, respectful, and collaborative. Motivation to face anxieties is undermined if one person simply imposes their ratings of difficulty and importance upon another. You can't make someone feel motivated just because you are. I recommend starting with an anxiety trigger that is *mutually* motivating. Then, initial success is more likely. Later, with improved skills and confidence, you can turn to other anxiety triggers for which there is less shared purpose.

In this way, the team leader helps everyone choose the first anxiety trigger for exposure therapy. Try to include the key players. Consider ease, importance, and shared motivation. Pick a trail.

View from the Top

Each member of the hiking party should take a moment to visualize victory. For the targeted anxiety, ask, "What will it look like to conquer this fear?" Start from the child's perspective, then ask the same questions of each relevant participant in the anxiety system: What will life be like when this worry is crossed off the list? What will you be able to do that you couldn't do before? How will it feel to experience comfort and freedom in situations that now cause distress and limitation? What does it mean for that anxiety or fear rating to come down into a truly acceptable range? The view from the end of the trail represents the goal.

Children, parents, and other involved adults may describe their goals in similar terms, or the same anxiety trigger may suggest related but different goals or "summits." Either way, each and every hiking companion should be clear on what success means to them. Your child and each hiker should write in their definition of success and mastery at the top of the trail.

Dr. Oh asked Jordanna and other members of the hiking party, "How will you know when Jordanna has conquered her anxiety about going to school? What would it look like if this problem disappeared?" Some of these goals were communicated to Dr. Oh directly. Others were guessed by her or Linda.

- *Jordanna: Going to school would be no big deal. I wouldn't get upset or feel scared. I wouldn't feel like such a baby. Everybody would stop yelling at me to hurry up.*
- *Linda: Jordanna would just get up, get ready, and go to school like a regular kid. No more crying. I wouldn't feel so tense and exhausted. I wouldn't get as frustrated with Sanford or be so dependent on my mother. I'd be able to give the other kids more attention. And I'd get to work on time for a change.*
- *Sanford: Mornings would be peaceful. Linda wouldn't be so stressed. Her mother wouldn't make me feel quite so worthless. My kids would give me a little more respect.*
- *Grandma: Everybody wouldn't be calling out for me to come upstairs and help. I wouldn't have to do damage control every morning. Maybe I could even read the paper and have my coffee. And this family wouldn't be so helpless.*
- *Brianna: Jordanna would be a normal kid for a change. I would get some attention instead of Jordanna being such a drama queen. Everybody would stop yelling at each other every morning.*
- *Frank: Jordanna would be happy. Maybe we'd have time to play before school.*
- *Mrs. Smith: Jordanna would come in with a smile on her face instead of wiping away tears. She would talk and play with the other kids, then settle right into the morning routine. I wouldn't feel so torn about trying to help her. I'd be able to give more attention to the other kids.*
- *Mr. Fred: Jordanna would just get on the bus and sit with the other kids. Maybe she'd even talk with them. I wouldn't worry about her. I could just relax and drive the bus.*
- *Dr. G: Linda would give me some good news. I'd feel hopeful—like this family was starting to get it together. I'd feel less frustrated and more confident about being able to help all my patients with mental health problems.*

- *Dr. Oh. If Jordanna is successful getting to school, I'd feel happy for the whole family. Also, I'd feel like my whole approach is validated.*

Marking a Trail

The view from the top—the summit—tells you where you're going. For each anxiety trigger, your ratings of difficulty tell you where you're starting. You could think of this starting point as your base camp or trailhead. To get from start to finish, you need to mark a trail.

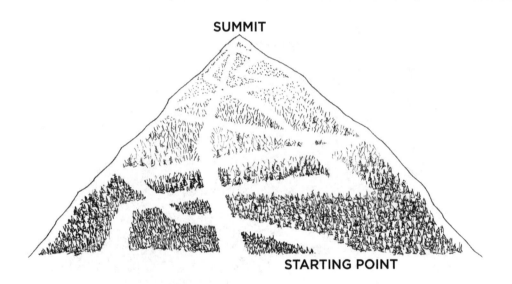

Setting Markers

It's important to set clear and achievable markers—or blazes—along each trail. Each marker indicates the direction of the trail and sets easily attainable sub-goals. If you're hiking the Appalachian Trail, there are intermittent tree trunk blazes: white, vertical, single strokes of paint. Other trails might be marked by tree or log carvings, signs, sticks, poles, flags, or rock piles.

Even experienced hikers experience alternating feelings as they seek each successive marker. Deep in the woods, you feel just a bit of anxiety. You wonder, "Are we going the right way?" Then suddenly, "There it is!" Then a little anxiety again until you find the next marker. And so on, up the trail.

Exposure therapy should proceed just like hiking. After choosing a trail and visualizing the summit, set blazes or markers so that they are not too close together but not too far apart. If a trail seems too hard, just set the marker or sub-goal closer. If a trail seems too easy, you could set them farther apart. In this way, each trail marker represents just-right challenges. Not too hard. Not too easy. Each marker draws the hiking party closer to the ultimate goal. Remember: In parallel exposure therapy, versus traditional child-centered CBT, it's important to consider the difficulty ratings for each member of the hiking party when setting markers too.

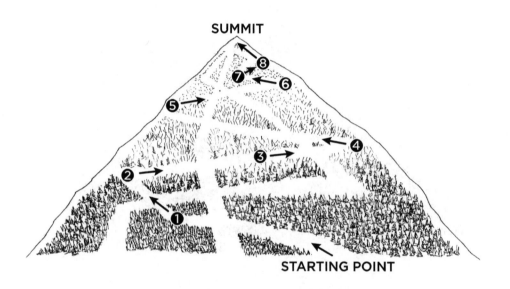

The whole idea of exposure therapy is to deliberately create situations that are incrementally more anxiety-provoking. The only way to conquer fear is to put yourself in situations that cause some discomfort. Children and adults undergoing exposures should remember that the discomfort is necessary but temporary. If not pushed at all, anxious children and others in the anxiety system will continue to avoid the source of their fear. Pushed too fast or too far, exposure backfires. Too much anxiety can be paralyzing and demoralizing.

The key is to push just right. Be optimistic, but be realistic too. Go for mastery, but ensure success. Set goals, but make the goals achievable. Your child, you, and others in the anxiety system should struggle some—but not too much. In this way, each successive mark on the trail should represent a slightly higher "dose" of the anxiety trigger.

Dr. Oh looked down her list of team members who would be directly involved in the morning home-school transition. She reviewed each player's responses—reported or assumed—to Jordanna's anxiety, in order to design just-right exposures while strengthening relationships within the anxiety system.

- *Jordanna: Jordanna's clinging, screaming, and resistance to school reflected her anxiety about separating from her mother. These feelings were complicated by her anxiety about being a middle child. Some other family tensions were hard for Jordanna to fully understand. For her to make progress, she would need to learn to face uncertainty without having her mother, grandmother, or teacher right there for comfort. This would mean loosening those dependent relationships and strengthening healthy bonds with her siblings, father, bus driver, classmates, and doctors.*
- *Linda: Jordanna's mom responded to Jordanna's anxiety by providing comfort and reassurance, or calling for Jordanna's grandmother to help. Linda got upset with anyone who seemed insensitive. She had her own anxiety about Jordanna's distress, and struggled with her own dependence on her mother, her own feelings of self-doubt and incompetence. Linda would need to be more forgiving of herself, give up some control, and trust her husband to step up. She would need to work on being less enmeshed with her children and strengthening her relationships with her husband and friends.*
- *Sanford: Jordanna's father responded with frustration, anger, or withdrawal—due to his own anxiety about his role in the family and his marriage. Sanford would need to work on being a more regular part of his children's daily routines. This would mean strengthening his relationships with his wife and children—and loosening his relationships with TV and beer.*
- *Grandma: Jordanna's grandma responded to Jordanna's anxiety with hugs and food. She communicated frustration*

toward Linda and Sanford, which reflected her anxiety about the overall health of everyone in her daughter's family and her own ability to continue serving them as an emotional safety net. Grandma would need to resist her reflex to rescue Jordanna and Linda, which would mean increasing her tolerance of other family members' imperfections and communicating greater respect to Linda and Sanford as a married couple. She needed to continue enjoying her relationship with her grandchildren without feeling guilty about taking better care of herself.

- Brianna: Jordanna's sister responded by ignoring Jordanna. If Jordanna's crying was too annoying, Brianna would call for her mother or grandmother to help. Brianna would need to feel more independent of Jordanna and less resentful of Jordanna's attention-getting behavior. This would mean establishing a more mature relationship with her mother and father, plus enriching her own social life with friends.

- Frank: Jordanna's brother understood that his sister was unhappy, but he didn't understand why. So he simply tried to cheer her up. This reflected Frank's anxiety about his sister's distress. But mostly, he just missed having her as a consistent playmate. Frank would need to learn more independence from Jordanna. He needed help strengthening his connection with his father and spending more time playing with peers.

- Mrs. Smith: When she could, Jordanna's teacher tried to reassure her and teach her to problem-solve. But Mrs. Smith was concerned about her lack of availability to Jordanna during the crucial transition from bus to classroom. And Jordanna was becoming more dependent on her. Mrs. Smith worried that she would not be able to give enough attention to other students in her classroom, some of whom also had special needs. She would have to find ways to help Jordanna feel less dependent on her and more connected to other classmates and adults. This would mean trusting others, delegating some responsibility, and becoming less of a perfectionist.

- Mr. Fred: Jordanna's bus driver was concerned about Jordanna. He responded by giving her positive attention and pleasant (musical) distraction. He worried about whether *it was enough. After all, what was going on in her life? Did her parents and teacher know how upset she was every morning? Mr. Fred would need to become a better-informed member of Jordanna's team and not underestimate the potential importance of his—subtle but significant— role in her life.*

- *Dr. G: Jordanna's pediatrician would not be directly involved in this exposure but she would be a very interested bystander. She knew that Jordanna's responsiveness to this intervention would have some bearing on any decisions about medication. Dr. G. was a bit concerned about relying entirely on non-pharmacological treatment. She wanted to help but she didn't want to venture too far outside of her own comfort zone. Dr. G. would need to learn to be okay with asking for help, to work with a team without feeling that her authority was threatened.*

- *Dr. Oh: Jordanna's psychologist was confident that she could help. She believed in her approach but every new patient presented unexpected challenges. Would Jordanna and her team stick with the plan? Would it work? If needed, Dr. Oh was open to medication, but—if she was honest with herself—she considered a medication prescription to be a type of failure. Dr. Oh needed to learn more open-mindedness about working with other medical professionals. This would mean better communication with Jordanna's pediatrician. In addition, Dr. Oh tended to trust mothers more than fathers. She would need to give Sanford the benefit of the doubt and not underestimate his ability to help.*

For each and every member of the anxiety system, carefully designed exposures should stir these anxieties and strain these relational complexities. Not too much. But not too little.

Increasing the Difficulty of Exposures

There are several ways to gradually increase the difficulty of exposures. In general, the difficulty of an exposure varies with intensity, duration, frequency, support, warning, and motivation. Keep in mind, whenever a child is exposed to their anxiety trigger, others in the anxiety system are challenged as well, each in their own way. When the difficulty of exposures is increased for one member of the system, everyone in the hiking party is affected. Parallel exposure therapy brings down anxiety for everyone in the anxiety system and gradually repairs relationships—all at the same time.

Intensity

The intensity of exposures should be dialed up or down, as tolerated. Usually, it's best to begin with exposures that provoke only moderate levels of distress. If the distress is too severe, the exposure will not be able to be maintained long enough for habituation to take place. The intensity of the exposure should be high enough to trigger some anxiety but low enough that subjects will be able to stay with the anxiety for a meaningful length of time. The goal of the exposure is to help the individual face the trigger, experience the anxiety, and realize that their fear was unfounded—nothing bad happened! Once there is acclimation to one level of intensity, we can gradually work up to more difficult tasks. There are several ways to modify the intensity of the exposure.

Type of exposure. Not all exposures are created equal. Some anxiety triggers will be more intense than others. And sometimes, delaying confrontation altogether isn't feasible or advisable. Daily attendance at school is required. If an anxious child is allowed to stay home from school, we are not helping them take steps up their mountain trail. School avoidance only digs the child and parents into a deeper emotional hole.

> *Dr. Oh realized that she should not offer Jordanna options that prolonged her school avoidance. That would only make her separation anxiety worse. Just talking about it or other indirect exposures, like creating a "going to school" storybook, might be helpful, but Jordanna would still have to go to school. The good news was that Jordanna's anxiety trigger was all about anticipation and transition. Once in the classroom, Jordanna would gradually settle in.* "First," *Dr. Oh said to Jordanna,* "let's take a look at different ways to face your fear about going to school. Then I'll ask you and your mom to tell me which ideas seem the scariest and which seem the easiest. Then we can try them out here, easiest ones first." *Linda was surprised by her own reaction to Dr. Oh. Just talking about Jordanna's fear made Linda feel anxious!*

Low-tech preview. For some very sensitive children, the first and easiest trail marker may be just a mental rehearsal. The first exposures might entail just imagining what would be too overwhelming to confront in reality. This kind of soft, gentle preview can be accomplished in any number of ways: discussion, sharing stories, drawing a picture, reading a book, or relevant TV shows, movies, pictures, or videos. Before actually facing a clown directly, a boy who is afraid of clowns could be asked to just think about clowns, then talk about them, then look at a picture, then watch a video. In this way, the intensity of the exposure could increase and there could be a degree of habituation before facing a real clown.

> *Dr. Oh and Linda had previously discussed some of Jordanna's general likes and dislikes. Jordanna was not into books, drawing, or even talking. But she loved imaginary play and movies. To help Jordanna visualize conquering her school fear, Dr. Oh set up a doll house and play school. They acted out a little pretend drama about a girl crying but then conquering her separation anxiety. Linda had found a good YouTube video that, in a very reassuring way, modeled bravery. Although these indirect means of exposure would not solve Jordanna's problem, the pretend play and video at least introduced Jordanna to the benefits of overcoming her fear.*
>
> *Dr. Oh elaborated on the play themes in her office. She suggested that Linda, Sanford, Grandma, Brianna, and Frank take turns—each in their own way—getting in on these play and YouTube exposures at home. Although they all liked Dr. Oh, having an outsider involved in their family business felt awkward. Everybody in the family was a little bit uncertain about the whole process. All this strategizing was definitely outside of their comfort zone. But despite their reservations, the family decided to give it a try. And as their plan unfolded, they began to feel a bit more connected and less frustrated with each other. Instead of anxiety controlling the family, the family would work as a team to help each other.*
>
> ◆ *Marker #1 would be tolerating indirect exposures to school anxiety through pretend play and YouTube clips. This would include Dr. Oh, Linda, Sanford, Grandma, Brianna, and Frank.*

High-tech preview exposures. Greater degrees of exposure can also be simulated through virtual reality or augmented reality technology.

With *virtual reality,* you're immersed in the anxiety-provoking imagery. Usually this means wearing goggles and headphones. As an example, virtual reality exposure for fear of flying would make you feel as if you're in an airplane. Or in the case of our clown-phobic boy, he could be virtually—but not actually—at the circus or maybe even encountering a clown on a walk down the street.

With *augmented reality,* the anxiety-provoking image is projected onto you or your environment. This is achieved by computers that are equipped with special software and projectors. For someone with a spider phobia, the video image of a spider would crawl off the computer screen onto their arm.

> *When Dr. Oh explained exposure therapy to Brianna, Jordanna's big sister got excited about an idea. She could use a digital camera to make a movie: "Jordanna the Brave Goes to School." She could record Jordanna saying good-bye to Mom, leaving the house, getting on the bus, riding to school, and walking through Jordanna's classroom door. Dr. Oh thought her idea was brilliant. They would not be able to get permission from the school for the bus and school scenes. But they could do the transition and good-bye scenes at home. Dr. Oh thanked Brianna for her great suggestion: "You're thinking like a real psychologist!"*
>
> ◈ *Marker #2 would be making a video, "Jordanna the Brave Goes to School." Brianna would be the writer and director, Jordanna would be the star. Other family members would play supporting roles.*

Actual exposures. Once a child has mastered increasingly difficult previews of the anxiety trigger—whether low-tech or high-tech—the next markers on the trail would represent brief or partial exposure to the real-life trigger. For the boy in our example, the therapist could put on a clown mask, then build up to opportunities for the child to see a real-life clown. The ultimate exposure might entail going to the circus or a birthday party. The intensity of the exposure can be softened with just the right amount of individualized support and positive incentives.

Duration

There are two ways to determine the just-right duration of exposures: 1) SUDS and 2) graduated lengthening.

Duration of Exposure Based on SUDS

Usually, short exposures are easier than long exposures. But if the exposure is too short, the child doesn't have enough time to habituate. The duration of an exposure is commonly determined using a variation of the Subjective Units of Disturbance Scales or "SUDS," originally developed by Dr. Joseph Wolpe (1992). SUDS ratings are essentially the same thing as the Anxiety Rating Scale described previously: 10 could mean "unbearable," 0 could mean total peace and relief, with 1–9 corresponding to intermediate emotional states.

At various intervals—before, during, and after the exposure—children, adolescents, or adults can be asked to give a real-time rating of their distress. Usually, the exposure is continued until the anxiety is reduced by at least 50 percent. For example, as the exposure continues, there is habituation and the SUDS rating of 8 becomes a 4. If the exposure can't be maintained long enough for the person to habituate and bring down their level of distress, they should start with a lower-intensity task that triggers a more tolerable intensity of discomfort.

For example, a boy with a fear of clowns thinks he could look at a series of still photos with relatively friendly clown faces for at least 10 minutes (SUDS rating of 5) but he doesn't think he could handle watching a video of a scary clown for even 3 seconds (SUDS rating of 9). So, the therapist has him look at the still photos until his SUDS rating dropped from 5 to 2. Then he will be able to look at progressively scarier still photos, long enough for his SUDS ratings for those to come down as well. Finally, he will able to work up to watching the video. Then he will be ready for more real-life clown exposures.

Another example using parallel exposure: A boy and his father were both extremely afraid of my little lap dog. Whenever they came to my office, just the sound of her barking from another room would send them both through the roof. Despite my reassurances that the dog was at the opposite end of my home office, behind two sets of doors, father and son both remained on high-guard, as if the doors would not offer sufficient protection from my 12-pound Bichon.

So, we designed a parallel exposure. I promised them that I would hold the dog in my lap on the opposite side of the room. I gave a 100 percent guarantee that I would not let the dog go. When I described the exposure, son and father SUDS ratings were 8 and 4 respectively. With their permission, I got the dog and held her as promised. At first, their SUDS ratings went up to 9 and 5. Without providing any distraction, I asked them to simply monitor their anxiety. After 5 minutes with the dog in my lap, their SUDS ratings came down to 7 and 4; after 10 minutes, their SUDS were 6 and 3; after 15 minutes, 4 and 2. Each time the dog stretched in my lap, they reported minor increases in distress. But then, within seconds, their numbers settled right back down. From 9 and 5, their paired anxiety had decreased by 50 percent, to 4 and 2. The father said seeing his son calm down helped him calm down too. The son said the same thing. Parallel success.

SUDS Ratings Based upon Duration of Exposure

Sometimes it's not as feasible or practical to base the duration of the exposure on SUDS ratings. Another option is to ask the child for SUDS ratings based on the duration of the exposure. Using this strategy, you start with a very short duration of exposure that causes a tolerable degree of anxiety. When the child's SUDS rating for the short exposure comes down, then it's time to gradually increase the duration of the exposure. In the case of the clown-phobic boy, this technique would mean starting with a very short exposure to a moderately scary still photo of a clown and gradually increasing the duration of the exposure.

On school days, Dr. Oh's strategy cut the duration of Jordanna's transitional period. For starters, there would be no long farewells. With her mom going to work and her grandma going to the diner, Jordanna would spend much less time in the process of separation. Mom and Grandma didn't sneak out, but their good-byes were designed to be quick and matter-of-fact. Eventually, Dr. Oh would have Mom and Grandma linger a bit more in the morning. This would gradually acclimate Jordanna to tolerating more time in transition.

Frequency

Exposures work faster and better if they occur more frequently.

Habituation to anxiety triggers depends upon very regular encounters. It takes many exposures, over and over, for the level of distress to come down. For example, I have a fear of flying. If I only get on an airplane once a year, my fear of flying intensifies. However, if I have to fly much more frequently, I get used to it faster, unlearn my anxiety more completely, and reduce the chance of relapse. Frequent practice is an important key to conquering anxiety and maintaining real-life mastery. For the best results, practice exposures should take place at least daily; if feasible, many times per day.

Some anxiety triggers don't ordinarily happen with sufficient frequency to ensure habituation. Unless required to by work, most people with fear of flying don't have much occasion for air travel. Likewise, children with clown phobias don't usually see clowns every day. For these infrequently occurring anxiety triggers, artificial exposures might be necessary. For other anxiety triggers, exposures are inescapably regular. Under ordinary circumstances, children have to go to school, do homework, and attend recess every weekday. Such unrelenting exposure actually makes habituation more natural and effective.

Dr. Oh asked Linda and Sanford, "Is Jordanna's separation anxiety worse on Monday mornings?" They looked at each other and rolled their eyes. After weekends—and especially after vacations—Jordanna's fears seemed to go through the roof. When there was no school, Jordanna liked coming to her parents' bed in the morning. Linda and Sanford were so tired, they just let her stay and cuddle. Consequently, Monday mornings felt like an even bigger shock to everyone's system. This was when Jordanna was most likely to have stomachaches. And the whole family system was at its worst. Everybody in the house was more irritable.

Dr. Oh explained that this pattern was not unusual, and suggested that Jordanna might need to keep up the new school-day routine even on weekends and vacations. At least for a while, such maintenance exposures would mean coming up with some playdates and other extracurricular activities. Nobody liked this idea, but they knew that avoiding separation when school was out just made it that much harder when school was in. To prevent backsliding, they would have to increase the frequency of morning separations and structured transitions from five to seven days per week.

Support

With the first exposures, you may need to provide a very high level of support. This might mean the steady presence of a therapist, parent, counselor, teacher, other adult, sibling, friend, or pet—prompting, encouraging, or simply being a steady presence. At the beginning of each trail, support personnel might need help too. That's okay. In learning to face fears, some mutual interdependence is better than avoiding discomfort altogether.

Over time, these supports should be removed, as the child and others in the anxiety system learn to navigate challenging situations more successfully. Children and adults should choose some easier exposures that they can practice facing on their own. For somewhat harder tasks, where support is temporarily necessary, removing it should not be too fast or too slow. The ultimate goal is to gradually increase everyone's confidence.

For example, our clown-phobic boy could first learn to handle exposures with just his therapist, then with his mother, then with his brother, then with a few other trusted individuals. Finally, the boy would be able to deal with clown exposures entirely on his own. At the same time, the support personnel would become better equipped to deal with similar situations in the future.

On your trail map, it's important to specify the expected level of independence at each marker—not just for the child but for other members of the anxiety system too.

> *For Jordanna's transition from home to school, Brianna would be her primary source of support. Dr. Oh laid out the markers to indicate gradually decreasing levels of dependence.*
> - ◈ *Marker #3 represented Brianna sitting next to Jordanna on the bus and walking with her to her class.*
> - ◈ *Marker #4 represented Brianna sitting next to Jordanna on the bus and walking with her to the class hallway.*
> - ◈ *Marker #5 represented Brianna sitting next to Jordanna on the bus and walking with her to the front door of the school.*
> - ◈ *Marker #6 represented Brianna sitting next to Jordanna on the bus and Jordanna walking all the way in on her own.*

◆ *Marker #7 represented Brianna sitting right behind Jordanna on the bus and Jordanna walking all the way in on her own.*
◆ *Marker #8 represented Brianna sitting three rows behind Jordanna on the bus and Jordanna walking all the way in on her own.*
◆ *The summit represented Brianna sitting all the way in the back of the bus and Jordanna walking all the way in on her own.*

Different members of the hiking party will need different levels of support. For some members of the anxiety system, participating in the exposure isn't a problem. Once the goals of exposure therapy are made clear, their own anxiety may be mild or relatively easy to manage. However, other members of the anxiety system might need more coaching during the exposure or more rehearsal and deliberate habituation before the exposure.

Dr. Oh asked each member of the hiking party to consider how much anxiety they would have at each of the markers. What would be the hardest part for Linda? Sanford? Grandma? Brianna? Frank? Mr. Fred? And Mrs. Smith? Each adult could ask themselves, "What do I have to be willing to feel during this exposure?" After all, they would be climbing this mountain together.

For some adults, participation in parallel exposure therapy may require more direct and substantial intervention. Some adults may need feedback on their parenting skills; others, more help challenging relevant cognitive distortions; still others may need to address their own interpersonal issues or self-regulating problems. Furthermore, adult exposure to a child's anxiety trigger may also highlight adult needs that would have otherwise gone unmet.

For example, let's say exposure therapy for separation anxiety requires giving a child the opportunity to learn self-settling for sleep. A parent might privately listen to a recording of their child's crying to practice self-calming during the day, before they are able to tolerate their child's distress at bedtime. The spouse might need to unlearn catastrophizing about their marriage, in order to support the other parent's imperfect implementation of the exposure plan. Grandparents might have to deal with their own blaming and labeling if they are going to play a positive and supportive role in the exposures. Sometimes members of the family may even need their own treatment, with some sessions directed specifically toward them.

For other anxiety triggers, such as academic underperformance or psychosomatic symptoms, teachers or doctors, respectively, might need some help being less perfectionistic if they're going to maintain a calming presence.

This kind of parallel treatment can pose significant logistical, financial, and even ethical issues. Sometimes it makes sense to do family or team sessions. Other times, the therapist will do some sessions with the child and other sessions with adults, even including teachers. Professional boundary issues might require referral to a colleague. Complicated problems often require creative solutions.

Cognitive-behavioral therapists are famous for rising to the challenge, getting out of their offices and providing coaching in real-world settings. This means accompanying their clients to elevators, bridges, bee hives, zoos, storms, crowded malls, restaurants, playgrounds, basketball courts, classrooms, and—of course—in their own homes; wherever the anxiety might be triggered. More recently, many therapists are using technology to provide virtual coaching, remotely and inconspicuously, via earbuds or video conferencing. Such expert coaching can be crucial for any member of the hiking party. In some situations, more than one person in the anxiety system can be coached through the same exposure at the same time.

It's always best if these challenges in the hiking party can be identified and strengthened before the exposure, but sometimes fault lines become apparent only with implementation of the exposure plan. In those cases, without blame, shame, or judgment, the therapist can provide individuals with whatever level of support is necessary to follow through with the exposure. The system as a whole is strengthened. Proactive management of anxiety responses is always better than reactive repair. Laying out these principles and providing support to the whole team in advance increases the chances of system-wide success. Over the years, I have been pleasantly surprised how little reactive repair is needed when simple goals are stated clearly and shared with the team.

Warning

Early in the habituation process, many children will handle exposure to their anxiety trigger better if they know what's coming, when and why it's coming, and how to handle it. With plenty of warning, the child is more likely to experience success and self-confidence. Surprise exposures carry an increased risk of failure and distress. Generally speaking, exposures should be planned and structured. The boy in our clown phobia example could first practice exposures with a countdown. For example, his therapist or parent could say, "I'm going to count to 3, then show you this scary picture of a clown. You can do it. Are you ready? 1-2-3." Then he could progress to a slightly less specific warning: "You are going to see a clown sometime within the next minute." Then, "Now there's going to be a clown sometime within the next 15 minutes." Then, sometime within the hour, then sometime today, then sometime this week. Then without any warning at all. In this way, successive markers on the trail could represent exposures to the anxiety trigger with gradually less support and warning.

On the other hand, for some children and some types of anxiety triggers, less warning can be better. Under certain circumstances, there might be more distress for the child—and more tension throughout the anxiety system—anticipating the exposure than actually experiencing it. In these cases, more warning and more preview just prolongs the torture! Better to just plow through it. If the anxiety trigger occurs predictably, according to a regular schedule, then unnecessary prompting might only interfere with the development of independence.

Jordanna was okay with the pretend play and videos about going to school. But on weekday mornings, the more Mom and Grandma talked about going to school, the more anxious Jordanna became. She knew she had to go. And she was painfully aware of the minutes until 7:55 a.m., when she had to leave for the bus. The digital clock on the oven was obvious enough—she didn't need to be reminded. Sanford wondered why Linda and his mother-in-law kept going on about it. It was clear to him what was going on. The more interaction Jordanna had with her mom and grandma, the more she dreaded the impending separation.

Dr. Oh talked this through with Linda, Sanford, and Grandma. It was clear that the separation was making Linda and Grandma anxious too. The more Jordanna expressed her own distress, the more Linda and Grandma tried to provide comfort. They needed to practice not worrying too much about Jordanna.

So, they all agreed to minimize the time that Jordanna spent separating from—and being comforted by—the women of the house. Linda had to get to work anyhow. Grandma would love to walk up to the corner diner for a cup of coffee. So right after breakfast, Linda and Grandma would leave together. They would give each other support in just walking out the door and not responding to any last pleas for help, and get used to the idea of Sanford taking over.

Sanford liked the idea of being able to handle some things with the kids in his own way. Especially when he realized that after the girls left, Frank had 30 minutes before he got picked up by carpool for preschool. Sanford realized he would be able— for the first time ever—to have some regular father-son time.

Motivation and Rewards

Some children and adults are internally motivated to overcome their anxieties. They are eager for liberation. They understand the need for exposures and will do anything to achieve better control over their worries.

Others don't want to face their fears. They just want to avoid their anxiety triggers. Despite explanation and coaching, they might be too reluctant to change. They just might not understand the need for exposure. Lacking internal drive, they might need more external motivation, including positive incentives or rewards.

For some children and adults, well-timed and individualized positive attention might be more than enough motivation. For others, special prizes or activities might be necessary. The most effective reward systems are custom-designed, clear and simple. For motivation in exposure therapy, the reward can be written next to each marker; the reward is claimed upon reaching each marker. Rewards should be delivered reliably, soon after succeeding at each level of exposure. A grand prize is saved for reaching the summit and achieving mastery over the anxiety trigger. This final reward can be written or pictured at the end of the trail. Children should know ahead of time exactly what they are working for and what they need to do to get it. For a complete discussion of how to individualize positive attention and rewards, see *Parent Child Journey*.

In parallel exposure therapy, other key players in the anxiety system are required to overcome their own reluctance. Siblings and adults might need some kind of positive reinforcement too. Especially when members of the hiking party rate a trail as difficult or unimportant, they might need help with motivation.

How to help Jordanna get motivated? Linda knew that Jordanna was not driven by rewards. In fact, a reward system would probably just increase Jordanna's stress. Dr. Oh wondered if a more indirect approach might work.

Brianna had noticed Jordanna's interest in Mr. Fred's music. Linda talked to Mrs. Smith and the school counselor, who asked Mr. Fred if he had any ideas. Immediately, Mr. Fred got excited. He could ask Jordanna to give him some feedback on his songs. He would save the front right seats for Jordanna and her sister. Then he would slip Jordanna his iPod. On the way to school, she would listen and rate each song on a ten-point scale. She'd hand back his iPod and her score sheet when they got to school.

In a very natural way, this plan rewarded everyone concerned. Jordanna would get positive attention from Mr. Fred. Brianna felt great about being in a leadership role. Her parents practically glowed with pride. Brianna's old teacher Mrs. Smith gave her a huge smile and a high five each morning. Even the principal told her how much she appreciated what Brianna was doing to help her sister. And Brianna looked forward to her Friday night movie with Mom. Frank got special time with Dad each morning. Sanford got special time with Frank plus deep appreciation from his wife. Linda got to work on time, stress-free. Grandma got a morning to relax on her own with coffee and the newspaper. Mr. Fred got some attention for his music.

In my experience implementing parallel exposure therapy, members of the anxiety system usually feel rewarded just by being included in the plan and sharing in the success. Some positive, mutual and sincere expressions of appreciation are usually motivation enough.

Pace

The pace of the hike is just as important as the placement of markers. How quickly should hikers move from one level of exposure to the next? Behavior science provides a surefire way to set goals and move from one trail marker to the next.

In general, don't make the initial intensity and duration of the exposure so easy that it seems unimportant. The family and child must be sufficiently motivated. However, don't make the challenge so great that 80 percent success isn't achievable. In other words, the child and others in the family system should be able to implement the plan and handle the anxiety trigger without too much distress, four out of five times. If there's 80 percent success at one level, then it's time to increase the difficulty of the exposure. Increase the duration and the intensity. Decrease the support and warnings. But not too much. It's crucial to go slowly enough that your child and others continue to feel motivated. Success at one level should inspire a degree of optimism about facing the next exposure. Marker by marker, the child, parents, and other hikers should all feel a growing sense of accomplishment and confidence.

If your child or other members of the hiking party cannot tolerate a certain level of exposure at least 80 percent of the time, then you probably need more practice at that level. Don't advance up the trail yet. If there is too much distress, you might even have to dial back the expectations and firm up confidence at a slightly lower level—decreasing the duration or intensity of the exposure, increasing the support and/or preparation. Don't be tempted to raise the bar too quickly. You can repeat exposures at the current level to let everyone in the hiking party experience success and consolidate gains. Extra practice can firm up skills, instill greater confidence, and increase motivation for the next part of the trail.

Anxiety habituation proceeds at a tolerable pace, step-by-step, up a carefully marked mountain trail of exposure, moving incrementally but assuredly toward the summit and freedom from fear.

At the end of each day, Brianna and Mrs. Smith (by email) would tell Linda how things went. Sanford created a spreadsheet to track progress at each marker. They would not move to the next level until Brianna and everyone in the hiking party experienced success at least four out of five school days. If she didn't show steady progress, they would contact Dr. Oh by phone or meet in person to review and troubleshoot. Was everyone doing their part? If not, why not? Were the goals and expectations realistic? What modifications made sense?

Remember, not all members of the hiking party will make progress at the same rate. Some individuals will need these variables adjusted according to their needs. In general, the intensity, duration, frequency, pacing, and other exposure variables should be adjusted so that no one in the hiking party is paralyzed by their own anxiety. This can sabotage the team's progress. The exposures should be modified so that everyone has a fair shot at the summit.

Over-Training

Sometimes, after reaching the end of a trail, it's a good idea to push beyond the initial goals, creating even more advanced challenges. The idea is to design exposures of even greater duration, intensity, and independence than you might ever encounter in real-life. Over-training makes naturally occurring anxiety triggers feel like no big deal. For example, a child with a germ phobia at home and school could work toward tolerating the grungiest public restroom in town. The child with separation anxiety could target attending a sleep-away camp or (if old enough) flying on her own to visit grandparents. If you can run a marathon, running a mile is no sweat.

Maintenance training. Another form of over-training, maintenance training means deliberately continuing exposures, even after reaching the end of the trail. By continuing to practice exposures after the goal is met, relapse is much less likely. By conquering *extreme* challenges and then continuing maintenance exposures, mastery over *everyday* challenges becomes easier and more durable.

The Strategies Backpack

Exposures are supposed to trigger anxiety—that's how they work. But self-calming strategies come in handy if emotions might run too high. We don't want paralysis; excessive brain flooding could threaten the success of exposure therapy. The rationality switch needs to stay on. If the distress is rendered tolerable, then the exposure can proceed. Effective coping strategies should not eliminate anxiety, just buffer it. The purpose of the strategies backpack isn't to avoid anxiety, only to rein it in. A just-right amount of anxiety means successful exposure, not failure of self-calming strategies. Relaxation strategies that work too well may represent just another form of avoidance.

To stay just cool enough, each person in the anxiety system should be ready with a few self-calming strategies. Everybody's different. What works for one will not work for all. On each section of the trail, each hiker will have their own thoughts, feelings, physical sensations, and behaviors. To move from one level of exposure to the next, each person in the anxiety system will need their own self-control techniques. Each hiker's backpack will have different tools.

It might take time to find the best tools for each person. Start by considering a variety of options. Brainstorm good ideas and bad ideas. Ask others for advice. Go online. Get professional advice. Develop a menu from which to choose. Give each strategy a try. For children who are too young to choose their own coping strategies, adults can choose and experiment on their behalf. Over time, each hiker will learn to pack and use their own backpack of coping strategies. With regular practice, these tools can be used more automatically and effectively.

Your backpack of coping tools may include any combination of the following self-calming strategies:
- Simple noticing
- Positive self-talk
- Ordinary relaxation strategies
- New relaxation strategies

Let's take a quick look at each type of coping strategy. Consider which of these strategies will work best for your child, you, and others in the anxiety system.

Simple Noticing

Often, to get through an exposure, all you need to do is notice the anxiety and let it pass. Some call this "mindfulness" or "meta-cognition." Do not avoid the anxiety. Habituation comes through prolonging and repeating the exposure, without the need for any other relaxation strategies at all. Your child, you, and others in the anxiety system, can learn to just acknowledge the anxious thought or feeling. But then, do nothing. Everyone involved in the exposure should expect to feel uncomfortable. That's the whole idea. They should not fight the discomfort. They should just let themselves feels anxious.

Pay attention to your fear level during the exposure. Periodically, assign a SUDS or anxiety level rating from 0 (completely relaxed) to 10 (stressed out of mind). These ratings can be simply acknowledged, written down, or entered into cell phone apps.

Simple noticing might be the most effective and most underused strategy of all. Other tools would be necessary only if significant impairment or excessive distress interferes with the exposure. Commonly, simple noticing is combined with some type of positive self-talk.

Positive Self-Talk

Before facing excessive anxiety, children and adults should get ready with a self-empowerment script. Anticipation of an anxiety trigger or actual exposure can cue some good "fear-busting" lines. Modify the language to suit each person's developmental level and personal style. Again, for the word "anxiety," feel free to substitute more meaningful words, such as "worry," "fear," "stress," "freak-out monster"—whatever works. What would you like to say to yourself when your anxiety pops up?

Here are some examples of positive self-talk that you can present to your child:

- "*There* you are, Mr. Anxiety. You tried to surprise me but I'm ready for you!"
- "Hey, anxiety, you're not the boss of me. I'm the boss of you!"
- "I'm going to get rid of you with my anxiety-busting strategies. I've been practicing. I know how to be brave!"
- "It's normal to have some anxiety. Having anxiety doesn't have to be a big deal."
- "I'm not going to let anxiety stress me out or keep me from doing things I want to do."

After you've helped your child come up with a self-empowerment script, parents and others in the anxiety system can come up with some lines to use for themselves. For example:

- "These are just anxious distortions, out of proportion to what's actually happening."
- "This anxiety is just a temporary discomfort. I'm not going to

avoid it. I can just ride it out."
- "What's the worst thing that could really happen? And what are the odds of that actually happening?"
- "It doesn't help to make things worse than they are."
- "I need to control this, for the sake of my child, my family—and myself."
- "Exposure therapy works. I just need to stick with the plan."

You and your child should each put your favorite self-help scripts into your coping strategies backpack. Sometimes, for easy reference, it helps to actually write these lines on the back of the hand, or on index cards, posters, iPads, or cell phones.

Ordinary Relaxation Strategies

Many children just need a little coaching or reminding to use effective strategies they already have. Ask your child, "When you want to relax, what works best for you?" Ask yourself the same question. Remember, some strategies will not interfere with the exposure—they can be used in the face of the anxiety trigger. Others would cause avoidance of the anxiety trigger—they should only be used well before or well after the exposure.

Some examples of ordinary relaxation strategies include:
- listening to or playing music
- reading, writing, or drawing
- walking, hiking, exercising, dancing, hula-hooping, biking, or other physical activity
- engaging in conversation
- playing a game
- retreating to a quiet room or outdoors

New Relaxation Techniques

Many children and adults need help learning, testing, and choosing from a menu of novel relaxation techniques. Again, don't use new strategies that would directly interfere with the exposure.

For example, you and your child can check out:
- yoga
- neuro-biofeedback
- self-hypnosis
- progressive muscle relaxation
- mindfulness, breathing awareness, mental imagery, and different types of meditation

Packing Your Backpack

After considering a menu of coping strategies, it's time to pack your backpack for the chosen trail. Some children and adults rely on just one "go-to" coping strategy. Most people do best with a small collection from which to choose. After all, different situations may require different "tools." For example, some coping strategies, like playing outside, may be practical for home but not for school. Depending upon the anxiety trigger, the setting, and the people involved, you might need different coping tools. And again, what works for one person may not work for another. Each person will need their own backpack. The important thing is for you, your child, and others in the anxiety system to decide in advance, "What will work best for me?"

Rating strategies. How to choose? After brainstorming, you can have your child rate each strategy. Ask, "How do you think each of these strategies would work for you? Which ones will best help you face your fear and control your anxiety? Let's go down the list." Your child should predict the effectiveness of each possible strategy on the menu. Encourage a best guess. Use some kind of rating scale, not just binaries like "good" or "bad." For example, this coping strategy is:

0 = stinky
1 = bad
2 = okay
3 = good
4 = very good
5 = excellent

Or, as discussed previously, you can use thumbs (up, sideways or down), smiley faces (happy, neutral, sad), traffic lights (green, yellow, red), or any other type of scale, customized to your child's developmental level and interests. Whatever works. Then, choose a scale that works for you, to rate your own strategies.

You might want to just go ahead with educated guesses. But, especially for new strategies, you and your child might have difficulty predicting effectiveness. Before doing the rating scale, you might want to test-drive them. At first, without exposure to the anxiety trigger, just try the strategy. See how it feels. Of course, you won't know for sure until you try it in real-life, and one try may not be enough. Sometimes, our predictions are accurate. Other times, strategies work better or worse than expected. With experience, you can judge more accurately and change ratings accordingly.

> For her strategies backpack, Jordanna decided to use a "helping hand" technique. With Dr. Oh's guidance, Jordanna assigned a different strategy to each of five fingers. Using a permanent marker, she wrote a little letter to help her remember what to do when she started feeling nervous.
>
> - On her thumb, she wrote the letter "H," for say "hello" to the anxiety. This meant simply noticing the anxiety and calling it by a silly name that she chose, "Chi-Chi."
> - On her index finger, she wrote the letter "B," for telling Chi-Chi who's boss.
> - On her middle finger, she wrote letter "M," for using "music" to get her mind off Chi-Chi. Sometimes, this meant listening to Mr. Fred's songs. Other times, it just meant singing a song in her own head.
> - On her ring finger, she wrote the letter "F," for getting on the bus and going into school by just putting one foot in front of the other.
> - And on her little finger, she wrote the letters "OK," for it's okay to have some anxiety.

Promoting Self-Reliance

At first, children and adults may forget to "look" in their strategies backpack. Even with rehearsal, they may need help remembering, choosing, and implementing their preferred coping technique. Different people need different levels of coaching and support. As mentioned above, the level of support can be written next to different trail markers. More support goes with the earliest markers. Less support means you're higher up the trail.

Initially, to help your child develop a self-help habit, provide whatever prompting is needed. No more, no less. For example, "Hey, how ya doing? Don't forget about your worry-busting backpack." Over time, this level of support can be modified and faded to promote higher levels of independence. Perhaps you get to a point where it will be enough to just give a one-word cue, such as "backpack," or even a nonverbal reminder, such as pretending to adjust some imaginary backpack straps. As mentioned, it might help to write the anxiety-busting strategies on an index card or cell phone app for easy reference.

As you help your child organize their anxiety-busting backpack, you can get your own backpack ready too. Children and parents will have different backpacks but the same goal: good-enough self-control in the face of provocation.

Backpack Backfire

Some backpack strategies might provide temporary relief or short-term motivation but interfere with progress in the long run. Backpack strategies can backfire if they 1) contribute to avoidance, 2) reinforce undesirable behaviors, 3) interfere with the development of self-reliance, or 4) haven't been practiced enough. And sometimes, 5) strategies can both help and hinder. Let me explain.

1. *Strategies that contribute to avoidance.* Forgive me for belaboring this point. But avoidance—in all its many disguises—is the single most common pitfall. Strategies to overcome anxiety should not interfere with exposure to the anxiety trigger. Distraction, anti-anxiety medication, marijuana, and alcohol all have the potential to interfere with exposure and sabotage the treatment process. For example, Emily has a fear of choking. She might use an iPad while eating to distract her from the sensation of swallowing. At first, this works. But this electronic diversion works too well! The iPad is so powerfully engaging that it makes Emily oblivious to the act of eating. Now she is able to swallow—but only while watching YouTube! The whole idea of exposure is to face a just-right dose of provocation, then learn to tolerate gradually increasing doses. With Emily, it might be appropriate to use the iPad strategy before or after the exposure. This could help with preparation or recovery. Over time, Emily could use the iPad after one swallow of food, then two swallows, and so on. In this way, the duration of the exposure could be gradually increased, until ultimately, the iPad is allowed only after the meal is over.

2. *Strategies that reinforce undesirable behaviors.* Children make quick connections between their behavior and adult responses. Adults may respond to a child's distress by letting them escape from non-preferred activities. Commonly, children and adults get out of school, work, and other unpleasant situations if they express anxious thought and feelings or if

they have physical symptoms or disruptive behaviors. Adults may respond to a child's anxiety by providing attention, a desired object, or a favored activity. For example, children with separation anxiety learn to cry at bedtime if it gets them more hugs and stories. Here, the hugs and stories relieve the anxiety (temporarily) but reinforce the crying. The child doesn't learn to tolerate separation, and the adult doesn't learn to tolerate their own anxiety about separation. Reading stories in response to crying isn't a good coping strategy for either the child or the parent.

3. *Strategies that interfere with the development of self-reliance.* Whenever possible, anxiety-busting strategies should be ones that the children can provide for themselves. In the example above, a child who is anxious about separating from their parent at bedtime could get his or her own book to read. The parent could get their own book too! Both could read on their own, separately. Their anxiety about separating is softened but the separation itself proceeds. Rewards work best if they are earned for progressively greater degrees of independence. For example, two tokens (toward a reward) could be earned for complete independence in confronting an anxiety trigger. One token could be earned for one reminder from an adult to use their strategy and successfully complete the exposure. No tokens would be rewarded if the child needs more than one reminder. Rewards backfire if they are provided without regard to the level of adult support provided. We don't want to reward increasing levels of dependence—just the opposite.

4. *Strategies that have not been practiced enough.* It's hard to use new skills when stress is high. Good luck to the basketball player whose very first attempt at a free-throw is in double-overtime with a championship on the line. Any good coach makes sure that players have practiced thousands and thousands of free throws before placing them in a high-stakes/high-stress situation. Likewise, children should first practice their relaxation techniques when they are calm and not feeling threatened. A good time to practice self-calming strategies is every night at bedtime. Until strategies are mastered under calm circumstances, they will not be sufficiently automatic when emotions are high. When anxiety flares, only the well-practiced child will have the fluency and confidence

necessary for effective self-control. To begin, some coaching may be necessary. After a while, support can be faded. Think driver's ed. For many miles, practice is carefully guided. After a while, your teen has the skills to safely drive solo. Same thing with learning strategies to manage anxiety. At first, your child will need some help. Over time, the goal is self-management. Look forward to the day when your child can say, "I'm feeling that old anxiety again. But now I know how to deal with it myself. I've got this."

5. *Strategies that both help and hinder.* There are some strategies that could get mixed reviews. For example, consider a child with anxiety about background noise. On one hand, headphones could interfere with habituation and appear socially awkward. On the other hand, headphones could promote independent participation in otherwise intolerable situations. Like a medicine with possible benefits and side effects, these types of "double-edged sword" strategies must be evaluated carefully. For each person, in each situation, it's important to weigh the pros and cons.

Jordanna's Hiking Party Reaches the Summit

Using a combination of email, phone conversations, face-to-face coaching, and intermediaries, Dr. Oh helped each member of Jordanna's hiking party anticipate their own difficulties implementing the plan. Some, like Jordanna, needed explicit coaching. Others, like Brianna, just needed a script to follow.

To make it from one marker to the next, which members of the hiking party do you think would need to use self-calming strategies? Which strategies do you think they might choose?

Moving from one trail marker to the next, Dr. Oh had some troubleshooting to do. What kinds of difficulties would you anticipate? If you were Dr. Oh, what would you do?

Despite some spurts and sputters, Jordanna made good progress moving from one marker to the next. Eventually, she overcame her fear of going to school. The anxiety didn't go away entirely. But she did learn to handle it. With everyone's help, mornings were so much better. Jordanna was able to make the transition from home to school each morning without too much trouble.

In the process of reaching the trail summit, take a moment to consider the other system-wide benefits of Jordanna's parallel exposure therapy:

1. What happened to the relationships between each of the kids and each of their parents? What about between Linda and Sanford? Between Linda, Sanford, and Grandma? Between Grandma and grandkids? Between siblings? Between Jordanna and Mr. Fred? Between Jordanna and her classmates? Between Jordanna and her teacher? Between Dr. Oh, the family, and the school? Between Dr. Oh and Dr. G?
2. What happened to Jordanna's willingness to tackle the next anxiety trigger on her list? What about everyone else's confidence?
3. In helping Jordanna overcome her anxiety, what did other members of the hiking party learn about overcoming their own issues?
4. What if Dr. Oh had just worked with Jordanna and not the whole anxiety system? What would have been the likelihood of success? What about these other benefits of parallel exposure therapy?

Accommodation Versus Remediation

Often, children experience anxiety or avoid challenges because of real skill deficits. Anxiety often travels with other emotional, social, motor, academic, attention, and executive problems. In many of these cases, the anxiety may be mostly secondary. Even mild impairment or relative weaknesses can cause significant performance anxiety.

Parents, teachers, and coaches should be sensitive to these underlying weaknesses. To avoid humiliation and loss of motivation, a child's skill deficits should be accommodated in public and remediated in private. Improved performance might require hard work and considerable time. Complex tasks should be broken down into simpler subskills. Rendered more doable, each subskill can be practiced. When mastered, subskills can be combined. With increasing competence and comfort, children can gradually shift from supported private practice to independent public performance. In this way, step by step, anxiety and skill deficits are addressed simultaneously. Self-confidence increases with real success—not false praise. It's crucial to strike the right balance between accommodation and remediation.

Expectations and demands should be individualized and reevaluated over time. Some children need longer-term support. While working on these areas of weakness, adults can make sure to nurture and spotlight their child's natural strengths. Adults should take a good look at their own strengths as well.

With all of this attention on Jordanna's anxiety, Dr. Oh didn't forget about her problems with language processing and production. She recommended that Linda and Sanford ask the school for an education management team meeting, which Dr. Oh joined. They all talked about Jordanna's anxiety problems. But then, Dr. Oh asked for more feedback about Jordanna's reading and writing problems. Mrs. Smith reported that Jordanna was falling farther behind her classmates. Mrs. Smith had assumed that this was all about the anxiety. But the school speech-language pathologist agreed to a more formal assessment.

She found that Jordanna didn't just have anxiety. The results of a standard battery of tests were clear. Jordanna also had a language disability, with significant problems in oral expression, reading, and writing.

Linda was relieved. Sanford and Linda had always been concerned. After all, Sanford had his own problems with reading and writing when he was a kid. Even now, he struggled to read manuals at work. It dawned on him and Linda that his language problems had not just made things hard for him in school—they had affected his marriage, his relationship with his kids, and his friendships.

The school psychologist did some additional testing. She agreed with the speech-language pathologist about the language disability and ruled out any additional problems. The team drafted an individualized education program (IEP) for Jordanna's reading and writing disorder. They also added some goals for her anxiety and social difficulties; including, small group instruction for reading and writing, and a social skills "lunch bunch." Mrs. Smith would provide additional accommodations in the classroom; such as, making sure that Jordanna understood directions, helping Jordanna use graphic organizers before starting to write, and previewing a few questions with Jordanna before calling on her to answer in front of the whole class.

Dr. Oh reminded Linda and Sanford that Jordanna's language weaknesses affected home and social functioning too, not just school performance.

Dr. Oh knew that she had to practice what she preached. In talking about anxiety management with Jordanna and Frank, Dr. Oh deliberately kept her explanations short and clear, avoided technical jargon, and tapped into Jordanna's artistic side by using visual explanations. Knowing that Sanford was a software guy, Dr. Oh used computer metaphors with him.

Handout: Talking with Your Child About Anxiety

If your child is fearful or worried, you may try reassuring or instructing. You might even try to keep your child away from the source of his or her fear. But these parent maneuvers are often the product of your own anxiety. They rarely work and they often make a child's anxiety worse instead of better. Plus, your child doesn't learn to deal with his or her own worries.

Instead, parents can teach their children how to "STOP" and face their fears. Try it in a time and place when everyone is calm, not right in the middle of an anxious episode.

"STOP" and face your fears:

1. Scared?
2. Thinking about what?
3. Other things I can do or think to help myself relax.
4. Pat myself on the back for facing my fears.

Here's how to STOP:

1. *Scared?* Before children can solve their problems with anxiety, they must be able to recognize when they are feeling anxious. They can be taught to notice the signs: muscle tension, fast breathing, fast heart rate, abdominal discomfort, headache, nervous habits, shaky feelings, tearfulness, irritability, anticipatory dread, avoidance behaviors, obsessions, compulsions, etc. The earlier they recognize these red flags, the easier it will be to reverse the problem. Children should learn to say to themselves, "I can tell that I'm beginning to feel scared. I need to do my STOP."

2. *Thinking about what?* After recognizing their anxious feelings, children should learn to identify their source and put these anxious thoughts into words. For example, "I'm afraid that robbers will come while I'm asleep" or "I'm feeling nervous about flunking my exam" or "I'm worried that something might happen to my parents."

3. *Other things I can do or think to help myself relax.* Children need to be aware of irrational or distorted thoughts. They have to learn to frame their anxiety in specific and solvable terms. If children think ahead about possible solutions, pick the best one, and practice it, then they can face their fears with confidence. Initially, most children need parents

213

or professionals to coach them through this process. "Other things" might include: positive self-talk, muscle relaxation, breathing awareness, meditation, yoga, physical exercise, positive imagery, self-hypnosis, talking, playing, music, reading, drawing—any relaxing activity. After brainstorming about possible solutions, the child should choose the best one(s) to practice. By deliberately and gradually increasing exposure to the source of anxiety, adults can give children opportunities to successfully practice chosen strategies, lessening the child's sensitivity.

4. *Pat myself on the back for facing my fears.* After successfully choosing and using his or her own strategies, your child should feel very proud. Children are often quick to say negative things about themselves. The idea of self-praise might be foreign to some children. Your child might need help learning that the ability to help oneself is the ultimate reward. Initially, parents and professionals need to do some coaching. Eventually, the child should carry out his or her own plan. After effectively conquering some fears, the child should feel empowered that if they STOP and think, they can face just about anything.

These STOP steps work just as well for adults as they do for children. At first, you and your child may need some help learning to STOP. With time and practice, you can both learn to STOP and conquer anxiety more effectively and independently.

*Many thanks to Philipp Kendall and Kristina Hedtke, whose (2006) *Coping Cat* manual includes the "STOP" mnemonic.

Parallel Exposure Therapy and Larger Social Systems

We focus on larger social systems not only to help embedded individuals. In the long run, we hope to change these larger social systems too. By attending to systems, we help individuals change, and by attending to individuals, we also help systems change. Realistically, whether working toward change in individuals, school systems, or nations, we need to go slowly, marker by marker, exposing old nerve networks and old institutions to just-right doses of stress so that change is rendered possible and made durable. Much more on all of this in Excursions 4 and 5, when we turn our attention to social change and autism. But first, a brief view of the summit toward which this book is slowly climbing.

In *The Geography of Thought*, Richard Nesbitt describes different sources of anxiety in individualistic Western and communitarian Eastern cultures. For example, in the United States, anxiety might stem from "failure" of the individual to achieve self-reliance. In China, anxiety is more likely to stem from "failure" of the individual to subsume selfish drives for the good of the community. What about when these dissonant cultures come into contact? Consider the anxiety of bicultural individuals (Asian immigrants to the U.S. or American expats in Asia) who move between these two worlds. Consider how, over the years, gradually and incrementally, globalization has brought together previously isolated or warring countries. Dr. Nesbitt asks, will parallel exposure of cultures disparate to one another result in "victory" of Western culture over Eastern culture? Or will parallel exposure of these different cultures result in more tension, conflict, and warfare? Nesbitt concludes his mind-blowing book by pointing to evidence that, as the world gets smaller, we might be inching our way to a wonderful amalgam:

> "[W]e all function in some respects more like Easterners some of the time and more like Westerners some of the time. ... So I believe the twain shall meet by virtue of each moving in the direction of the other. East and West may contribute to a blended world where social and cognitive aspects of both regions are represented but transformed—like the individual ingredients in a stew that are recognizable but are

altered as they alter the whole. It may not be too much to hope that this stew will contain the best of each culture."

Applying Parallel Exposure Therapy to Other Conditions

Although CBT and exposure therapy have the strongest evidence base for the treatment of anxiety, the same principles and strategies are also effective for treatment of various other disorders of self-regulation. As described in *Parent Child Journey* (see the seventh mile), problem-solving "steps" of CBT can be applied across the entire range of developmental, behavioral, and social-emotional challenges.

Exposure therapy can be used to effectively treat:
- depression
- irritability
- inflexibility
- bipolar
- anger
- impulsivity
- post-traumatic stress
- schizophrenia, psychosis
- prevention of mental illness
- gambling, Internet, substance addiction
- eating disorders
- sleep problems
- psychosomatic (somatoform) symptoms
- pain, fatigue, or other symptoms related to medical conditions

Whether using exposure therapy to treat anxiety or any of these other issues, a system-wide approach is worth considering. Although application of parallel exposure therapy across this entire range of disorders is well beyond the scope of this book, the principles are entirely the same.

What If It's Too Hard?

Cognitive-Behavioral Therapy with an Expert

CBT, with a heavy emphasis on exposure, is the treatment of choice for anxiety. Not all anxiety requires the highest level of expert intervention. Some people do remarkably well reading a book about CBT and practicing on their own (known as "bibliotherapy"). Others respond nicely to brief CBT with a primary care provider or school counselor. However, if there isn't clear progress or the anxiety is severe, it's wise to seek expert help. A cognitive-behavioral therapist, usually a licensed clinical psychologist or social worker, should have received intensive training in evidence-based techniques. Be skeptical of online reviews. Ask your pediatrician for a referral, and/or ask other parents.

Medication for Anxiety

With careful prescribing, medication can safely and effectively minimize symptoms of anxiety.

Indications

When is it appropriate to consider a careful trial of anti-anxiety medication?

- *Unresponsiveness to CBT.* A medication trial may be appropriate if a child or adult is unresponsive to a good trial of exposure therapy. This usually means weekly sessions with an expert therapist, plus very regular exposures. After one to three months, an experienced therapist can tell if exposure therapy is likely to work. In some cases, a longer trial of six to nine months may be necessary. But either you're making progress or you're not.

- *Unavailability of CBT.* A medication trial may be appropriate if a good therapist is simply not available. Given the shortage of skilled cognitive-behavioral therapists and the importance of providing prompt relief, a medication might be necessary to get your child back on the road and to keep things from getting worse. Even in communities that are rich with mental health care providers, it can still be difficult to find a good therapist, whereas it may be relatively easy to get a prescription. As discussed below, you need to be careful with medication. But sometimes, medication without CBT is better than nothing at all.

- *Inability to participate in CBT, unrelated to anxiety per se.* Medication may also be indicated if a key member of the anxiety system—child or adult—isn't developmentally able to participate in CBT. Even with the most creative and skillful therapist, a child might be too young. Any individual— child or adult—might be too impaired. Right up front, a good therapist should judge each person's cognitive, verbal, attentional, and emotional readiness for successful therapy. A therapist might recommend medication for such a child or adult, while starting cognitive-behavioral training with other members of the anxiety system. Sometimes, this means medication for a child while working with parents; other times it could mean medication for a parent; sometimes both. It doesn't mean it's forever. Periodically, the therapist should reassess individual readiness for direct CBT.

- *Inability to participate in CBT because of severe anxiety.* Medication may be indicated if the child's or the parent's anxiety is causing persistent or severe impairment or distress. Sometimes, even with the best therapist and the simplest exposures, anxiety is just too overwhelming. A child or adult might become so easily flooded they cannot even begin to participate in exposures. In these situations, medication can knock the anxiety down into a more workable range, then CBT can be layered in. Ultimately, after CBT skills are learned, the prescriber can conduct a carefully controlled discontinuation trial. A trial off anxiety medication is done just the same as a trial off ADHD medication—apply the principles discussed in the first excursion on ADHD. If discontinuation of medication results in relapse, medication can always be restarted.

Medication for child and adolescent anxiety can be prescribed by a child psychiatrist, developmental-behavioral pediatrician, or specially trained nurse practitioner. In many relatively straightforward cases, primary care pediatricians can at least get things started with first-line medication. For adults, medication can be prescribed by an adult psychiatrist. Again, if things are relatively simple and good follow-up is assured, a primary care provider can do a good job.

Options

- *SSRIs (selective serotonin reuptake inhibitors).* SSRIs include Prozac, Zoloft, Celexa, Lexapro, Luvox, and others. Unfortunately, these medications are often referred to as antidepressants. In fact, SSRIs work much more reliably for anxiety than they do for depression. When anxiety medication is indicated, the SSRIs should be considered first-line drugs of choice for children, adolescents, and adults. If tolerated, these medications can be very effective. In children, overactivation is the most common side effect. Overactivation—also referred to as disinhibition—can take the form of hyperactivity, impulsivity, distractibility, mood swings, sleep disturbance, or increased bowel or bladder frequency. If one SSRI isn't a good fit, it may be worthwhile to try a second one. But if there is a particularly severe reaction to low doses of one SSRI, or side effects before benefits with a second SSRI, then it may be necessary to try another type of medication. Non-SSRIs may also be used to augment a partial or suboptimal response to an SSRI.

- *NRIs (norepinephrine reuptake inhibitors).* Some norepinephrine reuptake inhibitors are also serotonin reuptake inhibitors, and called SNRIs. They are just not selective for the serotonin receptor, like the SSRIs listed above. Two commonly prescribed medications that inhibit norepinephrine reuptake are venlafaxine (Effexor) and duloxetine (Cymbalta). Bupropion (Wellbutrin) and atomoxetine (Strattera) are also NRIs, sometimes used to treat coexisting anxiety and ADHD. If anxiety travels with poor appetite and insomnia, then mirtazapine (Remeron) can target all three of these issues. NRI medications should be considered second-line choices, usually indicated only if SSRIs prove ineffective or cause significant side-effects.
- *Tricyclic antidepressants.* This older class of medications includes imipramine and desipramine. They can be useful, especially if there is coexisting ADHD, insomnia, or bedwetting. However, since SSRIs became available, tricyclics are not prescribed nearly as much, since they are more likely to cause side effects, such as sleepiness, bowel/bladder changes, dry mouth, and cardiac arrythmias.
- *Beta blockers.* The most commonly prescribed beta blocker is propranolol. This medication is used for performance anxiety, rage, or panic attacks. It may also be effective in preventing coexisting migraine headaches. Beta blockers should not be prescribed to individuals who also have asthma.
- *Neuroleptics.* These medications, such as risperidone (Risperdal) and aripiprazole (Abilify), are used primarily for treatment of psychosis and severe mood dysregulation. They should not be used as a stand-alone medication for anxiety.

However, neuroleptics may be useful as a supplement under special circumstances, when very severe anxiety isn't sufficiently responsive to first-line medications.

- *Benzodiazepines.* "Benzos" include Valium, Xanax, Klonopin, Ativan, and others. They should not be used on a regular long-term basis because of their addictive potential. These medications are appropriately and effectively prescribed for situational anxiety. Unlike SSRIs, which can take weeks to build up, benzodiazepams usually provide immediate relief—for example, if a child might not be able to make it through a necessary medical or dental procedure, or there's a very important but very stressful family event, such as a funeral. If there is insufficient time for habituation through CBT or relief from SSRIs, then it may be entirely appropriate and necessary to use a benzo.

How to Do a Medication Trial for Anxiety

Many of the principles reviewed in the first excursion on medication for ADHD also apply to pharmacological treatment of anxiety. A full discussion of medication management for anxiety is beyond the scope of this book. For a more extensive discussion, see Timothy Wilens and Paul Hammerness's (2016) excellent book, *Straight Talk About Psychiatric Medications for Kids.* Here, I will just hit on the most practical points. It should be noted that not all the medications listed here are FDA-approved for treatment of anxiety in children. Consult your prescriber regarding up-to-date FDA status and the latest research regarding safety and efficacy.

Similar to the treatment trial for ADHD, here is a sample protocol with rating scales for SSRIs. These forms should be modified for treatment trials with other anxiety medications.

Directions for Serotonergic Medication Trial

1. Baseline ratings: Observers should complete baseline rating scales before starting medication for both target symptoms and possible side effects.
2. Starting medication and dose: _____.
   I recommend beginning medications and making any dose changes on Friday nights or Saturday mornings, so that parents can be sure that there are no side effects over the weekend.

3. Adjustments: Side effects tend to happen early, usually within days of each dose change. Although peak benefits happen late, usually after a month or two, you may see the beginning of benefits earlier, even within the first week. After one week at each dose, compare baseline ratings with updated ratings:

   a. "Looking good": If benefits are optimal (2s and 3s are down to 0s and 1s) and side effects are *in*significant (numbers on the bottom half of the page have not gone up), then stay with that dose.

   b. "Too low": If benefits are less than optimal and side effects are *in*significant, then increase the dose by an amount equal to the starting dose.

   c. "Hopefully just an adjustment": If benefits are optimal but there are significant side effects, try to keep the benefits but lose the side effects by decreasing the dose by one-quarter or one-half of the starting dose.

   d. "No good": If benefits are less than optimal and there are significant side effects, either decrease the dose by half and give the maximum tolerated dose a chance to work, or just stop and consider trying something else.

Serotonergic Medication Trial

Child's name: _____ Grade: _____ Year: _____

Person completing this form: _____

Relation to child: _____

Dear Parents, Teachers, and Student,

Thank you very much for your help. It's so important to conduct this medication trial in a careful and controlled fashion. Please complete the table below. Record observations for the week indicated. Your comments in narrative form are also very helpful; please record the date and elaborate on any side effects and benefits. Please contact me if you have any questions or concerns. Thank you.

How often did you notice the following? 0 = not at all, 1 = just a little, 2 = often, 3 = very often

Dose									
Target Symptoms Date (Week of)									
Inflexibility/frustration intolerance									
Meltdowns/tantrums									
Aggression									
Irritability									
Sadness									
General anxiety									
Specific worries/fears									
Obsessive/perseverative thoughts									
Compulsive habits/behaviors									
Tics /nervous habits									
Physical symptoms/body complaints									
Limited social interaction									
Possible Side Effects									
Trouble sleeping									
Agitation/tension									
Dizzy									
Bowel/bladder changes									
Nausea/vomiting/stomach pains									
Increased/decreased appetite (circle one)									
Drowsy									
Headache									
Restless, hyper, manic, impulsive, distractible									

For severe anxiety, the combination of CBT and medication works better than either intervention alone. Whether treating with exposure therapy or medication, parents should stay in regular communication with their clinician.

Trail-End for Excursion 2

We have now discussed the importance of a highly individualized approach to medication management for ADHD and cognitive-behavioral therapy for anxiety. Complexity is a theme that has run throughout these first two excursions. That theme continues as we turn, in Excursion 3, to the management of conflicting internal tendencies, when ADHD, Anxiety and Autism coexist.

EXCURSION 3

Balance—Combined Medication and Parallel Exposure Therapy for Coexisting ADHD, Anxiety, and Autism

———◆———

All extremes are dangerous. It's best to keep in the middle
of the road, in the common ruts, however muddy.
—Virginia Woolf, *The Common Reader*

*Raph thought, If I get on the unicycle and try to chase Dog, I go too
fast and fall on my beak. If I try walking or just sit like Turtle, I go
too slow and never find any Tambalacoque fruit.*

*Then Raph had an idea: I could ride the unicycle a little like Dog
and a little like Turtle. If I lean forward—just a little—I could go
forward but not fall on my beak. If I lean back—just a little—I could
slow down but not fall on my tuft.*

*Raph tried to find the right balance. Sometimes he got too excited
and fell forward. Sometimes he got too scared and fell backward.
But, instead of hurting his beak or his tuft, Raph learned to land
on his feet. At first, he could make it just one roll of the wheel. Then*

two. Then, very gradually, Raph learned how to lean and pedal just right. Seven rolls! Then 12!

Dog kept running too far ahead. Turtle lagged farther behind. But Raph made progress down the trail. Excited but cautious, moving ahead but not too fast, Raph got better at keeping his balance. He rode for longer distances without falling at all. The mountain grew closer and closer.

Signposts for Excursion 3

This excursion is a detailed discussion of medication and cognitive-behavioral therapy for coexisting ADHD, anxiety, and autism, including:

- A case for functional or transdiagnostic assessment.
- Seeing ADHD, anxiety, and autism, in part, as an imbalance of under-inhibition and over-inhibition.
- How to work with this imbalance, pharmacologically and non-pharmacologically.
- Applying this framework to other behavioral, neuropsychiatric, and developmental disorders.

Here, we focus on the complex interplay of neurophysiological, psychological, and behavioral tendencies.

Thinking Outside the Boxes

In Excursion 2, we focused on a systems approach to anxiety. We discussed how parallel exposure therapy deals with the fact that there is more to the anxious individual than just the individual. We also described conditions that commonly coexist with anxiety. But *treatment* of coexisting conditions was only mentioned in passing. Here, in Excursion 3, we'll go into more detail regarding management of diagnostic complexity: when there's more to the anxious individual than just the anxiety, and, more broadly, when there's more to any child than just one diagnosis. Using the common coexistence of ADHD, anxiety, and autism as an example, we'll explore a different way of describing developmental difference. Then we'll get into practical management.

Coexisting Conditions Are the Rule, Not the Exception

In previous discussions regarding ADHD and anxiety, I have emphasized that these conditions are complicated and usually don't travel alone. Regarding ADHD, there are many types of inattention and ADHD usually coexists with other developmental differences. The same holds true of anxiety disorders. Just to make the point clear, let's take a moment to review.

Remember this DSM list of potentially coexisting anxiety disorders:
- Separation anxiety
- Generalized anxiety
- Specific fears and phobias
- Selective mutism
- Obsessive-compulsive disorders
- Perfectionism
- Social anxiety
- Situational anxiety
- Agoraphobia
- Acute or post-traumatic stress disorder
- Panic disorder

Recall that any one of these anxiety disorders can coexist with any other anxiety disorder, in any number of combinations. Also, constellations of different anxiety disorders usually change over time. Depending upon the developmental phase and life circumstances, one type of anxiety can combine with or morph into any other.

Also recall how anxiety often coexists with many other disorders. Any combination of anxiety disorders can coexist with any combination of other developmental, medical, family, or environmental issues. Remember this list of commonly coexisting conditions:

- ADHD/executive dysfunction
- Learning problems and disabilities
- Mood disorders, including aggressiveness, explosiveness, bipolar illness, and depression
- Sensory differences: under- or over-reactivity
- Sleep problems
- Gross motor, fine motor, and writing deficits
- Movement disorders: tics, spasms, stereotypies, or other repetitive movements
- Autism spectrum disorders and other social skills deficits
- Medical problems or medication side effects
- Parent and other adult anxiety
- Cultural pressures
- Environmental stresses and trauma

Anxiety causes other stuff. Other stuff causes anxiety. And even when there isn't a cause-effect relationship, anxiety and other developmental disorders often coexist in dynamic interplay, each affecting the others. These overlapping and intertwined issues should not be treated as if they stand alone. Treatment of one condition can impact the coexisting conditions—in positive, negative, or mixed ways. Clearly, very few children with developmental differences can be placed in only one diagnostic box. Failure to describe actual diagnostic complexity often means failure of treatment.

Three Levels of Assessment

The brain is a complicated organ. Human beings are complicated organisms. We live in complicated environments. All of this intricacy can be viewed through different windows. Each window yields a different view; each view serves a different purpose. There are three types of diagnostic windows or levels of assessment: categorical diagnosis, etiologic diagnosis, and functional assessment.

Categorical Diagnosis

Categorical diagnosis is based on constellations of symptoms. This is the level of assessment that is most familiar. ADHD, anxiety disorders, and autism spectrum disorders represent just a few such categories. These—along with hundreds of others—are the types of diagnostic boxes found in the Diagnostic and Statistical Manual of the American Psychiatric Association, the International Classification of Diseases of the National Center for Health Statistics (ICD), and the World Health Organization. For the most part, DSM categories are based upon symptoms. For example, DSM5 defines:

- ADHD as "a persistent pattern of inattention and/or hyper-activity–impulsivity that interferes with functioning or development."
- Anxiety as "excessive fear and anxiety and related behavioral disturbances."
- Autism as "clinically significant, persistent deficits in social communication and interactions," plus "restricted, repetitive patterns of behavior, interests, and activities."

Specific symptoms are described in much greater detail but there is no discussion of causation.

These diagnostic categories serve a crucial set of purposes:

- They allow children to gain eligibility for special services, such as through the public-school system or federal government.
- They can be used to justify health insurance reimbursement.
- They often facilitate communication between parents, clinicians, teachers, and children.
- They can help explain and demystify developmental difference.
- They are crucial for funding and driving important research.
- They can bind people together for mutual support, civil rights activism, and social-cultural movement.

For these reasons, I certainly don't advocate throwing DSM5 and ICD10 in the trash can. However, as discussed throughout this book, we should not rely too heavily upon these diagnostic categories for management. Given our previous discussions of ADHD and anxiety, the reasons should be clear:

- *There is always more to an individual child than just a diagnostic category.* Many children have more than one diagnosis. Many children have complicated profiles. Each facet of a child's profile affects the others. All children change over time. Children with one diagnosis will share some core features. However, in other ways, they may be more different from one another than alike.
- *There is always more to a diagnosis than just the child.* Children exist within families, schools, communities, and cultures. Effective management depends upon understanding the systems within which children are embedded, not viewing children as if they exist in isolation.

Etiologic Evaluation

Etiologic evaluation identifies specific underlying causes: neurobiological, genetic, metabolic, or environmental. Fetal alcohol syndrome, Down syndrome, phenylketonuria, and lead poisoning are examples of disorders for which the cause can be identified. Extraordinary advances in testing now allow for specific identification of subtle genetic variations in a large number of children with developmental differences. For example, specific genetic abnormalities can now be identified in roughly 35 percent of children with autism spectrum disorders. Subtyping disorders according to a primary neurogenetic or metabolic cause can serve some important purposes.

- It can promote research on prevention.
- It can guide certain types of management.
- It can inform families regarding origin, prognosis, and heritability.

However, there are some serious limitations to basing treatment on identifiable causes:

- Despite advances in genetic testing, for most developmental disorders, one ultimate cause cannot usually be identified. This is due to either the limits of science and technology or the existence of multiple contributing factors.
- Even when one specific genetic cause can be identified, serious ethical issues are raised regarding family counseling

and prevention (Silberman, 2016).

- Identification of a specific cause doesn't take the place of individualized management. Genotype doesn't equal phenotype. In other words, two people with the same gene will express that gene and turn out in very different ways. Environmental causes also have highly variable effects. Despite some similarities, two individuals with fetal alcohol syndrome will be more different than they are alike. Most often, etiologic diagnosis doesn't lead to sufficiently individualized management. Phenylketonuria or PKU is the exception that proves the rule. It's one of the very few diseases where diagnosis of a very specific enzyme deficiency determines a very specific and effective dietary treatment. Usually, nature and nurture combine too unpredictably to make reliable presumptions regarding treatment.

Functional Assessment

Functional assessment determines an individual's real-life abilities and capacities. With this approach, we describe an individual's functional level overall and, more important, within a broad range of specific developmental domains. For example, an individual can be described according to their overall academic success, specific skills in geometry, and their achievements in learning to play the piano. As described in *Parent Child Journey,* the Gander is one such assessment tool. It covers temperament, sensory profile, specific skills, and environmental factors. (For a free copy of the Gander and detailed instruction manual, go to www.parentchildjourney.com/journey.) Functional assessment is the most reliable and practical guide to individualized care because:

   a. It moves beyond diagnostic generalizations (lumping) to explain individual variation (splitting).
   b. It describes each child across multiple domains of development and multiple real-life settings.
   c. It highlights disparities between potential and real-life capacities.
   d. It establishes a sufficiently detailed baseline against which progress can be measured.

I am not suggesting that we should only do functional assessment. For the reasons stated above, it's still important to identify diagnostic categories, such as ADHD, anxiety, or autism. It may also be important to find specific causes or contributing factors. However, these first two levels of assessment, categorical and etiologic, are usually not enough to guide individualized management. One person often has more than one disorder. Disorders in one diagnostic category or with one etiology present in different ways, in different settings, across different tasks, in different people. Functional assessment cuts across categories and causes to describe individuals in real-life situations. Treatment of coexisting conditions requires moving beyond simplistic diagnosis to a more nuanced description of interrelationships across categories and causes.

Having covered the theory, let's see how this "transdiagnostic functional approach" works. Let's take a deep look at medication and CBT for three commonly coexisting conditions: ADHD, anxiety, and autism. Then, in more general terms, we'll discuss application of these principles to other coexisting conditions.

Complicated Problems with Self-Control and Attention Dysregulation

The Self-Control and Attention Dysregulation Spectrum (SCADS)

As discussed in our first two excursions, ADHD and anxiety are at opposite ends of an inhibitory control spectrum. On one end of this spectrum, ADHD can be thought of as a disorder of under-inhibition and distractibility. On the other end, anxiety can be viewed as a disorder of over-inhibition and perseveration. Autism is a multifaceted disorder that usually contains elements of both over-inhibition and under-inhibition; a core feature is inflexibility. To better describe this complex interplay, let me introduce the idea of a "Self-Control and Attention Dysregulation Spectrum" (SCADS).

On one end of the SCADS spectrum, ADHD is a disorder of inadequate inhibition. It's like the brain's brakes are too loose and the gears shift too easily. These children (and adults) are impulsive. They often leap before they look. They shoot a hand up even if Simon doesn't say to. They bore easily and crave novelty. They live too much in the moment. All too often, they act with insufficient consideration of past experience and future consequences. This spontaneity can be fun, but it can also lead to inappropriate or unsafe behavior. Poor cognitive inhibition underlies their distractibility. Their attention span is too short; their focus is too shallow and fleeting. People with ADHD often pay attention to too many things, to the exclusion of one.

On the other end of the SCADS spectrum, anxiety is a disorder of too much inhibition. With anxiety it's hard to shift gears. The brakes are too tight. As a result, people with anxiety are often inflexible, avoidant, stuck, or even paralyzed. They tend to take steps back when they should take steps forward. They keep their hand down even when Simon says to raise it up. When faced with unfamiliarity, they are predisposed to avoid. They too easily become overwhelmed or shut down. They have a narrow comfort zone, preferring repetition and ritual. They tend to fixate on past and future and not so much on the here and now. When they don't pay attention, it's because they perseverate or hyperfocus. In other words, they get stuck on one thing to the exclusion of others.

The Self-Control and Attention Dysregulation Spectrum (SCADS)

ADHD ←――――――――――→	Anxiety/Autism
under-inhibition	over-inhibition
distractibility, poor focus	perseveration, hyperfocus
brakes too loose	brakes too tight
gears shift too easily	stuck in one gear
impulsive, prefer novelty	inflexible, prefer repetition and ritual
leap before looking, dangerous	step back, avoid, shut down
too much in the moment, here and now	too much in the past and/or future
focus on too many things instead of one	focus on one thing, exclusively

Mixed Profiles and Autism

Let's peel back a few layers of complexity. Many children with anxiety also have ADHD. Many children with ADHD also have anxiety. Many children with autism have both anxiety and ADHD.

In the past, clinicians were supposed to diagnose *either* autism *or* ADHD—not both in the same person. This was just one example of faulty either/or thinking. Only in May 2013, with the publication of the DSM5, was there formal acknowledgment that autism and ADHD often travel *together*.

Recognition of this common association between autism and ADHD was slow in coming because autism is primarily considered to be a disorder of over-inhibition and anxiety. Indeed, core features of autism include difficulty shifting and transitioning. People with autism have problems breaking from routines and rituals. They perseverate and hyperfocus. They have repetitious thoughts, behaviors, and speech, including echolalia, scripting, and motor stereotypies. They are genetically predisposed to primary coexisting mood disorders and they almost always have anxiety secondary to their social disability, inflexibility, language challenges, sensory reactivity, and other associated deficits. As children with autism grow up, they become more aware of the differences between themselves and others. They experience more adverse life events, such as bullying. They perceive their social environment as unpredictable and confusing. They have difficulty with changes in rules and schedules. They have unusual worries related to their special interests and fears about distorted sensory experiences.

With that said, many children with autism also show symptoms of under-inhibition. They can be very impulsive. Many (but not all) are extremely hyperactive. They may run off. They may have involuntary motor mannerisms, such as flapping, spinning, and fidgeting. They may self-injure. They may have excessive vocalizing, shouting, and talking. They may touch others inappropriately. They may have significant problems with distractibility, short attention span, rapid shifting, flitting, mind-wandering, and flights into fantasy.

Clearly, autism is a disorder of self-control, including *both* under-inhibition *and* over-inhibition. As such, we can learn a lot from children with autism about mixed profiles. After all, these opposing tendencies coexist in all of us, whether we have autism, another developmental disorder, or just normal human variations. In this discussion, ADHD and anxiety will function as archetypes for understanding under-inhibition and over-inhibition. Autism will be our model for understanding coexisting disorders. However, as we'll see, there are many other disorders that can be thought of in the same ways.

Flipping Profiles

Many social psychologists question the whole idea of specific labels or profiles (Mischel, 2014). So much of human behavior depends upon situations and relationships (Gilovich, Keltner, Chen, & Nisbett, 2015). Depending upon the task and setting, a child with a mixed profile may flip between symptoms on one end of the SCADS spectrum to the other.

For example, it's not unusual for some children to be "more ADHD" (impulsive and distractible) for auditory-verbal situations, "more anxious" (avoidant) for social situations, and "more autistic" (stuck and perseverative) for visual-motor activities. Parents and professionals might wonder: "If he can sit there and play video games or Legos for hours, why can't he sit still and listen in class or at the kitchen table for more than five seconds?" Other children have very different patterns of dysregulation that depend entirely upon the activity or situation. If these children could speak for themselves, they might explain: "Please don't be confused by my inconsistent attention and self-control. Just because I can attend appropriately to some things sometimes, that doesn't mean that I can skillfully sustain and shift engagement for all things all the time. My problem is with complicated attention dysregulation, not just one simple pattern across the board."

Treatment of SCADS

In Excursion 1, we covered treatment of ADHD as a disorder of under-inhibition. Treatment of ADHD is like saying, "Use your brakes. Slow down. Stop and think, about past experiences and future consequences. Please, be a little more anxious." The primary treatment for ADHD is medication to increase inhibition. This is why Excursion 1 is titled "STOP."

In Excursion 2, we covered treatment of anxiety as a disorder of over-inhibition. Treatment of anxiety is like saying, "Take your foot off the brake. Let it roll. Don't stop and think so much. Don't worry about the past and future. Just live in the moment. How about some action? Please be a little more ADHD." The primary treatment for anxiety is cognitive-behavioral therapy, while secondary treatment is medication—both work by decreasing inhibition. And so, Excursion 2 is called "GO."

Treatment of SCADS

Treatment of Under-Inhibition (ADHD)	Treatment of Over-Inhibition (Anxiety/Autism)
• Use your brakes, slow down	• Take your foot off the brake, let go
• Stop and think more	• Don't stop and think so much
• Don't just live in the moment	• Don't worry about past/future
• Consider past and future	• Live more in the moment
• Be more cautious	• Relax
• Narrow your comfort zone	• Expand your comfort zone
• "Be more autistic/anxious"	• "Be more ADHD"

In this Excursion 3, we'll tackle treatment of coexisting ADHD, anxiety, and autism as intertwined disorders of under-inhibition *and* over-inhibition. When these conditions coexist, how to STOP *and* GO? The simple answer: find the right balance between inhibition and excitation.

The treatment for coexisting ADHD, anxiety, and autism is complicated. At multiple levels, there is tension—even conflict—between therapeutic approaches. Treatment of these mixed disorders is like saying, "Not too fast, but not too slow. Not too impulsive, but not too inhibited. Let's find the middle course—the *golden mean.*"

Therefore, Excursion 3 is called "BALANCE." How to find the golden mean.

Daedalus, Icarus, Aristotle, and the Golden Mean

In a way, the ancient Greeks had a lot to say about developmental disorders such as ADHD, anxiety, and autism.

In one of the most famous Greek myths, Daedalus and his son Icarus tried to escape King Minos. Daedalus made wings of feathers and wax. Anxiously, he warned his son to fly the middle course, between the sea and the sun: *Not too low, or your wings will get wet. Not too high, or your wings will melt.* Impulsively, Icarus flew higher and higher. Although most of us think of the death of Icarus as a warning against flying too high, the same tragedy would have befallen him had he flown too low.

In *Nicomachean Ethics,* Aristotle wrote that we should find a healthy and moral middle way, or "golden mean," by moderating "excesses" and "deficiencies." For example, he suggested:

- *Courage* represents the golden mean between *cowardice* and *rashness*
- *Generosity* represents the golden mean between *stinginess* and *extravagance*
- *Ambition* represents the golden mean between *sloth* and *greed*
- *Modesty* represents the golden mean between *humility* and *pride*
- *Honesty* represents the golden mean between *secrecy* and *loquacity* (too much talking)
- *Good humor* represents the golden mean between *moroseness* and *absurdity*
- *Friendship* represents the golden mean between *quarrelsomeness* and *flattery*
- *Temperance* represents the golden mean between *self-indulgence* and *insensibility*
- *Composure* represents the golden mean between *apathy* and *irritability*
- *Self-control* represents the golden mean between *indecisiveness* and *impulsiveness*

Today, such myths and admonitions might strike some readers as quaint. However, the idea of finding the middle way is still relevant, practical, and powerful. Aristotle's suggestion that self-control represents the golden mean between indecisiveness and impulsiveness could have been written by any modern neurophysiologist about competitive excitatory and inhibitory brain networks, or by any cognitive-behavioral therapist about rational thinking and self-regulation. Especially for children with extremely conflicting tendencies, effective pharmacological and non-pharmacological treatment depends upon finding this middle course.

Jimmy is an eight-year-old boy with autism. Jimmy's parents and teachers were concerned about his difficulty paying attention, at home and in school. He could play forever with his Legos and trains but he'd wander and roam during group instruction and meals. He resisted shifting from preferred to non-preferred activities. He could not sustain engagement for play. When other children approached, he'd shut down, run away, or lash out. Unexpected noises set him on edge.

Jimmy's parents consulted a child psychiatrist, Dr. Totle, who explained that Jimmy had a complicated profile, including sensory reactivity and language problems. But Jimmy's inconsistent focus and poor self-regulation were mostly due to the combination of three core factors:

- *Autism (social learning disability and perseveration)*
- *ADHD (distractibility, impulsivity, and hyperactivity)*
- *Anxiety (with sensory and social triggers)*

Medication for SCADS

Finding the Golden Mean with Medication

When ADHD, autism, and anxiety coexist, treatment is about finding the golden mean—the sweet spot—between not enough inhibition and too much inhibition. Although research continues in earnest, currently there is no effective medication for the core symptoms of autism: namely, social disability and repetitive, restricted, ritualized thoughts and behavior. On the other hand, there is very effective medication for coexisting problems with ADHD and anxiety (Mahajan et al., 2015; Vasa et al., 2016).

With medication management of ADHD, you want just enough stimulant (methylphenidate or dextroamphetamine) to fix impulsivity and distractibility (brakes too loose) but not so much that you amplify autism or anxiety (brakes too tight). With medication management of anxiety—especially when there is coexisting autism—you want to give just enough SSRI (selective serotonin re-uptake inhibitor, such as fluoxetine) to fix rigidity and distress (brakes too tight) without amplifying ADHD (brakes too loose).

It's all too easy to mute tendencies on one end of the Self-Control and Attention Dysregulation Spectrum while amplifying opposing proclivities on the other end. Especially in this population, the most common side effects of stimulants for ADHD are irritability, inflexibility, and social withdrawal—that is, magnification of anxiety and autism. The most common side effects of SSRIs for anxiety are disinhibition and overactivation—that is, intensification of ADHD.

When ADHD, autism, and anxiety coexist, there is a greater predisposition to side effects and a narrower therapeutic window. Side effects kick in at relatively low doses. All too often, even if the dose of medication is increased very gradually, side effects appear before benefits.

Suggested Approach

Just because medication management of co-occurring conditions is tricky, that doesn't mean it's impossible. In fact, medication can be a huge help for many. For pharmacological treatment of SCADS of children with coexisting ADHD, autism, and anxiety, here are a few suggestions.

1. *Find a doctor with lots of experience treating these coexisting conditions.* As you can see, this stuff isn't simple. Find a child psychiatrist or developmental-behavioral pediatrician with deep expertise and good communication skills who is reliable and responsive. Unfortunately, just finding the right doc might be the biggest stumbling block of all. The decision to treat—and what to treat—should only be made after a careful and comprehensive assessment. You might end up targeting ADHD, anxiety, or both.

2. *Set up a sufficiently nuanced treatment trial with a team of educated observers.* Target one set of symptoms at a time. Using detailed rating scales, as described in the preceding discussion of ADHD and anxiety, collect baseline and follow-up data. The scales should be explicit regarding the difference between distractible and perseverative types of inattention. Likewise, raters should be clear on the difference between impulsive and inflexible types of behavior. Observers should understand that medication often makes some aspects of attention and behavior better, even while making others worse. Multiple observers—parents, teachers, and therapists—should report task- and setting-specific differences in medication response. (For free medication trial scales, go to the Resources page at ParentChildJourney.com.)

3. *Dose for singles; not home-runs.* As emphasized above, children with coexisting ADHD, autism, and anxiety are notoriously prone to side effects. Start with extremely low doses of medication, and titrate up by small increments, to find a sweet spot where benefits appear before side effects. If there's 25–50 percent improvement in the target symptoms, try tuning up a bit more to see if you can do better. But if higher doses cause side effects, you might decide that partial response is still much better than no medication at all. Home runs are nice. But singles can still score runs and make a big difference.

4. *Don't chase your tail.* Once people understand the idea of balance between under-inhibition and over-inhibition, they might fall into the trap of trying to treat the side effects of one medicine with the other. This usually doesn't work. For each medication, it's better to find the minimum dose that's sufficiently effective or the maximum dose that avoids side effects. Then, decide if that's good enough. For example, if a stimulant helps ADHD but causes more anxious perseveration, don't try to offset these side effects by increasing the SSRI. Rather, decrease the stimulant, try another stimulant, or try a non-stimulant, such as guanfacine, clonidine, or atomoxetine. If an SSRI causes overactivation, don't try to offset these side effects by increasing the stimulant. Instead, decrease the SSRI, try another SSRI, or try a non-SSRI, such as duloxetine or buspirone.

5. *Remember, it's not all about medication.* Although stimulant medication is a mainstay of treatment for ADHD, behavioral therapies should be front and center for anxiety and autism. Moreover, children with ADHD, autism, and anxiety usually have other co-occurring differences. Commonly accompanying problems with learning, language, and sensory-motor function, plus family and other environmental stresses, should always be considered for their effects on self-control and attention. Although medication may be an important part of a comprehensive management plan, it's never the whole answer. For children with ADHD, autism, and anxiety, even the best medication management in the world doesn't take the place of educational, cognitive-behavioral, family, and other non-pharmacological supports.

Where to Start: ADHD or Anxiety?

Whether or not there is autism, when ADHD and anxiety coexist, how do you decide where to start? Consider these three factors:

1. *Genetics.* Some family trees are loaded with one disorder or another. Say there are tons of relatives with ADHD and not much anxiety. Or tons of family members with anxiety—or other mood disorders—but not much ADHD. Such strong family patterns might factor into treatment decisions. However, not all family histories are accurate. Furthermore, biology isn't destiny; environment and circumstance also matter.

And despite its rising popularity, as discussed previously, pharmacogenomic testing isn't yet reliable enough to guide treatment, especially when it comes to choosing treatment targets.

2. *Developmental history.* Better than family history, take a look at the child's own past. If symptoms of one condition—either the anxiety or the ADHD—first made a strong appearance at an earlier age, this could mean that it's more hardwired. However, there are at least three reasons why the first condition up might not be the best first target:

   a. Remember that ADHD and anxiety will present in different ways at different ages. The younger the child, the less specific the symptoms and the harder it is to have diagnostic certainty. For example, irritability in an infant could be an early sign of either the emotional impulsivity of ADHD or the inflexibility of anxiety.

   b. ADHD and anxiety can both present with obvious symptoms or no obvious symptoms at all. ADHD can appear as either glaring hyperactivity and impulsivity or as a more hidden problem with internal distractibility. Likewise, anxiety can cause either very disruptive fight, flight, or freeze reactions, or very private internal distress. Sometimes, anxiety can fly completely under the radar if triggers are avoided altogether.

   c. Lastly, different disorders can blossom at different ages but still have equally deep roots. The old dogma was that ADHD presents young and anxiety tends to present later. Now we know that some people with ADHD don't have signs of impairment until they are older. Some slow-to-warm-up or fussy babies are really just showing their anxious colors early in life. Still other anxiety disorders are more situation- or task-specific but just as impairing and deserving of treatment.

3. *Relative importance.* Despite the importance of considering genetics and development history, clinical assessment of here-and-now impairment is usually more reliable. An effort should be made to see if one condition seems to be causing more impairment. Ask parents, teachers, and the child, "If you could only have one magic wand, would you choose one for ADHD or one for anxiety?"

a. Primary and secondary conditions: Sometimes, there is a consensus. Each observer, without hesitation, might choose the same magic wand. One condition is clearly the primary source of impairment, across settings and people. If so, use that magic wand. Start by treating the primary condition and hope that the secondary condition improves as a result.

b. Coequal conditions: Other times, reports are mixed or uncertain. Different observers might choose different magic wands. Individual observers might say, "The anxiety and the ADHD are both a big deal. I need two magic wands." Here, anxiety and ADHD are more equally at play, truly coexisting. Stirring together genetics, developmental history, and current impairment, you feel compelled to treat both; one isn't more important than the other. In that case, it's generally best to start with medication for ADHD and CBT for anxiety. Then re-evaluate. This approach is supported by research. And, as a practical matter, doing a treatment trial with stimulants is relatively quick and easy. For anxiety, it takes much more time to implement and assess the response to treatment, whether CBT or SSRI. Plus, treatment of ADHD might make it easier for a child to successfully participate in CBT.

Case Study: Jimmy

Remember Jimmy, our eight-year-old boy with coexisting ADHD, autism, and anxiety? After thorough assessment, Dr. Totle explained to Jimmy's parents that there was no medication for autism but they could try treating the ADHD and anxiety. But which to treat first? Both the ADHD and the anxiety were significant problems. Jimmy would certainly benefit from successful treatment of either or both. They hoped that treating one might help with the other. But teachers and parents agreed that the anxiety seemed like the bigger problem. Anyhow, because of Jimmy's very limited social engagement and communication skills, they could not see him effectively participating in CBT. They decided to try medication for anxiety first, then see about the ADHD second.

To monitor benefits and side effects, Jimmy's parents and teachers completed baseline SSRI rating scales off medication, then weekly follow-up ratings as the dose was increased. Dr. Totle explained that, especially for children with autism, he liked to start very low and go very slow. One week of fluoxetine 0.2 mls (0.8 mg of the standard 20 mg per 5 ml concentration) did nothing. Cautiously, they increased the dose. But 0.4 mls (1.6 mg) caused overactivation. Jimmy would not settle to sleep and his ADHD seemed much worse. They stopped the fluoxetine and tried escitalopram, hoping it might be less activating. But the same thing happened. As the dose was increased, again Jimmy seemed to lose self-control. Dr. Totle explained, "With SSRIs, two strikes, you're out. For now, let's stop the anxiety medicine. Apparently, Jimmy is one of those super-sensitive kids. This is a common problem. We shouldn't give up."

Dr. Totle made a course correction: he shifted back to targeting the ADHD. At Jimmy's age, given his complicated profile, Dr. Totle advised against starting with hard-to-split tablets or capsules. He suggested one of the long-acting liquid stimulants (Quillivant XR or Dynavel XR). This would allow them to start with a very small dose and fine-tune incrementally. This time, Jimmy's parents and teachers completed baseline stimulant rating scales off medication, then twice-weekly follow-up scales as the new medication was increased. Each step of the way, Dr. Totle reviewed their scales and notes. He and Jimmy's parents stayed in close touch with regular email, occasional phone calls, and periodic visits.

Here's what happened. The first several days, Quillivant 0.25 mls (1.25 mg of the standard 25 mg per 5 ml concentration) did nothing. Then, through the second half of the week, 0.5 mls (2.5 mg) resulted in 25 percent less distractibility and motor restlessness. When the dose was increased to 0.75 mls (3.75 mg), Jimmy got irritable and more perseverative. They decided that 0.5 mls was his maximum tolerated dose. Twenty-five percent improvement, without side effects, was worth keeping. The 7:30 a.m. dose of Quillivant seemed to wear off at 12:30 PM. Apparently, Jimmy was a rapid metabolizer. So they added a second dose at lunch. This extended Jimmy's duration of coverage through the rest of school, and through his afterschool program too. Given Jimmy's sensitivity to even slightly higher doses of Quillivant, they decided to stay with the 0.5 mls and not try a different stimulant. Instead, they would try layering on guanfacine liquid, a non-stimulant, hoping for better ADHD control without more side effects.

Dr. Totle advised starting with just one dose of guanfacine in the morning. They tracked Jimmy's response with non-stimulant rating scales. Using a 1 mg/1 ml solution prepared by a compounding pharmacist, they moved up every three to five days, from 0.25 mls (0.25 mg), to 0.5 mls, to 0.75 mls. Combined with the Quillivant, the guanfacine 0.75 mg resulted in an additional 25 percent improvement in ADHD symptoms. Could they do even better? Nope. 1.0 mls (1.0 mg) made Jimmy too sleepy and irritable. So, they backed down to 0.75 mls. With these very small doses of stimulant and non-stimulant combined, Jimmy's ADHD was 50 percent better overall. And no side effects. Not bad.

Now for a little more fine-tuning. Just like the Quillivant, the morning dose of guanfacine lasted about five hours. Dr. Totle advised Jimmy's parents to add a second dose with lunch, so that both medications would be taken twice daily. This helped get Jimmy through the day. But the Quillivant and guanfacine both wore off around 7 p.m., and he was too wild for the evening routine. Plus, he started having some rebound waking at 3 a.m. So, they added a third dose of guanfacine at 6:30 p.m., and that worked. His BP decreased from 92/60 before the medication trial to 88/56. But Jimmy was not at all sleepy or dizzy. Dr. Totle monitored carefully. On subsequent visits, the blood pressure remained stable and Jimmy still had no symptoms of hypotension. Next, they tried stopping the Quillivant to see if the guanfacine alone would be good enough. But Jimmy did much better on the combination than either the Quillivant or guanfacine alone. They restarted the Quillivant, liked what they saw, and stayed with the combination.

The ADHD was now under good enough control but Jimmy was still a bundle of nerves. His anxiety was no worse but it was certainly no better. Due to previous overactivation, Dr. Totle was reluctant to try a third SSRI. When SSRIs fail, he explained, different doctors have different strategies. Most of these additional options are not FDA-approved treatment of anxiety in children. Some doctors and parents would reasonably opt to just stop and be satisfied with this degree of partial treatment. But Dr. Totle and Jimmy's parents thought it was important to see if they could help him do better. For older kids, duloxetine might be an option but it was not well studied in children Jimmy's age. Given Jimmy's fight/flight/freeze reactions, they considered trying "the stage-fright medicine," propranolol. But Jimmy also had asthma and propranolol is known to cause some constriction of bronchioles. Besides, duloxetine and propranolol didn't come in a liquid.

Dr. Totle said he'd had good luck with buspirone, which did come in a liquid. Like the guanfacine, buspirone can cause a lowering of blood pressure. They could super-tune the dose, monitor the blood pressure carefully, and hope to get lucky. Starting with a small dose—just 0.5 mg—they titrated up, slowly and carefully. Ultimately, 2.5 mg of buspirone twice daily resulted in in a 50 percent reduction in the frequency, severity, and duration of Jimmy's anxious reactions. He still reported worries and still avoided some situations, but on the buspirone Jimmy was calmer. It took the edge off. He seemed more responsive to redirection and encouragement. Jimmy's blood pressure remained in the normal range. As each dose kicked in, he was just a little drowsy for only 10 minutes. Jimmy's parents didn't want to increase the dose any higher but thought this degree of improvement was worth keeping. Jimmy's teachers agreed that he seemed more relaxed and engaged. He was participating much more consistently in class.

Although his ADHD and anxiety were both under better control, Jimmy's parents didn't like the idea of having their eight-year-old on three different medications. Even so, they were reassured by Dr. Totle's careful monitoring, encouraged by the teacher's positive reports, and convinced that this combination was making a crucial difference at home too. Jimmy was doing better and so was the whole family! Jimmy still had some problems with self-regulation. But, for the first time, he was playing a little with some of the kids in the neighborhood. Dr. Totle was pleased but he reminded Jimmy's parents that medicine was only part of a comprehensive treatment plan. There was more work to do.

Seeking the golden mean doesn't just apply to medication management of coexisting ADHD, anxiety, and autism. Now it's time to apply our understanding of SCADS to cognitive-behavioral therapy.

CBT for SCADS

Non-pharmacological care encompasses a wide range of psycho-social supports: parent behavior management training, family therapy, educational care, and child psychotherapy. Psychosocial supports may include CBT. Remember that medication works well for both ADHD and anxiety but not for autism. CBT works well for anxiety and autism but not for ADHD. In fact, the presence of ADHD can make it harder to do CBT. In this third excursion, I will focus on cognitive-behavioral therapy for when ADHD, anxiety, and autism coexist. At the end of this excursion, I will describe applications of this approach to other conditions. Finally, in the fourth and fifth excursions, we'll further broaden golden mean thinking to include autistic complexities and social-cultural change.

Finding the Golden Mean with CBT

For SCADS of children with coexisting ADHD, anxiety, and autism, golden mean thinking guides CBT just like it does medication management. Finding the middle ground may prove just as difficult in CBT as it is with pharmacotherapy. The therapeutic window is just as narrow, the sweet spot just as small. Even so, the goal with CBT is the same as with medication: that delicate balance between too much inhibition and too little.

With CBT, as with medication, the idea is to moderate excesses and deficiencies. In Excursion 1, I emphasized that CBT by itself isn't an effective treatment for the core symptoms of ADHD. However, CBT combined with medication can be very helpful for some children with ADHD, especially if there's coexisting anxiety or social difficulties. CBT for children with ADHD means teaching them to slow down their thinking but not get too stuck. CBT for children with autism and anxiety means encouraging them to loosen up but not get too scattered. Finding the right balance between "too impulsive" and "too perseverative" may prove just as elusive in cognitive-behavioral therapy as it is with pharmacotherapy. But again, just because it's delicate doesn't mean it's impossible.

There were so many things that Jimmy's parents wished they could discuss with him. He had problems with other kids, diffi-culties getting through daily routines, and a long list of worries.

But every time they tried to talk, he would either shut down, get distracted, or get stuck on some tangential thought.

How to do CBT for SCADS

For a detailed discussion of how to teach problem-solving to children, see the seventh mile of my first book, *Parent Child Journey*. There, I started with one of my favorite quotes, from Rollo May's *The Courage to Create:*

> *Human freedom involves our capacity to pause between the stimulus and response and, in that pause, to choose the one response toward which we wish to throw our weight.*

The pause is what's important. But for children with complicated profiles like Jimmy, effective CBT means pausing just right: not too little and not too much.

I first learned about problem-solving STEPS from Philip Kendall and Lauren Braswell's (1993) *Cognitive-Behavioral Therapy for Impulsive Children,* a CBT manual for ADHD. Different variations on these STEPS are common to all CBT.

- Say what the problem is.
- Think about all possible solutions.
- Examine each possible solution.
- Pick the best solution.
- See how it works.

Hard as it is for all of us to stop and think, children with coexisting ADHD, autism, and anxiety have extra difficulty navigating these STEPS. Some of these children pause too much. Others pause too little. Many bounce back and forth, between these two opposing tendencies, from one end of the Self-Control and Attention Dysregulation Spectrum to the other. Sometimes, children need prodding to move along. Other times, they need to slow down. In teaching these children how to use problem-solving STEPS, cognitive-behavioral therapists might feel like they have to keep moving their modulating foot from accelerator to brake.

Dr. Totle suggested a trial of CBT, to see if Jimmy could learn to use the problem-solving STEPS. First, they would practice the STEPS on some simple and easy problems, like a game of tic-tac-toe. Then, if it looked like Jimmy could handle the basics, they would apply the STEPS to progressively more complicated and challenging problems. Jimmy would need help learning to stop and think, but he would also need help learning not to stop and think too much!

Many children need help finding the golden mean between over-inhibition and under-inhibition, the middle ground between distractibility and perseveration, the right balance between pausing too little and pausing too much. Fortunately, we can use the problem-solving STEPS to teach these children how to pause just right.

CBT for Children with Under-Inhibition (ADHD)

Kendall's manual includes techniques for teaching impulsive kids to *slow* their pace through the problem-solving STEPS and think more carefully. Whether applying STEPS to a simple game or a complicated social dilemma, Kendall instructs therapists to give the child immediate feedback about their tempo and depth of processing.

Here's how it works. At the beginning of each session, children with "inconsistent brakes" receive a set number of tokens—say 10. As they proceed through the STEPS, impulsive children lose a token each time they:

1. Skip a step
2. Go too fast
3. Give a wrong answer

For children who need extra motivation, the remaining tokens can be redeemed for favored items or activities. This immediate feedback teaches impulsive children to slow down and go more carefully.

CBT for Children with Under-Inhibition (ADHD) and Over-Inhibition (Anxiety)

After years of doing Kendall's version of CBT with impulsive children, it occurred to me that we could also use his approach to help children at the other end of the self-control spectrum. Unlike children with ADHD, who tend to move through the STEPS too quickly, I found that children with anxiety and/or autism got stuck and moved through the STEPS too slowly. They often obsessed on one isolated detail and failed to move along. How to help these perseverative children navigate the STEPS more fluently and flexibly? Why not employ Kendall's immediate feedback system with a twist? Just like his strategy for children with ADHD, children with autism and/or anxiety could also start with ten tokens—but they would lose one token for getting stuck on a step or moving too slowly.

Over the years, I made two other modifications to Kendall's immediate feedback rules.

First, I decided not to take away tokens for wrong answers. To me, this feels less like constructive feedback and more like punishment. If a child went through the STEPS carefully but made a mistake, I preferred to just let them learn through natural consequences. This was already covered by the last S in STEPS: "See how it works." After all, the goal of therapy isn't perfect performance. To the contrary, we want to teach frustration tolerance and learning from mistakes.

Second, a major stumbling block for many children during problem-solving is getting too upset. Sometimes, this represents the emotional *impulsivity* of ADHD; other times, this is the emotional *inflexibility* of autism and anxiety; often, it's both. Whatever the underlying factors, many easily frustrated children respond well to explicit instruction regarding emotional self-control. For example, "Remember, stay calm and cool so you can keep your thinking cap on." Children can understand that too much emotional flooding makes it impossible to do effective problem-solving. So, when I took away Kendall's penalty for "choosing the wrong answer," I substituted a new one for getting too upset. This isn't a prohibition against any negative emotion. Rather, it's just a proactive suggestion to exercise sufficient self-control.

And so, for children with mixed profiles who might alternate between impulsive and perseverative tendencies, the STEPS are the same but the rules have been modified. Expanding upon Kendall's immediate feedback system, the child with coexisting ADHD, anxiety, and autism is brought from either extreme of attention dysregulation to a more functional middle ground. Specifically, while working through the CBT problem-solving STEPS, such a child would be given 10 tokens for starters, then instructed, "You lose a token if you ... "

1. Go too fast *or* go too slow
2. Skip a step *or* get stuck on a step
3. Get too upset and don't stay cool

In this way, whether children with opposing tendencies go too fast or too slow, they get immediate feedback about effective pacing, depth of processing, and self-control. Whether they are functioning at one end of the spectrum or the other, the middle is still the middle.

> *Dr. Totle's STEPS approach was relaxed, gentle, and playful. Jimmy looked forward to his choice-time at the beginning and end of each session. During STEPS-time, Jimmy learned to follow the rules. At first, Jimmy and Dr. Totle used the STEPS to play games and solve simple puzzles. Sometimes Jimmy lost a chip for skipping or zooming too quickly through the STEPS. Other times, Jimmy lost a chip for going on and on about a trivial detail or insisting that there was "no way to win!" But Dr. Totle gave Jimmy just enough help to head off too much frustration. Jimmy ended up keeping more chips than he lost. To help Jimmy stay motivated, Dr. Totle and Jimmy's mom agreed that Jimmy could trade chips for extra minutes on the iPad when he got home.*

Just like medication, CBT should be implemented on a trial basis. It's important to set out with realistic expectations. The middle ground with these complicated children can be hard to find, and CBT doesn't always work. As with pharmacotherapy, the therapeutic window is narrower for these kids, the sweet spot smaller, the chance of treatment failure higher. When coached to slow down, they may be more likely to get stuck. When coached to speed up, they are more likely to flit from one thought to another. Despite best efforts, they may not be able to sustain sufficient focus on the problem-solving process. Or they might get too stuck on the STEPS process and not concentrate on the problem itself. Even with the most skillful and sensitive coaching, many of these children will just get too frustrated and shut down. If this approach isn't working, modify it or stop.

Other Applications of Golden Mean and SCADS

So, you see how a functional approach to assessment can move us beyond categories and causes. Finding the golden mean between under-inhibition and over-inhibition provides a useful framework for medication and CBT when ADHD, anxiety, and autism coexist. But the common coexistence of these three conditions is just one of many possible applications.

Other Behavioral Disorders of Over- and Under-Inhibition

Much of childhood behavior management and early human development is about finding the right balance between stop and go. Let's shift gears a bit and consider some standard advice for children with excesses or deficiencies of inhibition in eating, sleeping, toileting, talking, moving, and motivation for school. Whether children start from a point above or below average, the golden mean is the same.

too little >>>>>>>>>> golden mean <<<<<<<<< too much

It doesn't matter if a child needs to move down from "too much" or up from "too little." Traveling in either direction, we target the same zone of moderation. Quite simply, some children need to dial it down, others need to dial it up. Either way, they should end up in roughly the same mid-range.

It's worth emphasizing that we're not talking here about behaviors that are just a bit off center. There's plenty of room on the planet for healthy, normal, and desirable degrees of human variation. Promoting a move to the mean is important only for those who are functioning at the unhealthy, impairing, or distressing extremes. For very dysregulated children, we should not get hung up on defining the exact boundaries between normal and abnormal or healthy and dysfunctional behavior. We just need to shift away from obviously impairing extremes to the sufficiently functional middle. A very rough idea of the golden mean is good enough.

To demonstrate this common theme, here are some examples of golden mean thinking as applied to ordinary pediatric issues:

Golden Mean for Eating

Whether dialing down the child who eats too much or dialing up the child who eats too little, the golden mean is roughly the same. The *broad* middle ground for good eating habits includes set times, set places, three to five meals per day, decent minimum table manners, reasonably balanced diet (see FDA food plate), and roughly one to two child's-fist-size portions of food per meal. Over-eaters and under-eaters should both follow these same guidelines.

Golden Mean for Sleeping

Whether dialing down the child who sleeps too much or dialing up the child who sleeps too little, the golden mean is roughly the same. The *broad* middle ground for good sleep habits includes approximate bedtime and wake-up time. According to the National Sleep Foundation, such times should allow 12–15 hours of sleep for infants, 11–14 hours for toddlers, 10–13 hours for preschoolers, 9–11 hours for school age, 8–10 hours for teens, and 7–9 hours for adults. Remediation means that over-sleepers and under-sleepers should both end up in the same range.

Golden Mean for Toileting

Whether dialing down the child who pees or poops too much or dialing up the child who pees or poops too little, the golden mean is roughly the same. The *broad* middle ground for good bathroom habits involves scheduling by the clock (e.g., urinating every two to four hours), or by daily routines (urinating on waking, morning departure, lunch, mid-afternoon, dinner, bedtime.) A normal range of bowel movements usually means one to two times per day, or according to a schedule, such as after breakfast and/or after dinner. Whether overly retentive or frequent, a healthy degree of moderation is the goal.

Golden Mean for Talking

Whether dialing down the child who talks too much or dialing up the child who talks too little, the golden mean is roughly the same. The *broad* middle ground for socially appropriate talking involves awareness of indoor voice versus outdoor voice. There should be somewhat balanced turn-taking and participation. Any one individual should take the social lead approximately half of the time if talking with one other person, one-third of the time if talking with two others, and one twentieth of the time if participating in a class of 20 students. For both the mute and the loquacious, social expectations point to the same middle ground.

Golden Mean for Physical Activity

Whether dialing down the child who moves too much or dialing up the child who moves too little, the golden mean is roughly the same. The *broad* middle ground for physical activity involves awareness of indoor versus outdoor expectations, at least 30 minutes of cardiovascular exercise per day but no more than compromises health or interferes with other activities of daily living. Both the couch jumper and the couch potato should modulate their motor activity level in each other's direction.

Golden Mean for Doing Homework

Whether dialing down the child who does homework too much or dialing up the child who does homework too little, the golden mean is roughly the same. The *broad* middle ground for homework should be roughly 5–10 minutes of homework per grade per day. That means 5–10 minutes per day for a first-grader, 10–20 minutes per day for a second-grader, 30–60 minutes per day for a sixth-grader, and 50–100 minutes per day for a tenth-grader. With moderation, the under-worker and the over-worker should end up putting in more similar amounts of time.

Regulating Up and Down

Popular mood and behavior self-monitoring tools, such as "zones of regulation" and "How's your motor running?" might lead parents to believe that children need only down-regulate. But, of course, opposing tendencies often exist in the same individual across situations. The same child might have to crank it up sometimes and turn it down other times. Individual health usually correlates with homeostasis, balance, and equilibrium. Consider the adolescent who overeats between meals but undereats at the kitchen table. Or the child who talks too much at home but too little at school. The golden mean exists between both of these extremes.

Keeping It Positive

This golden mean framework emphasizes positive messaging *toward* the middle ground, not negative messaging *away* from extremes. By defining the middle ground, we can shift the emphasis from deficiencies to goals. Then the focus is off failure and on success. A healthy self-image and improved adult-child relations are important fringe benefits of golden mean thinking.

The Existence of Twilight

In all of these examples, there's a broad range of normal. Although it may be difficult to say where normal ends and abnormal begins, we should have no problem recognizing *extreme* excesses or *extreme* deficiencies. As Samuel Johnson might say, "The existence of twilight doesn't obscure the difference between night and day." We just want to move away from *obviously* dysfunctional extremes toward an *obviously* healthier middle ground. A case for treating impairment and distress at the extremes of inhibitory control isn't an argument for uniformity, conformity, or artificial norms. As Daedalus might have counseled Icarus, "There's plenty of room to fly between the sea and the sun."

Mountain STEPS: Combining Parallel Exposure Therapy and Golden Mean Thinking

When we combine the golden mean thinking of Excursion 3 with the Parallel Exposure Therapy of Excursion 2, we can address any number of problems.

> *Gradually, Dr. Totle and Jimmy shifted from simple games to simple problems. Deliberately, Dr. Totle had Jimmy learn the STEPS on problems that were not too complicated, personal, or emotionally loaded. They started with simple children's books. Jimmy liked Thomas the Train. In one of Jimmy's favorite stories, Thomas and another train got into a spat. Using his STEPS to generate possible solutions for Thomas, Jimmy came up with a good conflict-resolution plan. During this process, Dr. Totle removed a chip if Jimmy did the STEPS too fast or too slow. Jimmy was getting the hang of proper depth and pacing—and he was becoming a good problem-solver. Then Dr. Totle and Jimmy used the STEPS to problem-solve a few other fictional problems. At the end of table-time, Dr. Totle gave Jimmy his leftover chips.*
>
> *Sometimes, Jimmy's parents sat in on sessions with Dr. Totle so that they could learn the STEPS too. It wasn't long before they found themselves using the STEPS for problem-solving at home—with Jimmy, his siblings, and even for their own adult problems. Jimmy's mom showed the STEPS to Jimmy's teacher too. The teacher liked the STEPS so much that she ended up using them to do group problem-solving with her whole class.*

Once your child has learned the STEPS and demonstrated an ability to solve simple problems, it's time to tackle some more complicated real-life problems. Parents, children, and teachers should start by listing the most common problem situations. Problems might be related to poor impulse control, anxiety, social difficulties, school challenges, or ordinary parent-child issues. Anything can go on the problem list.

To varying degrees, many of Jimmy's problems were related to some combination of anxiety, ADHD, and autism. Other problems were just ordinary issues that any child could have. Some problems were Jimmy's alone. Other problems involved different combinations of other people. Thinking about Jimmy's typical day, from morning until night, Jimmy, his parents, and his teacher came up with the following problem list.

- *Getting ready in the morning*
- *Sitting for morning meeting at school*
- *Doing math assignments in class*
- *Not interacting with other kids at school, especially during lunch and recess*
- *Fighting with his brother and sister about what to watch on TV*
- *Disagreements with Mom about video game restrictions*
- *Doing homework*
- *Trying new activities outside the house*
- *Sitting at the dinner table*
- *Going to bed on time*

After creating a problem list, rate each problem situation according to difficulty and importance. Different people are involved with different problems. For each problem, consider getting ratings from all of the important players. Arrange the problem situations in order, from easiest to hardest. You, your child, and anyone else in the system may want to start with the easiest problems first. Or everyone might be motivated to tackle a harder problem because of its importance.

Considering everyone's ratings, Dr. Totle, Jimmy, and his mom decided to start with sibling disagreements about TV choices. Although it wasn't the biggest problem on the list, TV conflicts were a regular source of turmoil for the whole family. Jimmy and his sibs, Amy and Luke, each wanted to watch their own show. These daily disagreements usually escalated from yelling to punching and kicking; their parents had to intervene. It usually ended with nobody watching TV and everybody being angry. Compared to other problems on the list, everyone gave these TV conflicts a medium rating for difficulty and a relatively high rating for importance. Everyone was motivated to consider a change from the status quo.

For each problem on the list, adults and children should work together. Anybody who is central to the problem should participate in defining the problem, brainstorming possible solutions, then choosing, implementing, and reevaluating.

Jimmy's parents called a family meeting to solve the TV show problem. Using STEPS and poker chips, they brainstormed a list of possible solutions. Everybody contributed their ideas. Then, everybody in the family system ranked each possible solution.
   0 = stinky
   1 = bad
   2 = okay
   3 = good
   4 = very good
   5 = excellent

How Can Kids Decide What to Watch on TV?

	Jimmy	Amy	Luke	Mom	Dad
Keep having arguments	1	0	0	0	0
Draw straws	0	4	2	3	4
Kids take turns choosing	2	3	2	4	4
Buy more TVs	5	5	5	0	0
Parents choose	3	3	0	2	2
Random draw of approved shows from a hat	0	1	0	3	3
No TV at all	0	0	0	3	5

The goal was to find a solution that everybody would be okay with. They agreed to put a red line through any of the possible solutions that got a 0 or a 1. They would put a yellow line through any of the possible solutions that got a 2 but not a 0 or a 1. They put a green line through possible solutions that got all 3s or higher. As it turned out, "take turns" was the only solution that didn't get a red line. What if someone choses a show that the others hated? They used the STEPS to come up with a list of mutually acceptable shows. How would they keep track of turns? They used the STEPS again and came up with a "Whose turn is it?" chart.

Choosing a solution is usually easier than implementing it. Things are easier said than done.

Dr. Totle wanted to help the family avoid conflict. But he also wanted the kids to learn to solve problems for themselves. At first, some parent support would be necessary. Gradually, with practice, the parent support could be faded out. Dr. Totle helped them draw a mountain trail map.

- *Summit. Kids take care of choosing and watching entirely on their own.*
- *Fifth marker. Parent pops in and out of the room.*
- *Fourth marker. Parent just stays in room to watch kids use the chart, turn on, and watch the show on their own.*
- *Third marker. Parent actively coaches and supervises use of "Whose turn is it?" chart, then leaves for kids to turn on show and watch on their own.*
- *Second marker. Parent actively coaches and supervises use of "Whose turn is it?" chart, then leaves after show is on for kids to watch on their own.*
- *First marker. Parent actively coaches and supervises use of "Whose turn is it?" chart, and stays during TV show to ensure compliance.*
- *Starting point. Kids fight about TV shows.*

The kids were excited when their parents suggested a reward. "Each time you take turns choosing and watch a TV show without any fighting, everybody wins a bonus show that day. And each week that you go without any fighting, you get a bigger bonus for that week."

Dr. Totle was pleased. Once they were making progress with the TV show plan, they would move to another problem on the list, including school issues.

Dr. Totle knew that Jimmy's parents were very concerned about his lack of friends. On the playground and in the lunchroom, he just kept to himself. Helping Jimmy connect with some other kids would require help from Jimmy's teacher and others at the school. Not everyone at school really understood autism. The school wasn't really staffed to help Jimmy at recess. And other kids just didn't seem interested in playing with Jimmy. He was different. Although very helpful, medicine and family problem-solving only went so far. Dr. Totle and Jimmy's parents knew that this would be a taller mountain to climb.

Other Neuropsychiatric and Developmental Disorders of Over- and Under-Inhibition

If we employ principles of functional assessment, many neuropsychiatric and developmental disorders can be reclassified as disorders of over- and under-inhibition. Let's list, then analyze how the following disorders might be represented on the Self-Control and Attention Dysregulation Spectrum.

	Over-Inhibition	Under-Inhibition
Mood disorder	depression	mania
DMDD/irritability	inflexibility	impulsivity
Anxiety	freeze	fight/flight
Thought disorder	OCD, autistic repetition, ritual	psychosis
Inattention	Sluggish Cognitive Tempo	ADHD
Social disability	"Classic" autism	Williams Syndrome

Mood Disorders

Disorders of mood regulation can cause over-inhibition, under-inhibition, or both. The most obvious example is bipolar illness. Afflicted individuals cycle between the paralyzing over-inhibition of depression and the dangerous under-inhibition of mania. Likewise, the severe irritability of Disruptive Mood Dysregulation Disorder can be the result of either difficulty shifting (over-inhibition) or emotional impulsivity (under-inhibition). Likewise, anxiety can present as freeze (over-inhibition) or fight/flight (under-inhibition). Obsessions and compulsions can be driven by the dysphoria of anxiety (over-inhibition) or the enthusiasm for special interests of autism (under-inhibition).

Attention Disorders

Inattention can be secondary to over-inhibition, not just the under-inhibition of ADHD. As already discussed, on the over-inhibited end of the spectrum, there can be inattention from anxiety and/or autism. For these individuals, inattention is associated with trouble shifting, perseveration on one thing to the exclusion of others, and emotional inflexibility. We all have limited mental energy. Emotional distress uses up brain fuel that is necessary for initiating, shifting, or otherwise directing focus.

In addition, and also distinct from ADHD, there is something called Sluggish Cognitive Tempo or Concentration Deficit Disorder (Barkley, 2013). Wisely, Barkley recommends using the latter, less pejorative term. Children with this more recently recognized type of attention disorder are low-energy and daydreamy, not at all impulsive or hyperactive. Furthermore, the whole range of learning disabilities could be reclassified as executive function disorders of over- or under-inhibition. For example, reading disability can be seen not just as a skill deficit but also as a disorder of pacing. In other words, some children have difficulty decoding because they pace too slowly, others too quickly (Wolf & Bowers, 1999).

Social Disability

Social disability can stem from either over-inhibition or disinhibition. The first descriptions of "classic autism" were published in the mid-1940s by Dr. Leo Kanner, a pioneering child psychiatrist at Johns Hopkins University. He suggested that these children were disengaged because they were too bottled up. Since then, we know that autism presents in many different ways. Sometimes, the social disability is much more the result of disinhibition rather than excessive restraint. The most obvious example of disinhibited autism is Williams Syndrome. Aside from their extraordinary musical sensibility, these individuals have very severe ADHD. They are unexpectedly friendly, talkative, and gregarious. For example, they sprint up to—and exuberantly hug—complete strangers.

SCADS of Other Ideas

In example after example, across ordinary behaviors and diagnostic categories, hopefully you now see how brain brakes may be applied too quickly or released too easily. Competing nerve networks inhibit and excite. Individuals stop and go. The Self-Control and Attention Dysregulation Spectrum represents one of many different ways to move past arbitrary diagnostic categories to a more functional description of human behavior.

More broadly, the over-inhibited brain can be viewed as too captive. Over-inhibition is about confinement, repetition, and rumination. In out-of-date Freudian terms, the ego is overactive. The individual follows the same script over and over. Nerves that fire together become too tightly wired together.

Conversely, the under-inhibited brain is too free. Under-inhibition is about plasticity, entropy, even psychosis. In some manifestations, the ego is dissolved. Things fall apart. The center doesn't hold. This mindset is the stuff of mysticism, spirituality, meditation, and psychedelics (Pollan, 2019). LSD and mushrooms can be thought of as disordering agents, the ultimate disinhibitors. There is liberation from overly rigid cognitive habits and expansion of consciousness. But what is left of the self wanders aimlessly through a virgin forest, every step representing a new path.

Beyond SCADS

The Self-Control and Attention Dysregulation Spectrum (SCADS) is just one of many different ways to look at developmental and behavioral variation. The spectrum from under-inhibition to over-inhibition represents just one domain for functional assessment.

Human variation and developmental disorder can be described in many other ways. Mel Levine (1993) employed a functional approach to educational assessment, in domains including language functions, motor functions, attention, visual-spatial functions, etc. Chess and Thomas (1990) were the first to systematically study function in terms of temperament over time. Their temperament domains include: attention, motor activity level, initial reaction, intensity of reaction, adaptability, sensory profile, and mood. Under the direction of Tom Insell, the NIMH (2019) has promoted Research Domain Criteria (RDoC). RDoC constructs include negative valence (e.g. threat, loss), positive valence (e.g. reward), cognitive systems (e.g. attention, perception, memory, language), social processes (e.g. facial and non-facial communication), and arousal and regulatory systems. From the NIMH website:

> RDoC is a research framework for new approaches to investigating mental disorders. It integrates many levels of information

(from genomics and circuits to behavior and self-reports) in order to explore basic dimensions of functioning that span the full range of human behavior from normal to abnormal. RDoC isn't meant to serve as a diagnostic guide, nor is it intended to replace current diagnostic systems. The goal is to understand the nature of mental health and illness in terms of varying degrees of dysfunctions in general psychological/biological systems (NIMH, 2019).

My own Gander (Shapiro, 2016) is another such attempt at comprehensive functional assessment. Each of these transdiagnostic approaches has its strengths and weaknesses.

I have chosen to explore inhibitory control in this book because it's so basic to behavior and cuts across so many common diagnostic categories—especially ADHD, anxiety, and autism. But in doing so, I don't want to imply that SCADS is the only way to think about assessment and management. Golden mean thinking can be applied to a wide range of conflicting tendencies—not just the inconsistent inhibitory controls of the three conditions featured in this book.

Trail-End for Excursion 3

In this discussion of coexisting conditions, I emphasized that conventional diagnostic categories are of limited use in guiding effective treatment. Meaningful understanding and individualized care require a much more nuanced approach, especially for the many children who have more than one diagnosis. In the next excursion—Excursion 4, on autism and social development—we'll again explore the importance of moving beyond diagnostic categories to a more functional style of assessment and management. But we'll take a different approach to functional assessment, viewing developmental difference not in terms of inhibitory control but from the perspective of development in another domain—social skill.

EXCURSION 4
Change—Social Engineering for Autism

———— ◆ ————

Thus, it can be seen that mental health is based on a certain degree of tension, the tension between what one has already achieved and what one still ought to accomplish, or the gap between what one is and what one should become. Such a tension is inherent in the human being and therefore is indispensable to mental well-being. We should not, then, be hesitant about challenging man with a potential meaning for him to fulfill. It's only thus that we evoke his will to meaning from its state of latency. I consider it a dangerous misconception of mental hygiene to assume that what man needs in the first place is equilibrium or, as it's called in biology, "homeostasis," i.e. a tensionless state. What man actually needs isn't a tensionless state but rather the striving and struggling.
—Viktor Frankl, *Man's Search for Meaning*

Grieve if you must, for your own lost dreams. But don't mourn for us. We are alive. We are real. And we're here waiting for you. ... The tragedy isn't that we're here, but that your world has no place for us to be.
—Jim Sinclair, *Don't Mourn for Us*

Dog ran ahead and got to the mountain first. Raph rode his unicycle and got there second. Finally, even Turtle crawled his way there. They were all thrilled to have finished the trail. But after such a long journey, there were still no Tambalacoque trees. How to get over the mountain? It was too steep and too high. Raph's hungry tummy rumbled.

At first, Raph felt sad. Then, Raph's sadness became anger, and, much to his surprise, his anger turned into rage! They had come so far. Now this! Raph exploded, screaming furiously at Dog and Turtle and anybody else who could hear: "Who put this mountain here anyhow? I need my Tambalacoque!" With each anguished screech, Raph smashed his beak into the mountain. Again and again, he cried out and chiseled away.

Turtle pleaded, "What are you doing? You're going to break your beak!"

Raph shrieked at Turtle, "If we can't get over this mountain, we'll have to dig right through it!"

Dog agreed, "Ruff!" and started pawing away at the mountain.

Turtle thought for a second, then put out his forelegs and started burrowing away at the mountain too.

Raph thought, I didn't know turtles could dig. The three friends dug together.

Signposts for Excursion 4

This Excursion is an exploration of comprehensive care for individuals with autism and other social disabilities, including:

- A brief review of autism, coexisting conditions, and other differences in social development.
- A brief review of child-centered therapies for autism.
- A detailed discussion of functional assessment and individualized accommodations for children with a range of differences in social development.
- A general discussion of social engineering for social disability.

Here, we move beyond changing the child with autism, to changing the world in which all children live.

In Excursion 3, considering ADHD, anxiety, and autism, we explored just one type of functional assessment. At the levels of neurophysiology and behavioral style, we described a range of issues in terms of under-inhibition and over-inhibition. I called this one type of functional assessment the Self-Control and Attention Dysregulation Spectrum, or SCADS. In Excursion 4, we'll be using a different type of functional assessment. Here, at the level of life skill acquisition, we'll describe social development. Just as SCADS provided specific guidance regarding medication and cognitive-behavioral therapy, this description of social development will guide an individualized approach to social success. Most of Excursion 4 will be devoted to this alternative approach, called social engineering.

Why social engineering? Those of us who spend our lives in

the world of developmental difference know the limits of individual therapy. Even when available, the most expert medical, psychological, and family supports don't address significant barriers presented by schools, insurance companies, governments, and society at large. Despite extraordinary progress, there are still "miles to go before we sleep." In this fourth excursion, I will focus on social disability, with autism serving as an archetype. Throughout the discussion, the emphasis will be on striking a balance between intervention and accommodation, "preparing the child for the road" *and* "preparing the road for the child."

Language Matters: "Diversity" and "Disability"

Before we go on, a word about terminology. Throughout this book, at the risk of unintentionally offending some, I have deliberately used the language of diversity *and* the language of disability. Understandably, many people in the neurodiversity rights community object to the term "disability" as a pejorative social construct. As explained by my friend and colleague Dr. Tom Holman:

> Just like white privilege, male privilege, and heterosexual privilege, there is neurotypical privilege as well. People with privilege "know," from early on, that they are "normal" and others are "aberrant." They are so "normal" that they don't even notice their own privilege. Likewise, neurotypical people "know" they are "normal." They have normal brains, normal lives, and normal relationships. Naturally, everybody without this neurotypical privilege is considered "disabled."

In a wonderful children's book, *Why Johnny Doesn't Flap: NT Is OK!*, the hero is a boy with autism who is trying to understand the weird behavior of his neurotypical friend, Johnny (Morton & Morton, 2015). The boy with autism concludes that Johnny is "too obsessed with social relationships" and is therefore missing out on many of the things that make life worthwhile.

I believe that this is a valuable perspective. I use the language of diversity because not all human variation causes impairment. All too often, when difference is associated with difficulty, it's the culture that's disabling, not the developmental variation per se. When it comes to accepting differences in others, maybe it's the people without autism who need flexibility training. Typically developing individuals need to be more open and accepting of atypical people. No one should have to be "less different" just to conform with cultural norms and expectations. After all, we all have strengths and weaknesses that require varying degrees of accommodation or intervention.

So why use the language of disability at all? Because some conditions are truly disabling, according to the people who have these conditions. A person having a grand mal seizure doesn't need a broader sense of success in life—they need an anticonvulsant. Same goes for certain other developmental disorders. Suffering and success deprivation are not all about cultural bias. Even with optimal social acceptance and support, there can be pain and deprivation. Even in a community that nurtures and celebrates diversity, there can be increased challenges and failures that negatively impact individuals' everyday function and long-term health. It's the language of disability—not difference—that guarantees a right to special education and freedom from job discrimination. The language of disability provides social security and health insurance. The language of disability drives scientific research and evidence-based interventions.

The language of diversity prepares the road for the child. The language of disability prepares the child for the road. One can—and should—speak of both.

Autism: A Critical Overview

As mentioned in Excursion 3, DSM5 defines autism as: "clinically significant, persistent deficits in social communication and interactions," plus "restricted, repetitive patterns of behavior, interests, and activities." Here, we'll move beyond this definition, because autism is much more complicated than that. In addition to these core deficits, people with autism always have a broad range of other developmental and behavioral differences (Soke, Maenner, Christensen, Kurzius-Spencer, & Schieve, 2018). In my view, the complexity of coexisting conditions, both weaknesses and strengths, renders people with autism (at least) as wonderfully different from one another as neurotypicals are. Autism presents diversity on top of diversity. Truly, if you understand autism, you understand the whole range of human development and behavior.

The Case for Functional Assessment

As discussed in Excursion 3, there are three levels of assessment: categorical, etiologic, and functional. Here, with autism in mind, let me review the case for functional assessment.

The Limitations of Categorical Diagnosis in Autism

Making a categorical diagnosis of autism is important in many ways. First, it may be necessary to obtain special education, public funds, and health insurance reimbursement for an important range of services. Second, a categorical diagnosis of autism suggests a helpful menu of accommodations and interventions. Third, it may enhance the understanding of developmental difference. Fourth, a diagnosis of autism can bring people together for mutual support, social activism, and clinical research. Despite these useful purposes—and as we'll discuss throughout this excursion—just saying that someone has autism doesn't determine the specific types of interventions and supports needed for any given individual. Although categorical diagnosis describes some important common features, it doesn't capture the uniqueness of the individual or their life circumstances.

The Limitations of Etiologic Diagnosis in Autism

The same limitations hold true for etiologic diagnosis. It has become standard practice to do genetic testing for anyone with a diagnosis of autism. An etiologic diagnosis is crucial in such conditions as Tuberous Sclerosis, phenylketonuria, and other rare conditions. However, for the overwhelming majority of people with autism, a specific genetic or other etiologic diagnosis isn't found. Furthermore, even when an etiologic diagnosis can be made, it doesn't guide individualized management. Ironically, these days, genetic diagnosis is held up as the gateway to "personalized care." Unfortunately, undue focus on specific causes can lead well-meaning clinicians to depersonalize care and treat very different children as if they are all alike.

Last but not least, identification of specific causes of autism raises complicated issues about the ethics of prevention and treatment. Subsequently, people who search for cures ignore the compelling cases for neurodiversity, inclusion, and individual rights. Much more on this to follow.

The Inner Life of the Person with Autism

Individuals with autism are not just defined by behavior check-lists or lab results. They have inner lives too. Despite our modern emphasis on biology and behavior, it's crucial to understand each child's experience of life; the meaning they attach to people, activities, events, and places; their personal life story. In this book, unfortunately, I will not do justice to these important considerations. I trust readers to remember: underneath all the diagnostics and therapeutics, there is a person.

The Case for Functional Assessment in Autism

Children who may share the same categorical and etiologic diagnoses are, in fact, more different from one another than they are alike. This should be obvious. But all too often, when we focus on categories and causes, we fail to see people with autism and other developmental differences as unique individuals. For truly personalized care, we must turn to functional assessment. Through detailed description of behavioral style, sensory profile, skills, and environmental factors, we move beyond boxes and labels to a deeper understanding of the unique human being. It's this type of assessment that truly guides care.

Autism and Co-Existing Conditions

There's much more to people with autism than just their autism. Beyond the categorical diagnosis—in addition to core problems with social interaction and repetitive, ritualized, restricted tendencies—commonly co-occurring conditions include the following:

- Broad range of temperaments and behavioral styles
- Special interests, enthusiasms, and perspectives with strengths and talents that are idiosyncratic, distinctive, eccentric, or very self-directed
- Complicated disorders of attention and executive functions, including ADHD, Sluggish Cognitive Tempo; problems with initiating, sustaining, inhibiting, shifting, planning, organizing; deficits in time awareness
- Language-based learning disabilities, verbal and nonverbal, including problems with oral motor function, phonology, semantics, vocabulary, syntax, language comprehension and expression, pragmatics, inferencing, context-reading, and more

- Full range of intellectual abilities, ranging from profoundly gifted to profoundly disabled, and everything in between; often including scattering of skills, from relatively high to low, across different domains of cognition
- Mood disorders, including various anxiety disorders, obsessive-compulsive disorder, depression, bipolar illness, and severe emotional dysregulation
- Thought disorders, including schizophrenia
- Uneven sensory profiles, including both hypersensitivities and hypo-sensitivities
- Motor disorders: fine, writing, oral, and gross motor disorders
- Movement disorders; chronic tics, Tourette Syndrome, stereotypies
- Disorders of sleep, eating, bowel, and bladder function
- Psychosexual and gender identity differences

Traveling along with autism, these associated features appear in any number of combinations, modes of expression, and degrees of severity. And all of this complexity changes over time. Associated conditions wax and wane, come and go. Even the core deficits of autism can harden or soften. Challenges can morph depending on the demands of the child's environment. The level of necessary support changes; the ability to provide that support might change as well. To varying degrees, some people become more impaired and marginalized. Others "grow off the spectrum" or learn to compensate for their autism and succeed in a mainstream environment.

Autism in the Context of Larger Systems

Adding to this complexity, there's more to the autism than just the individual. Children and adults with autism live within different social systems. Think about the variety of families, schools, neighborhoods, religious communities, developmental and medical services, governments, and countries within which individuals with autism find themselves. Some children with autism go to specialized, self-contained classrooms. Others are in general education, without any individualized support at all. Some families may be able to adapt and support. Others may struggle to muster the necessary financial and emotional resources.

Any of these milieus and circumstances can be a source of

neglect or nurturance, abuse or support, impairment or resilience. Teaching and modeling can be negative or positive. Cultures can be in conflict or harmony, disabling or empowering, stigmatizing or inspiring. These systems too evolve in spurts and sputters; stagnating, progressing, and regressing; exerting an ever-changing and powerful influence on the individual with autism, even as the individual with autism has an impact on his or her world.

General Principles of Care for People with Autism

Care for individuals with autism must account for this diversity and complexity.

For example, the National Research Council (2001) suggests that a management plan should be designed "To improve the overall functional status of the child by promoting the development of communication, social, adaptive, behavioral, and academic skills; lessening maladaptive and repetitive behaviors; and helping the family manage the stress associated with raising a child with autism." Quite a broad and comprehensive mandate.

Similarly, the American Academy of Pediatrics espouses the following general principles of care for children with autism (Myers & Johnson, 2007):

- Begin *early*
- Continue across the *lifespan*
- Ensure sufficient *intensity*
- Provide sufficient *structure*
- *Individualize* the plan based on functional assessment
- Remediate *and* accommodate
- Address weaknesses *and* strengths
- Be *comprehensive* and address all aspects of development
- Use a multi-disciplinary *team* with a case manager to set goals, choose strategies, and coordinate efforts across all settings
- *Empower* the child and the family
- Promote *inclusion* and mainstreaming
- *Generalize* learning across real-life settings and *maintain* learned skills over time
- *Measure* baseline and *monitor* progress toward goals
- *Modify* the plan if there is insufficient progress

Of course, general principles don't provide families, clinicians, and educators with sufficiently specific and individualized guidance.

A Shift in Language

Within the above guidelines for helping children with autism, there are two points worth highlighting:

1. We should move beyond the category of autism to focus on the individual.
2. We should *also* move beyond the individual with autism to focus on the world within which they live.

Although most people agree with these two general principles, they are too often missing in practice. Therefore, this excursion covers individualized child therapy *and* social engineering. Accordingly, as we move ahead together, you will notice a shift from the language of categorical diagnosis (autism as a group) to the language of functional assessment (social development in individuals).

Categorical Quackery

Many treatments for autism are promoted as if they help everyone with this diagnosis. These categorical recommendations not only fail to treat people with autism as unique individuals—despite their popularity, they have no scientific basis whatsoever. American Academy of Pediatrics and National Standards Project publications help separate wishful thinking from science, magical fantasizing from honest research, and quackery from solid evidence (Maglione, Gans, Das, Timbie, & Kasari, 2012; National Autism Center, 2015). Paul Offit wrote a brave book on the history of misguided and unethical interventions. He called it *Autism's False Prophets*. But, given the financial incentives and conflicts of interests, a history of autism could just as well have been titled *Autism's False Profits*. Treatments without a strong evidence base might seem promising, but innocent families are well-advised to exercise a high degree of skepticism and self-inhibition, and to seek guidance from trusted experts.

Non-Standard Interventions Without Evidence of Effectiveness

Time, money, and energy are all in limited supply. Finite resources should not be wasted. Besides lack of effectiveness, many interventions that are marketed to families with autism may be harmful. Recommendation of any of the following "therapies" (to name just a few) should cause parents to at least tap— better yet, slam—the brakes:

- Nutritional "cures," including both supplements and elimination diets
- Immunoglobulin therapy
- Secretin
- Chelation therapy
- Auditory integration training
- Developmental optometric training
- Interactive metronome
- Facilitated communication
- Chiropractic or craniosacral manipulation
- Acupuncture
- Hyperbaric oxygen

People want a quick fix. Anecdotal success may seem compelling. Parents may be drawn to promising new treatments despite limited data. Evidence-based treatments might seem expensive, complicated, and daunting. Experts are often unavailable. Parents get conflicting advice. Who to believe?

Hesitation and doubt are understandable. Most families will need expert advice to see through the confusing swirl of false promises.

Evidence-Based Interventions for Autism

In sharp contrast to the non-standard interventions described above, there are many ways of "preparing the child for the road" that have a solid base of evidence for safety and effectiveness (National Autism Center, 2015). The following evidence-based interventions should be considered standard. Careful selection from the menu of interventions can make a huge difference in long-term outcome. Over the course of my career, decade by decade, the range of effective services for individuals with autism has steadily improved. So has the prognosis. Even so, as you read through this menu of treatment options, ask yourself the following questions:

- How do I know which of these interventions is most important?
- What will this look like for my child?

Autism Education, Training, and Support

All families should receive education about autism. Training and support should of course include the individual with autism but also parents, siblings, extended family, care providers, friends, classmates, and teachers. The type of coaching and counseling should be customized according to each family's needs. The range of potential issues is broad. Discussion should begin with understanding autism and associated conditions. Other topics should include disclosure of the diagnosis, genetic counseling, family planning, coping, long-term relationships, and more. Family members should be referred as needed for psychotherapy, psychopharmacology, and support groups.

Speech-Language Therapy

Speech-language therapy is a top priority for many children with autism. There's nothing more important than ensuring a functional system of communication. For nonverbal children, direct speech-language therapy can be supplemented by augmentative and alternative communication systems, such as visual schedules, "if-then" boards, Picture Exchange Communication System (PECS), sign language, electronic speech-generating devices, communication apps, and other video/computer-based learning technology. For verbal children, the emphasis shifts from the acquisition of language to literacy skills and social pragmatic language—that is, the functional use of language in back-and-forth interpersonal communication.

Behavioral Therapies

Behavioral therapies should be customized to address skill deficits, promote adaptive behavior, and teach self-care. Based upon the work of Watson and Skinner, applied behavior analysis (ABA) isn't one specific technique. Rather, ABA is a fully developed science of behavior, a set of evidence-based principles, that can be applied comprehensively, across all aspects of development. ABA answers the question: What is it about a specific *situation* (antecedent) and the *response* (consequence) that explains the behavior? How do the child's profile and the environmental circumstances explain the behavior? Does the behavior allow the child to get: attention or reaction, a desired object or activity, or sensory stimulation? Does the behavior allow the child to avoid: pain, discomfort, or difficulty?

A behavior management plan modifies the antecedent situation, to close the gap between expectations and abilities. Consequences are modified, to reinforce desired behaviors and extinguish maladaptive ones. Many people have outdated views of ABA. Modern applied behavior analysis employs these principles across all settings, tasks, and people. These days, the focus is on "natural environment teaching," not artificial "discrete trial" tabletop tasks.

School-Based Educational Care

School-based educational care is another cornerstone of support for individuals with autism. According to federal law, every child in the United States is guaranteed free and equal public education (FAPE) in the least restrictive environment (LRE).

An individual education program (IEP) is based upon comprehensive assessment of the child's functional levels. Assessment and programming are not just for academic skills; the IEP should address any developmental differences that significantly interfere with availability for learning. This includes—but isn't limited to—communication, social, emotional, motor, and adaptive life skills. IEP accommodations and interventions should ensure access to education, but in the least restrictive (most mainstream) environment. For children under the age of three years, these services are delivered by the state early intervention system. Over three years of age, services are provided through the local public-school system. Of course, families can opt out of the public education system and pursue private education or home-schooling. But the same principles of special education should still apply. A complete discussion of the IEP process and the rights of children in special education is beyond the scope of this book, but other excellent resources are available (Weinfeld & Davis, 2008).

Psychosocial-Emotional Therapies

Psychosocial-emotional therapies include a broad range of interventions. Often, children with autism require specialized opportunities for social and emotional development. This usually means more-structured activities with more explicit teaching, coaching, and facilitation. The level of support depends upon the child's needs in different situations. Goals should address: shared

275

engagement, reciprocity, context-reading, play skills, self-awareness, and self-regulation. Carefully selected social-emotional interventions can take place in natural environments, interaction groups, or in one-on-one psychotherapy. Children can learn social skills from play, books, and interactive technology. Social stories, cartoon conversations, and social scripts can be used to model appropriate social interaction for different situations. Children learn about social reciprocity from animals, adults and—whenever possible—other children. The family and the classroom are usually the best social learning environments of all.

Occupational and Physical Therapies

Occupational and physical therapies are often helpful for motor development and specific adaptive skills, including eating, toileting, dressing, writing, and keyboarding—and for developing social interaction, executive, and technical skills. OTs and PTs are also expert in sensory processing differences: hyper- (over) or hypo- (under) sensitivities that can affect mood, behavior, and availability for learning. These specialized therapists often have creative ways to help with behavior and teach self-regulation.

Medication

Medication doesn't treat the core symptoms of autism. At the time of this book's publication, despite ongoing research, there is no drug that directly treats social disability or repetitive, ritualized patterns of thinking or behavior. Even so, medication can make a dramatic difference (McCracken et al., 2016). By treating associated conditions, medication can improve availability for learning and socializing. Psychopharmacology can help relieve distress by alleviating symptoms that have a significant impact on a child's success and quality of life. Consequently, about 25–60 percent of children with autism take medication. The percentage increases with age. Potential targets and medications include the following (McPheeters et al., 2011):

- ADHD (stimulants, nonstimulants)
- Anxiety (SSRIs, buspirone, propranolol)
- Depression (SSRIs)
- Mood instability, irritability, aggression, self-injury (neuroleptics, mood stabilizers)
- Sleep problems (melatonin, clonidine, mirtazapine, trazodone)

- Seizures (anticonvulsants)
- Specific medical conditions, such as allergy, GE reflux, constipation, etc. (histamine antagonists, proton pump inhibitors, laxatives, etc.)

Transition Planning

Transition planning is now recognized as a crucial component of care for teens and young adults. Discussion of life beyond high school should begin years in advance. This includes coaching in disclosure of the diagnosis and self-advocacy, self-care, and other adult life skills, as well as sex education, higher education, vocational training, career planning, and on-the-job mentoring. Life-span planning should include the whole family. Some of the most important and complicated decisions concern long-term finances, living arrangements, and contingency preparation.

Nurturing Strengths and Interests

Nurturing strengths and interests is a crucial component of overall care. Each child's relative proclivities, unique affinities, and capacities for joy should be identified and fostered. This is crucial for the promotion of positive self-image, self-efficacy, social connection, finding a peer group, vocational possibilities, and simple pleasure. This kind of strengths-based care might include leisure activities, sports, drama, music, art, politics, technology, or any other special interests or enthusiasms. The "strengthening of strengths" is an important key to success, both short-term and long-term, especially for children who have many identified areas of weakness.

Comprehensive Autism Treatment Models

There are a number of comprehensive autism treatment models. These programs are designed to cover a range of developmental goals. Some are more "child-led" or "developmental"; others are more "adult-led" or "behavioral." Each has something to offer, but a deep dive into the pros and cons of these different treatment models is beyond the scope of this book (Odom, Boyd, Hall, & Hume, 2010; Wong et al., 2015; Zwaigenbaum et al., 2015).

Here are the names of a few programs (and some of their founding practitioners):

- Applied Behavior Analysis (Skinner/Lovaas)
- Applied Verbal Behavior (Sundberg/Carbone)

- DIR/"Floor-time" (Greenspan)
- Relationship Development Intervention (Gutstein)
- Pivotal Response Training (Koegel)
- TEACCH (Mesibov)
- Early Start Denver Model (Rogers)
- Play Project (Solomon)

The Importance of Case Management

These interventions are generally effective. Most children with a categorical diagnosis of autism should receive a combination of these services. However, just having a diagnosis of autism doesn't guide individualized implementation. When presented with this standard menu of autism-related treatments, most parents quickly become confused and overwhelmed.

> When Jimmy was first given the diagnosis of autism, his parents were given a long list of recommendations from a long list of people. Their heads were spinning. They stayed awake in bed wondering, "From all these options, what should we do for Jimmy? How? We have limited time, money, and energy. And Jimmy can't be in therapy 24 hours a day!"

The importance of a good care manager cannot be overstated. In an ideal world, the care manager is a true autism expert: a developmental-behavioral pediatrician or a specialist in psychology, psychiatry, speech-language therapy, or other related subspecialties. The care manager can also be a special needs case navigator or a developmentally attuned pediatrician. Along with other clinicians, it's the care manager's job to repeat periodic functional assessments, thereby measuring progress, describing current levels of function across developmental domains, resetting goals, determining priorities, and coordinating care.

> They were relieved to meet Dr. Totle. At the very first visit, he explained that a big part of his job would be helping them decide what was right for Jimmy, as Jimmy's case manager. He wanted to see every report, talk with key players on the team, and make sure everyone was on the same page. He reassured Jimmy's parents that they would not have to make decisions alone—he was in it with them and Jimmy for the long-haul. They would be using the diagnosis of autism to make sure

Jimmy got what he needed, but they would decide what he needed by looking at him as a unique individual.

Jimmy's parents quickly learned that good assessment and management went beyond the diagnosis of autism. Dr. Totle, along with various professionals at school and in the community, assessed Jimmy's real-life functioning in all the important domains of his development. From this nuanced understanding Dr. Totle, with other clinicians and educators, helped Jimmy's parents decide what he needed each step of the way and how to customize their approach.

At each phase of development, priorities change. To be effective, even standard interventions need to be delivered in an individualized way. That's where functional assessment comes in. A comprehensive discussion of functional assessment and individualized care is beyond the scope of this book, but it's covered in my first book, *Parent Child Journey: An Individualized Approach to Raising Your Challenging Child.* Although this excursion isn't as broad, we'll go deep into the single most important aspect of functional assessment for people with autism—social development. Then you will see, at least in this domain, how accurate description leads to individualized and effective support.

Helping Your Child Experience Social Success

Advocacy and Social Change

Progress for children with autism has not come about by treating just one child at a time. Life is better for people with autism and other disabilities because of a profound and ongoing cultural revolution.

Not long ago, individuals with autism were routinely killed, institutionalized, tormented, or abandoned (Silberman, 2016; Donvan & Zucker, 2017). They were often assumed to be "uneducable" and didn't receive anything remotely resembling modern interventions and supports. Estimates regarding the number of children identified with autism continues to rise. In April 2018, CDC estimates were reported at about 1 in 59 children or just under 2 percent of the population (Baio et al., 2018). This rise in diagnostic rates is a good thing, because it's mostly due to dramatic improvements in identification—*not* environmental toxins, immunizations, modern parenting, screen culture, or other such factors (Hansen, Schendel, & Partner, 2015; Amaral, 2017). That people with autism are no longer—figuratively and literally—hidden in basements is cause for celebration, not despair (Grinker, 2008).

In the past, most people with autism didn't receive any evaluation or support at all. Far from it. Those who did see so-called "experts" were usually misdiagnosed as "feeble-minded," schizophrenic, or mentally retarded. Now, a larger percentage of children with autism are properly identified. Thanks to self-advocacy and parent organizations—plus researchers, clinicians, governments, and schools—life for people with developmental disabilities is better than ever. Access to comprehensive care, outlined above, has improved dramatically. We still have a long way to go, but these positive trends will likely continue.

How can we keep the ball of progress rolling? We must continue our efforts to help individual children grow—and to change the world in which they live. After all, is it just the child who is disabled or the culture that is disabling? Which requires more treatment: the developmentally different child or the social environment in which they live? I believe that we must do both: prepare the child for the road *and* prepare the road for the child.

A Different Approach

Beyond Autism

We began this excursion with a focus on autism. However, as emphasized in the last section, every child with autism is different. Although we should carefully consider the standard menu of evidence-based interventions, we still need to customize care for individual children. This means moving beyond the diagnosis of autism and one-size-fits all treatment.

Also, as we proceed through this section, you will see that the same principles of assessment and management are relevant to children without autism. There are many children without autism who have difficulties with social interaction.

Autistic or not, all children with social disability are well-served by functional assessment and individualized care. Up to this point, I have used autism as an important archetype of social disability. But now, for all socially challenged children, we'll move completely outside of this categorical box. A bit further below, I will elaborate on "the many faces of social disability."

Beyond Social Skills Therapy

With increasing awareness of autism, there's been a remarkable increase in attention to social skills development for all children. Search the Internet for "social skills" and you will get more than a million results—in fact, it's difficult to keep up with the growing number of social skills training programs. Amazon lists more than 40 million books on social skills. In the Greater Washington, DC, area, where I live, there are dozens and dozens of social skills groups for children and adults of all ages. All of this research and program development has helped many children with autism and other social disabilities. However, such efforts to help children achieve real-life social success are not always effective.

Popular "cognitive" approaches for promoting social development call for direct teaching of social skills. A common concern about this approach is failure of generalization—failure of the child in individual or group therapy to use what they've learned in real life, outside of the therapist's office. Weekly sessions in a clinic are not the same as everyday peer interaction in the real world. Just because a child can get along in a therapist's playroom doesn't mean they can hold their own in the school cafeteria.

Don't get me wrong. Many children *do* benefit from explicit social skills instruction. However, there's nothing like hands-on experience. The whiteboard never works as well as the playing field. For most children, the best social learning takes place in their home, school, neighborhood, and community. For these reasons, effective social skills instruction must always be combined with regular homework, involving parents and teachers.

Many children with social disability might not need social skills groups at all. They might only need some modification of their social landscape. Helping children experience real-life social success is the best way to help them in their social development.

The "natural environment" approach outlined here emphasizes experiential learning in the real world. By proactively modifying everyday situations to better fit each child's developmental profile, parents and teachers can increase a child's chances of success at school, on the playground, and in the community. This natural environment approach corrects the discrepancy between abilities and expectations by adjusting the expectations, not just the abilities. For real-world success, we need to fix the world, not just the child. For many children, modifying the environment must come before doing. And doing comes before learning.

Beyond Intervention

When I use the word "intervention," I mean preparing the child for the road. When I use the word "accommodation," I mean preparing the road for the child. This isn't an argument for accommodation *instead* of intervention. This is a case against intervention *instead* of accommodation. We should do what we can to address the underlying causes of social disability. But we should not spend all of our energy trying to change our children to fit our culture. Neurodiversity is real. At least as much energy should be spent changing our culture to fit our children—as they are! Usually, this means making relatively simple adjustments at home, in school, and in the community. (Much more on this to follow.)

One question hangs over all our efforts to help children with social struggles: Is "disabled" an adjective (the "disabled" child) or a verb ("to disable" a child)? In other words, does the impairment come from within the child or from a failure of society to accommodate the child's developmental differences? Who needs to do the most changing, the child or the adults?

This isn't a case against individual therapy. Much can be done to help children learn to better navigate their existing social development. However, this is a case against therapy to the exclusion of accommodation. We need to find the right balance between changing the child *and* changing the child's world. In this excursion, to offset what I perceive to be an imbalance in our approach, I focus on accommodation, *not* intervention. But I obviously believe in doing both.

Despite positive trends, our world can still be disabling. I understand why the word "enabling" has gotten some bad press. True, the wrong kind of accommodation can lead to helplessness and dependency. But there is such a thing as a healthy degree of support. Should we not remove true barriers to success? And by throwing a rope to some, don't we provide a way for others to follow? By accommodating individuals in need, aren't we bending society toward progress?

A less disabling environment doesn't come easily or quickly.

Social progress requires patience and sustained effort. It's a long climb. However, by helping individuals achieve social success, we can improve diversity awareness and social connection for everyone—one mountain marker at a time. The bulk of this excursion will be devoted to functional assessment of social disability and social engineering.

So, beyond the diagnosis of autism, let's review social disability. Then, beyond clinic-based interventions, let's explore an individualized and natural environment approach to social change.

The Many Faces of Social Disability

Many children who seem to lack social interest really just lack social skill and social opportunity. Their loss of motivation is more often the result of success deprivation than the cause. Some children are much more socially attuned than their "self-absorbed" appearance or "inappropriate" behavior suggests. In fact, their "self-absorption" and "inappropriateness" represent a poor fit between their neurodevelopmental profile and social expectations. Just like most other developmental disorders (such as ADHD and anxiety), social difficulties are usually due to a complex combination of factors, primary and secondary, intertwined in dynamic flux, changing over time.

- *Biology.* All of us are equipped with different social brains. Some people are born with extraordinary social instincts. Others have neurogenetically-based social disabilities. Then there is everyone else in-between.
- *Environment.* We all grow up in different social milieus. Some privileged children thrive thanks to socially nourishing and enriching environments. Other children may be thwarted in their social development, due to adversity and deprivation.

Including but moving beyond autism, let's take a closer look at the primary and secondary causes of social disability.

Primary Social Disabilities

Normal interpersonal development depends upon the "social brain." Specific parts of the brain take care of sensory, motor, language, and other functions. Distinct cerebral regions and circuits regulate how individuals receive, process, and send social information. Primary disorders of this social brain include the following:

- Nonverbal learning disability
- Social pragmatic language disorder
- Schizophrenia and personality disorders
- Autism spectrum disorders and social communication disorder

Whether or not a child is thought to be socially disabled depends on the culture within which a child lives. For example, what is considered pathological withdrawal or failure to make eye contact in one culture might be thought of as respectful and appropriate behavior in another.

Social disability goes by many different names. Sometimes, the diagnostic categories depend upon the training and biases of a clinician, not just the features of a child.

- Nonverbal learning disability is a diagnosis usually made by psychologists via standardized testing, when there's a large gap between (higher) verbal IQ and (lower) nonverbal IQ scores.
- Social pragmatic language disorder is a diagnosis usually made by speech-language pathologists to describe skill deficits or atypical use of language in social interaction.
- Schizophrenia and personality disorders (such as sociopathy) are very controversial diagnoses in childhood, more often made by adult psychiatrists.
- Autism spectrum disorders include a broad range of social difficulties, diagnosed by a variety of neurodevelopmental specialists, including developmental pediatricians, neuropsychologists, child psychiatrists, speech-language pathologists, and other specialists.

In many cases, the real difference between nonverbal learning disability, social pragmatic language disorder, and autism spectrum disorders may be entirely semantic.

Secondary Social Difficulties

Social development and interpersonal success depend upon a wide range of comingled brain functions. Children can have social difficulties due to myriad combinations of underlying problems. A healthy brain and a favorable social environment are both important. Problems with social development can be secondary to any mishmash of the following:

- *Difficult Temperament, Challenging Behavioral Style, or a Combination of Minor Developmental Differences.* Simple differences in temperament or behavioral style represent the most common source of social challenge. Without having a specific disorder, many children still experience significant social difficulty. They may just have normal differences in motor activity level, attention span, impulse control, adaptability, intensity of reaction, initial reaction, sensory profile, and mood. In any one of the following areas of development, many children are below threshold for diagnosis of a disorder. However, minor developmental differences can still combine to cause significant social impairment. As Mel Levine would say, there is dysfunction at the junction of the functions. The whole may be greater than the sum of the parts.

- *Attention Deficit Hyperactivity Disorder.* ADHD affects life, not just school. For most children with ADHD, hyperactivity, impulsivity, and distractibility are just as problematic on the playground or in summer camp as in the classroom.

- *Executive Dysfunctions.* Social success also proves difficult for children with problems initiating, sustaining, inhibiting, shifting, organizing, planning, strategizing, and tracking time. Again, academic performance is only part of the problem. Social impairment caused by such executive dysfunctions can be just as important.

- *Verbal Language Learning Disabilities.* Although social disability is often equated with nonverbal communication deficits, social success also depends upon adequate expressive and receptive verbal language, including a broad range of processing and production disorders. A child can have significant social impairment from different levels of verbal language disability. Verbal disabilities range from basic problems with decoding (dyslexia), auditory registration, and phonological processing; to word meaning (semantics) and grammar (syntax); and extend to "higher-order" subtle problems with dysfluency, limited chunk-size, lack of central coherence, organization of language on demand, plus inferential and abstract reasoning. Any combination of these verbal challenges can impact social success.

- *Intellectual Disability.* Not every child with intellectual disability and interpersonal challenges has autism. However, every child with intellectual disability will have some social disability and many will have "autistic-like" behaviors. The lower the IQ, the more likely and severe the associated repetitive and ritualized behaviors. Again, these "autistic behaviors" don't necessarily mean autism; social disability and repetitive behavior may be entirely secondary to intellectual disability and not autism per se. Many children with autism do have intellectual disability too. But, in these cases, the diagnosis of autism is made only if the social impairment is substantially lower—out of proportion to—the degree of intellectual disability. In other words, it can only be autism if the intellectual disability by itself doesn't explain the severity—and flavor—of the social impairment.

- *Mood Disorders.* Any of the so-called "internalizing" disorders have a profound impact on external social behavior. Interpersonal relations are usually impacted by generalized anxiety, performance anxiety, social anxiety, obsessive-compulsive disorder, and depression. Bipolar illness and other mood regulation disorders can have cycles of both internalizing (depression) and externalizing (mania, irritability) symptoms, all affecting social functioning.

- *Sensory Dysfunction.* Children may be under- or oversensitive to all kinds of sensory stimuli: visual, auditory, tactile, internal, movement, taste, touch, and smell sensations. The sensory profile affects many facets of social comfort; impairment may be mild or profound. Common examples include hypersensitivity to clothing, noise, physical contact, and specific foods. *Hyper*-sensitivity can produce anticipatory anxiety about social situations; *hypo*-sensitivity can produce intrusive behavior that can seem rude or aggressive, but is actually an attempt by the person to gain a level of sensation that feels normal to them.

- *Motor Weaknesses.* Another set of potentially hidden factors in social success are fine motor, gross motor, oral-motor disorders, and abnormal muscle tone. Many social activities of childhood require motor skill, coordination, strength, and tone. Social standing (pun intended)—real or perceived— is often determined by physical prowess, fluency, and efficiency. In many cultures, again, socialization involves normative motor efficiency and comfort eating. People with low muscle tone are often seen as "lazy."

- *Movement Disorders.* Involuntary movements or vocalizations of any kind can have significant social repercussions. This includes children with motor and/or vocal tics (such as Tourette Syndrome and other tic disorders), stereotypies (such as the hand flapping and spinning of autism), spasms, tremors, and other motor habits.

- *Environmental Disadvantage.* Children may have social struggles because of deprivation or adversity. Many children lack social role models, social teaching, and social experience. They may face extremely difficult circumstances at home, in the neighborhood, and at school. Common challenges include marital discord, separation, or divorce; lack of safety and security; bullying and teasing. There is a staggering range of other potential family stresses. Children may be the victims of discrimination because of their status in racial or LGBTQI minorities. The screen generation may have too much time with TV, computer, cell phones, tablets, and other electronics. Online and social media content can have a disturbing impact on a vulnerable child's view of social norms and personal safety. All of this can have a profound impact on the quantity and quality of face-to-face relationships.

Avoiding Either/Or Thinking

Again, many children with social difficulties have a combination of developmental strengths and challenges. All facets of the child's profile overlap, each affecting the other and changing over time. For any child with social difficulties, we should try to address the underlying causes, primary and secondary. We need to beware of "either/or" thinking and remember that most social delays have more than one cause. This means that all resource eggs should not be put in one treatment basket. Rather, we need to give priority to the most important and treatable sources of impairment. Some causes of social impairment are more modifiable than others. For example, medication can make a dramatic difference if social disability is secondary to ADHD.

For the rest of this discussion, let's assume that you're doing the best you can to address underlying causes of social difficulty. For a complete discussion of ADHD and anxiety, see the first parts of this book. For discussion about the whole range of developmental differences, see my first book, *Parent Child Journey.*

Let's shift focus to the development of interpersonal relationships. No matter what the contributing factors or causes, or the degree of impairment, what can we do to help all children experience social success?

Functional Assessment and Social Engineering

For many children, suggesting they casually "call up" a friend just doesn't work. Most children with social difficulties need supported immersion. Even mild weaknesses in interpersonal ability may need to be accommodated to avoid frustration, humiliation, and loss of motivation. Understanding primary and secondary causes of social disability is important, but understanding isn't the same as supporting real-world interaction. How to do social landscaping for children with different types and degrees of social disability? It all starts with an accurate description of social development.

Current Level of Social Development

By way of analogy, social disability is no different than reading disability. If a ninth-grader is reading at a third-grade level, you assign third-grade material—not Shakespeare. Even when the cause of reading disorder is environmental deprivation without disability, you don't start with grade-level reading material; that would be like throwing a beginning swimmer into the deep end of the pool. Sink or swim approaches usually don't end well. Without making proper adjustments, the struggling child—and teacher—might just give up. Adjusting the reading material to the child's current reading level closes the gap between expectations and abilities. Successful child, successful teacher—both are motivated to forge ahead.

Whether we're talking about reading or social development, assessment of the current level of development is the best starting point for adjusting demands to skills. By closing the gap between social expectations and abilities, we give children the best chance for social success and learning.

Social development proceeds in spurts and sputters. Different children make progress at different rates, along different paths. For infants and toddlers, normal milestones are well-established. We know the ages by which most typical children tend to smile, reach, point, and share. However, starting in preschool, our social assessment tools become much less reliable. Unlike the assessment of reading ability, we don't have a battery of social development tests to tell us whether a child is interacting with peers at the 3.2 or 3.9 grade level. As children get older, the increasing irregularity, complexity, and immeasurability of social development makes accurate assessment fuzzier and fuzzier (Greenspan & Salmon, 1994).

Facets of Social Development

Despite this lack of age-adjusted norms, a child's social development level can be described roughly according to certain practical "facets" of social functioning.

Functional Assessment of Social Development

Facet	Beginner	Intermediate	Advanced
Structure/ Dependence	tightly scripted	outlined	free improvisational
Familiarity	frequent	infrequent/ previewed	new
Warm-Up Time	prolonged	moderate	short
Interest/ Competence	high	medium	low
Partners	parent/sibling	older/younger children	peers/diverse
Group Size	solo or hive	"two's company"	larger/diverse
Duration	short	medium	long
Sharing	attention	things	thoughts and feelings
Social Quotient	egocentric	other awareness	reciprocity
Emotional Quotient	all-or-none	primary emotions	in-between shades

For each facet of social development listed above, picture expanding zones of social comfort or ascending markers up a mountain of social competence. Each wider circle or each higher blaze can represent beginner, intermediate, or advanced levels of interpersonal skill. This system is qualitative and subjective, but it serves as a simple, practical, and effective guide to management.

Jimmy, the eight-year-old boy with autism, was doing better on his ADHD and anxiety medication. Plus, customized CBT was gradually helping him learn to do some problem-solving with Dr. Totle. But he was still struggling with peer interaction at school and finding friends outside of school.

His parents signed him up for a social skills training group. There, week after week, he did well enough participating in the play activities. With the help of the psychologist, he took turns, shared toys, and engaged in some limited back and forth conversation.

But none of this seemed to make much difference outside of the psychologist's office. In class, on the playground, and in the cafeteria, he still avoided interacting with the other kids. His mother took him to the park on weekends, but when other kids approached, Jimmy either retreated further away or yelled something inappropriate. Sometimes, he literally pushed them away. The kids learned to just leave him alone. At school, his teacher made suggestions and tried to jump-start some interactive games. But Jimmy and the other kids just didn't sustain any kind of meaningful connection.

Individual Description Leads to Social Prescription

In the following discussion, for each facet of social development, you will see how to describe your child's level as beginner, intermediate, or advanced. That simple rating will help guide the just-right level of accommodation for success and progress.

Think about specific activities and social situations that could be tailored accordingly. Usually, it's the child who is expected to change, conform, and fit in. Here, I emphasize the importance of changing the social expectations to accommodate the child's developmental differences. In other words, individual description should lead to social—not just individual—prescription. Facet by facet, we'll now see how to rate your child's social development and then use individualized accommodation strategies to promote social success.

Structure/Dependence

Early in development, children don't have much self-awareness, social awareness, or self-regulation. They depend upon parents and other adults for basic guidance. For example, a parent might have to explicitly coach a child: "Say hi to your friend," or "You two can go outside and play." As they get older, most children are able to navigate sibling and peer interactions well enough on their own.

But some children continue to need more social mapping than others. They just may not be able to navigate social situations with the expected degree of independence. This will be most apparent when parents are otherwise occupied or further removed. Plunked into open-ended situations, some children just don't know what to do or how to do it. Social beginners are simply more dependent upon others for planning, preview, and guidance. At school, children with social disability might be okay during classroom instruction but lost on the playground, in the cafeteria, in the hallways, and/or in restrooms. Such unstructured settings can be marked by chaos, confusion, cliques, and competition.

These days, parents are often criticized for micromanaging. But not all "helicoptering" is harmful or unnecessary. Many socially delayed children really do require more explicit social coaching and close facilitation. Social beginners might need to be prompted and cued. As these children develop, they will not need so much external support, and the assistance should be gradually withdrawn. They will get better at social improvisation that is more free, spontaneous, and independent. Some achieve this type of social competence more quickly and completely than others.

For children who continue to need a high level of support in middle school, social scaffolding carries a higher risk of stigmatizing and prolonging dependence. That's where the benefits of peer mentoring can be major.

Whatever the individual's trajectory, a developmental perspective allows us to move beyond sweeping generalizations and encourage parents and teachers to find the right level of support—the golden mean—for each child.

Strategies:

- *Provide sufficient structure and supervision.* Social prompting might be as subtle as a parent's smile or as explicit as a visual schedule. Across settings and activities, it takes a village to know a child's social profile and provide necessary supports. The child's social village includes parents, family, and teachers; recess and cafeteria monitors; coaches, instructors, and friends. Adults should not stand by passively if a child is being bullied or marginalized. For the social beginner, unstructured time should be structured. One excellent curriculum for the school playground can be found at remakingrecess.org. After a child is successful at one level of structure and support, the scaffolding can be gradually faded and spaced to foster independence.

- *Plan ahead/teach advance planning.* Customized structure requires advanced planning. Social success is all about the details. There are all sorts of complexities to problem-solve: scheduling, transportation, activities, materials, supervision, and more. Social plans made on the fly often don't fly at all. Pick a day to sit down and think about the week ahead. As soon as they are old enough, children should be active participants in their own social planning: "What would you like to do? Who would you like to do it with? Let's get out the calendar and see when that can happen."

At home, Jimmy's parents got more strategic. Before trips to the park, they used social stories to review specific play options. They had Jimmy choose what he wanted to do from a menu. At the park, he liked playing tag. Referring to the social story, Jimmy's dad helped him ask another boy if he wanted to play tag. Dad helped Jimmy and the other boy by reviewing the rules. Jimmy's dad knew that he would have to play along to keep Jimmy in the game. In the future, Jimmy would be able to play tag and other games on his own. But not yet.

At school, just before going outside for recess, Jimmy's teacher presented different play choices. Jimmy liked using toy trucks to build roads in the sand. His teacher matched him up with another boy. Together, they came up with a plan and took turns playing different roles. First, Jimmy shoveled, the other boy hauled away, and the teacher smoothed the road. Every ten shovels-full, they switched roles. At first, the teacher helped by counting and cueing the switch. Then she gradually had them take over counting and shouting, "Switch!" She could not spend the entire recess just with Jimmy. But, at least for starters, she was determined to devote 5–10 minutes each day giving him this necessary level of support.

Familiarity

Children experience different people, places, and activities with varying frequency and regularity. Social beginners usually do best with routine and predictability, thus the preference many children have for repetition and ritual. Autism and other social disabilities usually stem from an impairing degree of context-blindness (Vermeulen, 2012). These children have relative difficulty reading new social situations and understanding expectations. They may not be able to navigate unfamiliar activities and environments. To expand their comfort zone, they may need gradual and incremental exposure to novelty.

At the intermediate level of social development, some preview is still necessary as a bridge to the unknown. But such preparation works more consistently, requires fewer specifics, and feels less crucial. Over time, the socially mature person may not require any rehearsal at all. At the advanced level, there is comfort with novelty and surprise, maybe even joy in uncertainty.

Strategies:

- *Limit novelty.* For some social beginners, it's especially hard to relate to other people while experiencing new things. Anxiety and sensory overload can sabotage social success. Most children feel more comfortable and confident doing familiar activities, in familiar settings, with familiar people. Over time, the degree of novelty can gradually increase.
- *Preview/rehearse.* Children are more likely to relax and enjoy if they know exactly what to expect and have some advance preparation. Depending on the child's developmental profile, adults should choose the best type of preview or rehearsal technique: visual schedule, social calendar, social stories, cartoon conversations, social scripts, video, guided practice, dress rehearsal, pretend play, role-play, or rule review.

Deliberately, Jimmy's parents planned regular times at the playground. He knew that his mom would take him every Wednesday after school and his dad would take him every Saturday morning. Jimmy liked it there. He knew every inch of the

climbing equipment and every slope in the woodchipped land-
scape. Also, the same neighborhood kids were usually there at
the same times. Tag was the go-to favorite game. "You're it,"
was not just familiar to Jimmy—other kids could seamlessly
move in and out of the game too. Although the players changed
somewhat, the game was the same.

One day, one of the kids suggested playing hotdog tag. Jimmy
and his mom had never heard of hotdog tag. Jimmy shouted no.
But when they got home, Mom went online and searched, "Dif-
ferent ways to play tag." Jimmy looked over her shoulder. There
were many other versions: sharks and minnows, band-aid
tag, and more. She showed Jimmy the pictures and described
some of the simpler variations. Jimmy seemed reluctant but
intrigued. Some days, when there weren't other kids there, Dad
and Jimmy practiced hotdog tag. Gradually, he learned to like
this variation, and one day he was ready to try it with some of
the other kids. In this way, Jimmy and his parents gradually
expanded his play repertoire.

Jimmy's teacher emailed his mom to see if Jimmy might want
to bring some of his favorite action figures to school for recess.
That way, she could help him expand upon his play with the
other kids in the sandbox, while keeping it comfortable and
familiar for Jimmy. The little Batman and Superman action
figures were cheap, so Jimmy's mom bought some duplicates for
him to keep at school. Jimmy was excited. He understood that
the teacher would keep them and he could only use them at
recess, not inside the classroom. But Jimmy was excited.

Warm-Up Time

Closely related to familiarity, warm-up time is the time it takes
a child to transition and get comfortable in a new situation. For
the socially immature child, successful adaptation to novelty
might require gradual and incremental exposure. These children cannot just dive into the social swimming pool, and they
should never be pushed or thrown. They need time to acclimate
by sitting at the edge and dipping one toe at a time. Eventually,
they can enter, but only through gradual and incremental habituation. As they mature, or as specific situations become more
familiar, slow-to-warm-up children don't need such protracted
transitions. They get better at diving right in.

Strategies:

- *Prolong warm-up to allow gradual acclimation.* Slow-to-warm-up children should be allowed extra time to hang at the social periphery and acclimate. Parents who want to just throw them in need to adjust their expectations. With these children, a "sink or swim" approach usually causes social "drowning." Forced entry only increases the child's anxiety and the likelihood of future avoidance. Depending on the child and the situation, the necessary warm-up time may range from minutes to months. Once successful—80 percent of the time at each level of accommodation—the transition time can be shortened and the comfort zone expanded. Going slow is better than not going at all. As long as there is some progress, parents should keep faith and stay the course.

- *Shorten warm-up to avoid transition torture.* Some children appear to require prolonged warm-up when, in fact, they need a *shorter* transition time. Despite their negative first reactions, many children are quite adaptable. Given the chance, they can overcome their initial uncertainty and settle in just fine. These children should *not* do "one toe at a time"—that just prolongs the "transition torture." The longer the hand-holding, the greater the anxiety. They should have a shorter transition period and dive right in, giving them the opportunity to quickly adapt. For these negative "initial reaction/high adaptability" children, parents should focus on controlling their own worries, communicate confidence in their child's resilience, and quickly fade support.

One day at the playground, there was a new kid who liked to yell—loudly. Startled, Jimmy ran away to the corner of the fence. He turned his back to the other kids and put his hands over his ears. Jimmy's dad decided to just wait and see what happened. After two minutes, Jimmy still hadn't moved much. After five minutes, Jimmy still had his hands over his ears. But he had turned his body 45 degrees toward the commotion. After a few more minutes, he edged along the fence, a few steps closer. The other boy was still yelling. Jimmy took one step back. But in this manner, Jimmy gradually re-entered the game of tag. Eventually, he took his hands away from his ears.

Interest and Competence

From early on, children have their own affinities and strengths. Social beginners are most comfortable playing and participating within their zone of natural talent and pleasure. As social development proceeds, successful interactions can include activities further removed from islands of aptitude. Only socially advanced individuals might deliberately put themselves in situations of little intrinsic pleasure, completely outside of their skill set, just for the sake of a relationship.

Children of the same age might have very different play skills. In her Developmental Play Assessment, Dr. Karen Lifter of Northeastern University has described different levels as follows:

- Level I: *Indiscriminate Play.* Actions when all objects are treated alike: waving, mouthing, banging, feeling, and throwing.
- Level II
  - *Discriminative Play.* Interacting with an object in a manner consistent with the properties of that object: pushing a car, squeezing a stuffed animal, and pushing buttons on a pop-up.
  - *Take Apart Combinations.* Separating the configuration of objects: taking all of the pieces out of a puzzle.
- Level III
  - *Presentation Combinations.* Re-creating combinations of objects according to their presentation configuration: putting pieces back into a puzzle.
  - *General Combinations.* Using objects based on global properties that are shared by many different objects: using an item as a container (nesting cup, bed of dump truck) to hold a variety of objects (blocks, toy cars).
  - *Pretend Self.* Relating an object to self with a pretend quality: bringing an empty cup to one's mouth to "drink."
- Level IV: *Specific Combinations (physical attributes).* Preserving the distinct and unique physical characteristics of objects in constructed configurations: stacking blocks, stringing beads, rolling a car down a ramp.
- Level V
  - *Child as Agent.* Using a replica of a person or an animal along with a prop to complete an act: giving a doll a drink with a cup, feeding an animal with a spoon.

- *Specific Combinations (Conventional Attributes)*. Preserving the unique and conventional physical characteristics of objects in configuration with another: placing a cup on a saucer.
- Level VI
  - *Single-Scheme Sequences*. Extending familiar actions to two or more objects: first feeding self with a spoon, then feeding a doll, then a stuffed animal.
  - *Substitutions*. Using one object to stand in the place of another: using a bowl as a hat.
  - *Substitutions without Object*. Pretending to use something that isn't there: shaking an imaginary salt shaker, drinking from an imaginary cup.
- Level VII
  - *Doll as Agent*. Manipulating doll figures as if they are capable of action: moving figures like they're walking, or having a doll hold a mirror as if to see itself.
  - *Multi-Scheme Sequences*. Extending different actions on the same figure: feeding doll with a spoon, wiping it with a cloth, and putting it to bed.
- Level VIII
  - *Socio-Dramatic Play*. Adopting various familiar roles in play themes: using a playhouse and assigning specific roles of baby, child, parent, pet, and friend.
  - *Thematic Fantasy Play*. Adopting various fantasy characters, such as Superman or Wonder Woman.

Beyond Lifter's levels, thematic pretend play involves perspective-taking, emotion recognition, processing, communication, problem-solving, and using everyday life in play.

Dr. Totle asked Jimmy's parents to consider Dr. Lifter's play levels. Jimmy could do puzzles and use objects according to their design, but he didn't use toys flexibly, to develop stories or expand upon themes. Usually, Jimmy just used his Batman and Superman to fly and fight. He would hold Superman in his left hand and Batman in his right hand. While Jimmy ran around in figure eights, the superhero figures would zoom back and forth, in parallel through the air, over and over. If Jimmy's mom or dad introduced another action figure or animal into the play schema, Jimmy's "guys" would swoop down and attack

297

while Jimmy made aggressive growling sounds. His parents tried making their figures act hurt or scared or even dead. But Jimmy would just keep playing as if nothing had happened. So, it seemed, he was good through Level VI.

At Level VII, he could use his toy figures as agents but he really didn't "extend their actions." He had been stuck at that play level for quite a while. It was always just the same flying and attacking. He needed some help using these figures in different ways and advancing to Level VIII, learning to develop some variation to play themes and creating a richer fantasy life.

Jimmy's teacher confirmed that the other kids at school were getting tired of Jimmy's repetitive play. He just wanted to do the same road building or superhero flying and attacking. Over and over.

Strategies:

- *Select activities in areas of interest and competence.* Shared interests lead to good relationships much more reliably than good relationships lead to shared interests. Schedule very specific activities that you know your child will find engaging and enjoyable. Do not expect relationships to develop spontaneously, or push your child into activities for which they have a lack of skill or interest. The best way to help a child make friends is to follow his or her bliss. Somebody out there has that bliss too. In social planning, the first question should be, "What do you want to do?" The second question, "Who do you want to do it with?"

- *Consider skill level.* Be careful to match playmates not just according to play preference but also with some consideration of expertise. For example, some children like sports but they are not very coordinated. Two children might share a love of video games, pretend play, or Legos, but their disparate levels of accomplishment could be a non-starter. Using Lifter's Developmental Play Assessment, think about your child's play skill level and consider the skill level of potential play partners. Use the same kind of developmental framework for other activities. Play partners don't have to be a perfect match. But, unless they are assuming teacher-student roles, their ability levels can't be too far apart.

- *Non-therapeutic/mainstream/inclusion social groups.* Although helpful to many children, therapeutic social skills groups and individual psychotherapy should not take the place of mainstream opportunities for social connection. Parents should work hard to discover "real world" group experiences that are in line with their child's strengths, interests, and developmental profile.
  - Clubs/classes/activities: Children can connect with each other through shared interests in video gaming, "hands-on science," dance, drawing, painting, software design, listening to or playing music, carpentry, design, sewing, knitting, crafts, animals, nature, robotics, card games, chess, other board games, cooking, or eating—whatever your child's area of enthusiasm. If such opportunities don't already exist, parents can help children start a club at their house, school, library, community center, or congregation.
  - Drama classes/theater: Many parents are pleasantly surprised to discover that their socially anxious kid comes out of their shell on stage. This is because theater can actually lessen the demands on social skills. Children are given a script on how to interact. What could be better for social education than drama practice? In addition, theater promotes a sense of belonging to a group, working together to produce something cool, and sharing applause for a job well done.
  - Sports: Team sports may represent a wonderful opportunity for social connection and social development.
    - Some children with social skills deficits are lucky to have compensatory athletic abilities. Just put them on the field or court and their social awkwardness disappears.
    - Other kids can participate in competitive sports only if accommodated. Specific skills training, such as preseason batting practice, can make a big difference. Children with attention deficits and/or visual-spatial processing deficits can still do well if their role on the team is customized. For example, in soccer, rather than playing midfield or forward, it may be easier to play goalie or defense. Then, the whole field is in front of them and everyone screams when the ball comes their way. Similarly, in volleyball, it may be easier to play the back line than the net. In baseball, it's

usually simplest to play first base, catcher, or right field.

- Many children do much better with noncompetitive—"personal best"—sports. For example: martial arts, fencing, hiking, kayaking, fishing, horseback riding, swimming, rock climbing, diving, skiing, weight-lifting, track and field, and biking.
- Some children with high interest but low ability can be part of a team as an equipment manager, statistician, score-keeper, or physical trainer. Sports-buddies can get together to watch professional or college sports, including eating popcorn and wearing team uniforms.

One thing Jimmy's parents knew for sure. He loved Legos. Jimmy's dad asked his teacher if there were any other kids in the class who were Lego-fanatics like Jimmy. She didn't have to think long—two other boys were always talking about their latest designs. And she remembered one of her students from a few years back was a Lego-maniac too. Their lunch times matched up, and it didn't take much effort to create the LLC: "Legos for Lunch Club."

The parents all pooled resources and donated a large castle-building kit. The older boy was the sub-contractor. Following the kit's very specific directions, he assigned each boy a part of the castle and oversaw assembly. Although they worked in parallel, the boys collaborated to build a series of truly extraordinary castles. Upon completion of each one, the teacher took a picture. The LLC members stood proudly behind each new creation. Over the months, their scrapbook of shared accomplishments grew and grew.

Partners

Early in development, infants and young children are usually most comfortable interacting with their parents. Over time, the social comfort zone widens to include siblings and other children. Socially immature children usually do best with either older or younger playmates. Interaction with same-age peers can be much more difficult. This is because older children can accommodate or follow the lead of a less mature child. Children with social delays function more comfortably at the same level with younger children. True peer interaction requires stricter adherence to social rules and higher behavioral expectations.

Only socially advanced children are able to move beyond like-minded peers and flexibly accept that everybody's different. Unlike socially immature children, they welcome social diversity and enjoy all types of play partners.

Strategies:

- *Non-peer partners.* If a child isn't able to meet the advanced demands of peer interaction, it's okay to have friends who are either older or younger. Sometimes, culturally determined differences in gender play allow boys to do better with girls and girls to do better with boys. This kind of cross-gender play may be less competitive and more flexible.

- *Helping others.* One of the best ways to help children is to put them in situations where they are helping others. This is especially important for children who are usually on the receiving end. Giving to non-peers might be very meaningful and easier to navigate. Parents and children should explore opportunities to volunteer, teach, coach, mentor, or baby-sit. Depending upon the child, such helper roles can be performed one-on-one. When feasible, helping partnerships or groups provide another level of social connection. Teachers can pair classmates or they can float students into younger classes to be a tutor or reading buddy. For lasting boosts to social awareness and self-image, it's truly better to give than receive.

- *Friends as specialists.* Children and parents should remember that there is no such thing as a universal friend: one go-to friend who is good for everything. Most of us have friends who are good for some types of situations but not for others. A child can have one friend for Minecraft, another for baseball, and still another for going to the zoo. It may even be useful to make a chart or list fitting favorite activities to specific friends.

Jimmy's parents were concerned that he tended to play with much younger children in the neighborhood. Dr. Totle reassured them that, at Jimmy's current level of social development, this was okay. With the little kids, he was the engine, while they were the freight cars and caboose. Although this type of follow-the-leader play was rather repetitive and rigid, Jimmy and the little kids loved it.

All too often, he had been teased, rejected, or ignored by the other kids his age. With the younger kids, Jimmy was a big hit. He taught them about different train types, railroad lines, and stations. Dutifully, they played their assigned roles. At first, parents of the little kids were concerned about this older quirky boy. But it didn't take long for them to appreciate Jimmy's help. They welcomed the chance to sit down, relax, and chat with each other on the benches nearby.

Group Size

The socially immature child needs to keep things simple. Usually, the complexity and difficulty of social interaction increases with the number of players. Two may be company but three can feel like an overwhelming crowd. It may be too difficult to simultaneously consider the thoughts and feelings of many people, and much easier to respond to just one person at a time. Over the years, children gradually develop the interpersonal capacity to navigate larger, more complicated groups. But early on, it makes sense to keep things small and simple.

But small doesn't always mean simple. Some large group experiences provide very uncomplicated social opportunities. Sometimes, it's easier to belong to a large, homogeneous group than it is to have individual friends. Think about the intense and effortless bond that exists between tens of thousands of sports fans, filling a stadium, cheering for their home team. Any interpersonal differences or social skills deficits are lost in the crowd as fans meld their individual identities. In victory or defeat, they celebrate or grieve as one.

The same differences that set some children apart can bind them together. Birds of a feather flock together. When people share a difference, there is safety in numbers. Many children with social disability and developmental diversity may not be able to find a single friend—but they can find a tribe. Andrew Solomon writes about the importance of belonging to a "horizontal family" of similarly different friends when the apple falls far from the "vertical family" tree. No matter how different one feels, there is a community out there for everybody, and finding one's horizontal family has become much easier in the Internet era.

Many writers, from Emile Durkheim (2007) to Robert Putnam (2001), have described the modern scourge of social isolation. In a dramatic cultural shift, too many people lack a sense of group belonging. As an antidote, social psychologists like Jonathan Haidt (2013) and Dan and Chip Heath (2010) discuss "turning me into us" and living more like bees in a hive than chimps in the jungle. By "flipping on the hive switch," people can experience group energy, buzz and flow. Belonging to a hive is about community rituals, not interpersonal skills; participation, not interaction; membership in a simple group versus relationship to complicated individuals; social identity versus isolated friendships. Of course, teenagers with social delays can be swept up into dangerous behaviors, drugs, and sex. However, there are many opportunities for membership in healthy communities. In many cultures, there is nothing more important than belonging to the society at-large.

Because interpersonal ease can be found in either the few or the many, strategies pertaining to group size might appear to be contradictory. But, depending on the nature of the group, sometimes it makes sense to limit group size. Other times it makes sense to seek out a larger group. Whatever works. Simplicity can come in different-size packages.

Strategies:

- *Limit group size.* For some children, social stress increases with the number of play partners. If this is a problem, keep it simple by keeping it small. For this type of interpersonal interaction, success one-on-one comes before success one-on-two (and so on). For example, early on, birthday parties might have to be relatively intimate affairs. Gradually, group size can be increased as children progress from one level of social success to the next.
- *Belong to a larger community.* Potential "hive" opportunities for children and adolescents include:
  - religious services and holiday celebrations
  - clubs (such as Cub Scouts, Pokémon, or Dungeons and Dragons)
  - group nature outings (such as field trips, hiking, climbing, kayaking, mountain-climbing, obstacle courses, summer camp)
  - crowd entertainment (such as movies, sports, concerts)
  - group games (such as chess)
  - group sports (such as biking, running, swimming, martial arts, yoga)

- group science and tech activities (such as robotics, mad science)
- group arts and crafts
- group work (such as construction, farming/4H, gardening)
- group drama (such as renaissance festivals, theater)
- group political activities (such as marches, protests, campaign work)
- group music (such as choir, drum circles, bands, orchestras)
- group dance (such as Irish, Israeli, Greek, square, clogging)

Every Sunday at one of the public parks, there was a drum circle. The first time they drove by, Jimmy's parents noticed his attraction to the throbbing beat. They decided to pull over and check it out. Jimmy was usually sensitive to crowds and noises, but something about the rhythmic pulsation drew Jimmy closer and closer. As his parents followed behind, Jimmy literally danced his way up to the center of the pounding beat. A kind man noticed Jimmy and offered his drum. Much to his parents' delight, Jimmy joined right in. Drumming along, he quickly became mesmerized.

At home, they found an old toy drum. Next thing they knew, drum circle had become a Sunday ritual. The regulars got to know Jimmy. He and his parents became a part of this joyful community.

Duration

For many children, playdates, recess, or other social situations are just too long and too exhausting. Interpersonal play or communication may go well for a while, but then an endurance threshold is crossed and things fall apart. The longer the time together, the greater the chance of misunderstandings, conflict, or just plain boredom. Over the years, as children develop, social stamina usually improves and social interaction becomes more sustainable.

Strategies:

- *Limited time.* In general, social beginners do better keeping interpersonal interactions brief. If you know that your child usually lasts only so many minutes, then plan to end the playdate 15 minutes earlier. Keep it pleasant by keeping it brief. As my father-in-law would say, "Thanks for coming. Thanks for going." Rather than "I never want to see him again!" or, worse, "He'll never want to see me again," it's far better to end on a positive note. Limit the duration so they say good-bye wanting to get together again soon. For example, you and your child can pick up another kid after school. Before dropping her off at her house, plan to stop by the ice-cream parlor for 10–15 minutes together. Short and sweet.

Although Jimmy loved going to the playground for tag, his dad knew that there was only so much fuel in Jimmy's little social interaction tank. If they stayed more than 20 minutes, something usually went wrong. Jimmy would get upset about getting tagged. He would run out of physical stamina. Other kids would get bored and move on. It would end in tears. Sometimes, Jimmy would even throw wood chips at the other kids. Deliberately, Jimmy's dad timed their arrival 15 minutes before the other kids usually went home for dinner. Better to have Jimmy a little upset about the other kids leaving than a lot upset about the other kids staying.

Sharing

Normal infants don't just *pay* attention; they *share* attention. I see you; you see me. One person smiles; the other person smiles back. Back and forth, they exchange a whole range of facial expressions, vocalizations, touches, and gestures. A triangle of shared engagement forms between two people and one object—we see it together. They learn to give, receive, and mirror an increasingly nuanced set of social signals. Over the years, the content of these social exchanges becomes more complex, deep, and abstract. The nature of the sharing evolves.

Social beginners are egocentric and controlling. They don't consistently share attention or objects. Over time, there is more give and take. They learn to play games for mutual pleasure, and evolve from not sharing at all, to sharing things, to sharing thoughts, feelings, and experiences. Early on, friendships may be based on proximity, possessions, and physical abilities. With time, friendships depend more upon shared values, goals, and interests. There is true reciprocity.

Strategies:
- *Parallel play.* If your child is at a beginning level of social development, parallel play is better than nothing. Parents

who expect or insist upon a higher level of interaction might cause unnecessary frustration, loss of motivation, and isolation. Sometimes, just being close to others promotes social comfort. At different ages, there are different types of parallel play. For young children, there is ordinary floor play with figures, trucks, and blocks. As children get older, there's bowling, arts, movies, and meals—activities that bring people together without requiring too much interaction and stress.

- *Intrinsically social games.* There are many games that require a degree of social interaction. For example: Go Fish, I Spy, 20 Questions, you're getting warmer/colder, hide and seek. Also, board games require varying degrees of joint attention and interpersonal awareness. For higher levels of social development, there's Pictionary, charades, sports, arts, and music, to name just a few. For teens and adults, even higher-level board games facilitate sharing thoughts and feelings.

At his early stage of social development, Jimmy's parents learned to accept his limitations. They would have loved to see him move beyond parallel play with Legos and trains. Other children his age were doing imaginative back-and-forth pretend play.

They decided to start with short and simple card games: Go Fish and Uno. At least Jimmy would get practice taking turns and responding to a play partner. This would be a foundation upon which he could build, slowly but surely.

Social-Emotional Quotient

SEQ refers to the tightly intertwined development of social awareness, social skills, emotional flexibility, and emotional intelligence.

Often, there are substantial discrepancies between standardized measures of IQ and real-life SEQ. "School-smarts" and "people-smarts" don't always match up. Just because a teen can get straight As in school and perfect scores on the SATs doesn't mean they do well hanging out with peers on the playground, in the cafeteria, or at parties. Conversely, others who can't read well enough to take the SAT might have very strong social-emotional functioning.

SEQ goes by many different names. As opposed to linguistic, logical-mathematical, and other "types of smart," Howard

Gardner (2011) calls SEQ "interpersonal intelligence." Simon Baron-Cohen (1997) introduced the term "Theory of Mind": the ability to form a theory about another person's unique thoughts and feelings. According to Martin Buber (1971), the socially immature person relates to other people as objects: "I-It." The socially mature person sees others as subjects: "I-You." But it's all SEQ to me.

As children move through levels of social development, they develop a more varied social-emotional palate. Beyond simple acknowledgment that other people have minds, much more lies beneath the surface. At first, children's emotional vocabulary is limited to binaries: happy or sad, friend or enemy, mean or nice. The conspicuous absence of "in-between" emotional states and social relationships underlies the immature child's interpersonal inflexibility and poor coping skills. The result, often: pessimistic generalization, aggression, depression, withdrawal, denial, arrogance, passivity, paranoia, or anxiety. But then, they learn a few more fundamental emotions (happy, sad, angry, and sacred) and gradations (big deal, little deal, no problem).

Over time, with more social maturation, the child shifts from these few emotional states and types of relationships to a more complete range of tones and intensities—beyond simplistic labels to a more nuanced understanding of inner and outer complexities. They fill their social-emotional palettes with more subtle hues, such as confused, embarrassed, jealous, remorseful, grateful, annoyed, frustrated. They learn to use more nuanced rating scales to quantify degrees of intensity. Increasingly nuanced emotional understanding leads to greater tolerance of social demands and more mature coping strategies. The result: acceptance, compromise, and collaborative problem-solving. High SEQ makes it easier to handle the full spectrum of social challenges.

Higher SEQ includes understanding that there is no such thing as a perfect friend. Rather, we have different friends for different situations and phases. Higher SEQ means accepting that expectations cannot always be met, that people can be unpredictable, and that much of human behavior is situational. Socially mature individuals don't insist on always having things their way. They learn to give up some control and "go with the flow" for the sake of the relationship. This requires a high level of social awareness, self-awareness, and self-control.

In addition to social-emotional knowledge, social success requires a large set of social skills. There's a lot to learn. How to share, take turns, and cooperate. How to do social problem-solving, reconciliation, and relationship repair. Across different social situations and different people, what are the hidden rules, norms, and expectations? How to read social context, grasp the situation, and modify your behavior accordingly. How to understand (receptive) and send (expressive) nonverbal language through voice tone, volume, and texture; through facial expression, body posture, and gesture; through interpersonal space, grooming, and touch. How to enter and leave a group. How to participate in a conversation. How to be a good sport, a good team member, a good co-worker, a good classmate, a good friend. It's a miracle that so many children pick up on these complicated skills instinctively, and no surprise that others need explicit teaching, supervised practice, and accommodation.

Strategies:

Again, this discussion isn't a case against raising SEQ and teaching social skills. I'm all for that. But social development takes time. How can you accommodate your child's current social-emotional intelligence, to help him or her experience a degree of social success today? We should definitely teach social awareness, flexibility, problem-solving, mind-reading, active listening, and nonverbal communication. More on all that below. But until that higher-level social-emotional software gets downloaded into your child's brain, we need to work with what they've got.

- *Preview.* Don't overestimate your child's need for explicit teaching and supervised practice. Many social norms that seem obvious to us are hidden to children with low SEQ (Myles, Trautman, & Schelvan, 2004). You may need to provide a very detailed script, with clear rules for sharing, collaborating, turn-taking, entering and leaving a group. As emphasized previously, a clear road map will relieve much of the SEQ burden.
- *Translate.* Until your child learns to send and understand appropriate nonverbal cues, some situations will require you to serve as prompter and interpreter. Temple Grandin teaches that the challenge of navigating the social world, for someone who's autistic, feels like being dropped in a foreign country or being "an anthropologist on Mars" (Sacks, 1996).

Parents and teachers might have to serve as real-time cultural guides to ever-shifting social contexts, strange rules, and subtle signals.

- *Accept and support.* Children with social development delays often experience overwhelming anxiety. This can appear as obvious dysregulation and disruptive behavior. Or social anxiety can remain under the surface, as avoidance and inner tension. All too often, children with social anxiety are misunderstood. Teachers tell them to consider their classmates' feelings. Parents advise, "Put yourself in your brother's shoes." But if these children could speak for themselves, they would say, "I would if I could." These difficult moments may not be the best time to do social skills teaching. Better to just reflect upon the source of your child's difficulty. Distract, redirect, empathize, calm, or hug. Sometimes, stepping forward to "help" only adds to a child's anxiety, embarrassment, or humiliation. In these situations, it might be better to take a step back.

General Approach to Social Engineering

By describing a child's social development in each of the above facets, a social facilitation strategy can be customized. This real-world approach to social success is very similar to parallel exposure therapy for overcoming anxiety. The same general principles apply. There is a golden mean between expecting too much and expecting too little.

Think Developmentally

Meet each child at his or her developmental level—where they actually are, not where you think they should be. Parents' wishes, conscious or subconscious, may not be in line with their child's needs. Some parents need to expect less and do more; other parents need to expect more and do less. For example, parents may have preferences about types of friends, activities, and level of independence. If the child's needs and preferences are different than the parents' preconceptions, then parents may need to be less idealistic and more pragmatic. What parents want may be very different from what works for their child. Expectations must be adjusted to match real, not imagined abilities.

This is all about developmental realities, not chronological age.

Problem: An eight-year-old child might have the verbal skills of a fourteen-year-old but the social skills of a four-year-old. Solution: Give that child Dostoevsky to read but Go Fish to play.

Of course, if a parent's expectations are below a child's developmental level, adjustments should be made in the opposite direction. For each child, there is a just-right level of social support.

Provide Positive Reinforcement

If we just set the stage for success, some children will need no encouragement. They will be so excited by their own achievement or so aware of positive natural consequences that external reinforcement only undermines internal drive. For them, environmental adjustment is more than enough. Other children, despite accommodation, might still lack motivation, especially when avoidance is easier or gratification isn't immediate. Some children need external motivation for social progress. Without some kind of reward or perk, there is no compelling reason to expand their comfort zone, be friendly, initiate interaction, show sympathy, or follow rules. Different children need different types of reinforcement: immediate or delayed, verbal or nonverbal, animated or muted, direct or indirect, material rewards or simple positive attention. The reward should be customized according to what is meaningful and motivating for the child, not what feels right to the parent. For a complete discussion of individualized approaches to motivation, see *Parent Child Journey*.

Jump-Start

It's important to ensure success at the child's current functional level. Sometimes, just to "prime the pump," we should start even a bit lower. Socially immature children need structure and support. Initially, parents and other adults might have to step forward to serve as social choreographers, matchmakers, and facilitators. They should deliberately design social situations that will lead to social success. Before expectations are raised, the child should experience repeated success, so that they can consolidate gains, build confidence, and enhance social motivation. If there is no progress at one level, then consider going back a level (-1), just temporarily, to get things going. When charging a car battery, we let the engine run for a while before shifting gears into drive. Let your child get a secure toehold at one level before expecting him or her to push off higher.

80 Percent + 1

After achieving success at one level, the child with social disability is placed in situations that are just a bit more challenging. Gradually and incrementally, the child is nudged along, just barely outside of their comfort zone. This means a minimum of 80 percent success at one level before going to the next. In other words, your child should be able to handle a social challenge at least four out of five times before you raise the expectations—and even then, you should not raise the bar too high. Just one notch up.

When ready to advance, as discussed in detail above, you can increase the variety of activities, expand the circle of friends, extend the length of time, require more independence, take away some structure, allow more uncertainty, and demand more social skill. Not too much. Just one notch up.

Fade Support and Space Positive Reinforcement

Even as a child makes progress, don't fade support too quickly. Don't assume that a child doesn't need significant support just because he or she is "older" or "should have" had enough time to learn. Early in social development, choices might have to be limited. But you won't need to continue providing the same high level of support forever. Just the opposite. For example, early on, even if you have to limit your child to certain play options, you can still allow a degree of self-determination.

As your child gets older, it's very important to give up as much control as possible. Your child should have increasing levels of autonomy choosing friends and activities. Of course, you should step in to prevent truly regrettable consequences—but the risk of drowning doesn't mean interfering with learning to swim. Children should not be denied the opportunity to learn from their own mistakes. Giving a necessary degree of support should not eliminate opportunities to learn through trial and error. A manageable degree of struggle is crucial to social learning. Gradually and incrementally, parents should lessen their degree of involvement, back off on external reinforcement, and give up larger degrees of control. After all, the overriding goal is independence, self-motivation, and autonomy. Again, it's just about finding that right balance between dependence and independence, that golden mean between expecting too much and expecting too little.

This approach pertains to children with persistent social difficulties. Normally developing children, who are experiencing good-enough social success, should be left well enough alone, without special accommodations. But many children need this kind of help.

Using the above guidelines, the child's current level of social functioning determines the necessary level of social support. Whether you call it social engineering, social choreography, or social landscaping, the general strategy is to accommodate the child's developmental level, setting by setting, situation by situation; not too much, not too little. This highly individualized approach increases each and every child's chance of social success, expands their circles of social comfort, and helps them move higher up the mountain of social development. Having experienced social success at one level, a child will be more willing and able to reach higher. Success deprivation, withdrawal, and apathy represent our failure to build a ramp, *not* the child's failure to climb the steps. This approach helps a child grow by first changing the environment—preparing the child for the road by first preparing the road for the child.

Finding the Golden Mean Between Social Accommodation and Individual Intervention

By design, this discussion of developmental difference has been imbalanced. The emphasis has been on adjusting our expectations rather than changing the child, social engineering more than individual therapy, acceptance over intervention, environmental support versus behavior modification, here-and-now success over future goals. But this advice is offered only as a counter-balance to prevailing cultural expectations.

I am all for helping children grow. But we need to help our society—and ourselves—grow as well. Although profound progress has been made, we still have a long way to go. Individuals with social-emotional differences still need a lot more acceptance and a lot less fixing. Our planet still needs more fertile space for neurodiversity to take hold and flourish.

In the pages ahead, I offer some supplementary comments—and a bit more balanced approach—regarding management across some common settings.

Social Engineering in Different Settings

Social Learning Begins at Home

Relatively context-blind children need a higher degree of consistency across settings. They have difficulty understanding why different behaviors are expected in different situations.

Modeling

Children learn what they see. Children who are more developmentally naive and vulnerable than others should not be left to depend too much upon peers, TV, or the Internet for social learning. Do not underestimate the importance and power of your own role-modeling. Parents, grandparents, and other family members should be mindful of their own social behavior. Parents want to feel pride—not regret—when they see reflections of their own interpersonal habits in their children. Your children need mature and positive exemplars to learn manners, conflict resolution, unselfishness, and empathy. In a natural way, not with parents functioning as 24/7 therapists, every moment together—dinner-time, play-time, and work-time—represents an opportunity for parents to demonstrate social-emotional intelligence and family values.

Sibling Relationships

Sibling relationships represent foundational and lifelong opportunities for social development. As discussed in detail in Excursion 2, sibling interactions can be very complicated, full of peril and promise. Given the potential risks and benefits, parents need to strike the right balance—find the golden mean—between intervening too little or too much.

Parents should recognize, notice, and encourage positive sibling interactions. All the social choreography principles discussed above work just as well for siblings as they do for peers. If social facilitation is required, it's best done proactively, not after the fact. Parents should analyze predictably problematic situations. What are the usual triggers? When and where does trouble tend to happen? When siblings fight, it's often for lack of something better to do. To head off sibling conflict, parents may need to preview rules and structure up unstructured time. More supervision can mean more opportunity to give attention for positive behavior. Don't wait for trouble to draw you in. It's much better to facilitate than police. After successful jump-starting, positive attention and guidance can be spaced and faded.

Sibling conflicts can be opportunities for collaborative problem-solving. Parents can validate each child's feelings, including negative emotions, without taking sides. Sometimes this requires teaching that equal isn't fair and fair isn't equal. If proactive engineering and collaborative problem-solving fail, parents should not underreact to abusive behavior, or allow serious or repeated injury, bullying or teasing, or serious physical or emotional harm. (For a complete discussion of collaborative problem-solving and behavior management, see my first book, *Parent Child Journey: An Individualized Approach to Raising Your Challenging Child*.)

Important as it is for parents to sometimes step forward, it's often best to take a step back. Parents should not pursue idealized relationships between their children, or feel as if they are responsible for each and every sibling interaction, or take responsibility for making siblings love each other. They should treat each child as a unique individual with their own needs and desires. Everyone in the family doesn't always have to get along. Siblings should not have to spend all of their family time together. Parents should take turns spending special time with each child, one-on-one. This de-triangulates parent-child relationships and allows each parent a chance to respond to each child as an individual, without their brother or sister around. Siblings should have favorite activities and friends separate from each other. Parents should encourage each child to develop their own peer/horizontal family relationships outside of the nuclear/vertical family.

Parents must learn to recognize, accept, and nurture different temperaments. As previously discussed, don't assign roles or reinforce cultural stereotypes, such as all-boy/girly-girl, the nerd/the jock, the shy one/the outgoing one, the youngest/the oldest, the emotional one/the stable one, and so on. Such labels lead to harmful comparison, feelings of favoritism, and constrained self-image.

Parents should not over-react to ordinary sibling conflict. They should allow minor injury, not reinforce negative behavior, dependence, and helplessness by giving attention to ordinary sibling conflict. They should be wary of sibling scapegoating, blaming, or "playing the victim." Parents should give siblings the opportunity to do their own problem-solving and learn from their own mistakes.

The Social Development School

The Fourth "R": Relationships

For most children, school represents their best opportunity for peer connection and social learning. Unfortunately, with increasing emphasis on academic performance and standardized testing, most schools give little attention to the social intelligence curriculum. Too much classroom instruction involves lectures, worksheets, videos, and computer screens. Recess is vanishing. From an early age, education has become geared toward admission to a "good" college. (Whatever that is.) We need to counter this trend and strike a healthier balance between academic and social-emotional goals. Success and happiness depend upon so much more than good grades and SAT scores—and good grades and SAT scores depend to a large degree upon social success and happiness.

In school, children should learn, work, and play together. They need to experience what it means to be a member of the class and the wider school community. Most children navigate the social world on natural instinct. But even those without social disability would benefit from more deliberate and explicit social teaching. In addition to "reading, 'riting, and 'rithmetic," socially attuned teachers and schools should give just as much attention to the fourth "r": relationships.

Social Problem-Solving

The social development teacher regularly interrupts or integrates academics with instruction in interpersonal skills. "It looks like we've got a problem over here. Let's all stop and brainstorm some solutions together." This social problem-solving can be done with the whole class, a small group, or just two kids.

Social Engineering

The social development teacher deliberately pairs socially delayed children with "popular kids." Or the teacher can rotate partners for small-group activities. The social development teacher designs, implements, and supervises plans for prosocial behavior, using different strategies for the classroom, playground, cafeteria, hallways, and bathrooms. She deliberately assigns academic and play projects that are intrinsically social, requiring interaction according to specific social scripts. With

315

children's help, she establishes prosocial protocols, rules, rituals, and games. (See www.remakingrecess.org.) Socially attuned teachers assign and rotate jobs to simplify social roles, creating a sense of teamwork and shared responsibility. She promotes friendships and shared interests outside of school.

Special Social Education

A social skills curriculum is important for all children but it's crucial for those with social disability. 504 plans or Individualized Education Programs should include specific social goals and strategies for all school settings and activities. The development of social intelligence is as important as academic achievement. However, according to federal law, school-based social-development goals must pertain to "availability for learning." Specifically, the academic curriculum requires a substantial amount of group learning. Without accommodation for social disability, most of these children experience secondary anxiety, depression, and distractibility. In these ways, social disability interferes with equal access to education. Some assignments and subjects (such as reading and writing in Language and Social Studies) require social pragmatics, social context-reading and social inferencing skills. Social support in a school depends upon strong leadership and good team work.

Case Study: T.

T. was having trouble connecting with classmates on the playground. Sometimes, he annoyed them by asking the same questions over and over. His parents and therapist (Dr. J) asked for a school team meeting. They were joined by T.'s teacher (Ms. H.), the head of school (Mr. N.), the school counselor (Ms. K), and learning specialist (Ms. D). Following the team meeting, there were a series of group emails.

Email from T.'s parents to the team:

Hi all,

Thanks for a great meeting. Afterward, T. met with Dr. J. and they came up with a few key things for T. to think about and say to himself during recess. We just wanted you to be aware so that we are all on the same page.

- *After I start playing with a group, I won't ask to play again—even if I'm separated for a bit or there's a little* break in the action. Note: *This is to keep T. from asking repetitive questions that might be annoying to other kids.*

- *I will not ask questions. I will just do what my friends are doing until I understand. Note: The idea is for T. to stop and observe, use his visual skills instead of needing language to interpret each unique situation.*
- *If I'm playing hide and seek, and I haven't been found in one or two minutes, I will come out and go hang with the group. I will also start to pick hiding places that aren't obvious but also aren't too difficult. Note: This is so T. really focuses on following along with the group and not being rigid about traditional rules of hide and seek.*
- *For now, when I want to change the game, I will ask my friends if they want to play a game we have already played in the past. Note: This is to gain success in leading a game and also increase the likelihood that other kids will want to play.*
- *When I feel confused, I will stop and look around. Then I will choose someone to hang around with who I feel comfortable with. Note: This is the stop and scan.*

T. seems comfortable trying these strategies out at recess. If you're outside with him and notice that he seems confused or isolated, you can prompt him, quietly, and privately: "Stop." This simple reminder seems to help him a lot. I did that myself with him, at a birthday party over the weekend at a busy gym—and he did fabulous!

Thank you all for all of your hard work, support, and understanding.

Warm regards,
T.'s parents

Email from Head of School:

Dear Team T.,

Thanks to T.'s parents and Dr. J. for passing these strategies along. I am cc'ing the team, including our recess monitor, Ms. H., who was not at our meeting last week and is definitely a part of Team T.

After the meeting, the school team met again to debrief. We identified the following next steps.

- *Recess data: We drafted a data collection document that*

we can use during recess time. We would appreciate your feedback as we are trying to make sure it's practical and provide the right data to help us monitor his engagement and progress.

- Schedule of observation: We will collect data two to three times a week for 20 minutes each. We can send the data sheet home at the end of each week.
- Structured play opportunities: I will be taking the lead with this. Next week, I will meet with the whole class to introduce some more-structured group games.
  - Kickball, foursquare, knock out, flag football, and bean bag toss.
  - I will be doing a little survey to see which games they want to try. I will let you know what the group decides, then you can go through rules and practice with T. at home.
- Time on the playground outside of school hours: You could also practice with T. at school when other kids aren't around. Please let me know if there is a certain day before school, after school, or on the weekend when you might want access to the playground. I would be more than happy to meet you here on a particular Saturday or Sunday and let you in.

Thanks again for sharing these strategies!
All the best,
Mr. N.

Mr. N attached a discussion draft of the data collection form:

T's Recess Success

Date.			
Activity. Minutes engaged. (5, 10, 15, 20) Prompt needed? (Y/N) Comments.	Activity. Minutes engaged. (5, 10, 15, 20) Prompt needed? (Y/N) Comments.	Activity. Minutes engaged. (5, 10, 15, 20) Prompt needed? (Y/N) Comments.	Activity. Minutes engaged. (5, 10, 15, 20) Prompt needed? (Y/N) Comments.

Another email from the Head of School:

Dear Team T.,

We are off and running with the recess plan at school and wanted to follow up with a quick update and copy of T.'s charts from recess this week. We got in three days of data collection. As you can see, there's been some nice sustained engagement with the other kids.

Regarding my introducing new team games at recess, I had a meeting with each of the third-grade classes on Tuesday and framed the conversation around their social development. I explained that, as kids get older, they often become interested in playing some team games that involve more than a couple students. I told them that I wanted their feedback on what would be particularly popular at our school. Based on what they said, I would make sure that we have the right equipment and that everyone understood the rules. The only criteria I gave them was that the activities needed to be able to be played safely on our playground. I walked them through the survey, which had some of my ideas, then we brainstormed. I invited them to write in ideas.

After we completed a list of possible activities, they each rated their interest in the games (4-point scale). In order of preference, here's their list.

Games to try at recess
1. Team Tag Infection
2. Foursquare
3. Football (two-hand touch or flag football)
4. Kickball and basketball/knockout (tied)
5. Capture the flag.

Next week I am going to be out on the playground Monday and Tuesday to introduce the rules and help launch Team Tag Infection (a.k.a. Zombie Tag) for students who are interested. Here are the rules in case you want to go through them with T.
www.wikihow.com/Play-Infection-Tag
I will keep you posted as to how popular this is and if T. decides to play or not. If he doesn't, I will try to introduce some of the other games. If he seems to be into it, then we'll let it play out and take our time before introducing another

game. Please share any thoughts or questions.
Have a great weekend!
Mr. N.

T. and his classmates loved zombie tag. Gradually, they learned
to play other games on the list. T.'s recess success chart kept
coming home with encouraging data. Now he was playing with
the other kids on a regular basis. He was having fun and so
were the other kids.

Some children with disabilities need self-contained special education classrooms. However, for many children with autism and
related challenges, inclusive classrooms and peer-mentoring
programs can be crucial for social development. In addition,
done properly, inclusive schools help typically developing members of the school community as well (Kluth, 2010). What better way to teach about developmental difference, empathy, and
social responsibility?

Bullying/Teasing

Any child can become either the victim or perpetrator of teasing
or bullying. Many children are both victims *and* perpetrators.
Children with social disability are at a much higher risk. What is
the right balance, the golden mean, between under- and overre-
acting (Bazelon, 2013)?

Strategies:

- *Take it seriously.* Peer abuse and isolation can have very serious health consequences, both mental and physical. Over the
  last few decades, the horrifying increase in school shootings
  plus persistently high youth suicide rates highlight the importance of early intervention for teasing and bullying—which
  are all too often associated. Less dramatic but equally worrisome is the high incidence of secondary anxiety, depression,
  and social isolation. School personnel should be vigilant,
  available, and responsive.
- *Setting school culture.* All schools should have no-bullying/
  no-teasing policies—clearly stated, posted, and enforced.
  Victims and perpetrators alike should know that parents,
  teachers, and bystander children will not react with indif-
  ference or ambivalence. If there is an incident, parents and
  teachers should meet immediately and present a unified

message to all children involved. They should agree on meaningful consequences for perpetrators and provide support for victims.

- *Create safe zones.* As a first step in prevention of recurrence, the school team should identify antecedent situations and circumstances. What was going on immediately preceding the bullying or teasing? Such incidents are most likely to occur when and where adults are not around: playgrounds, bathrooms, hallways, cafeterias, before and after school. High-risk situations should be avoided, modified, or tightly supervised. Preventative management plans should be written up, staffed, and reviewed periodically.
- *Beware cyber-bullying.* Although in-person bullying and teasing are still more frequent than the remote kind, abuse by cell phone and keyboard should be taken seriously. Many children and adolescents are subjected to harmful messaging through social media. Depression, anxiety and even suicide have been directly tied to this modern source of ubiquitous social pain (Truong, 2015).
- *Teach victims self-help.* Insisting that adults step forward to ensure safety doesn't preclude teaching self-advocacy and self-protection. Vulnerable children need help developing preventive strategies and emergency responses. At-risk children should be actively invested in their own safety. Parents, teachers, administrators, and counselors can help brainstorm a range of alternatives, choose an effective set of strategies, consider all the "what-ifs," and rehearse the plan. Whenever possible, parents, teachers and children need to try dealing with the problem head-on.
- *Work with the perpetrator too.* Just telling perpetrators to stop is usually insufficient. First, there should be an evaluation to determine the roots of their own behavior. As mentioned, many perpetrators are also victims. Perpetrators and victims are both at higher-risk for having underlying developmental and behavioral disorders, including autism, ADHD, anxiety, other mood disorders, learning problems, and more. When appropriate, they should receive some form of individual counseling, including sensitivity training and social problem-solving.

Supplementary (Not Alternative) Social Learning

As emphasized throughout this discussion, children learn best from real-life interaction. However, even with the kind of accommodation and support described here, some children will still struggle with social interaction. Natural play, conversation, and interpersonal dynamics might be too direct, too fast, or too uncomfortable. There are a variety of ways to provide meaningful social practice that is slower, more subtle, and less threatening. Indirect social learning opportunities can provide important preparation for the real thing.

Strategies and Techniques

A variety of strategies and techniques can be used to teach foundational vocabulary and concepts. Before children can apply emotional intelligence in real-life situations, they might need to be taught the fundamentals in private. First, children need to know the primary emotions: happy, sad, angry, and scared. Then they can learn more subtlety: confused, embarrassed, jealous, disbelieving, remorseful, grateful, annoyed, frustrated. They also need to learn about gradations of emotion. First, we keep it simple: big deal, little deal, no problem; red, yellow, and green. Then, multiple shades of gray, 0–10, etc. Similarly, we need to help children move beyond simplistic assessment of personality ("mean" versus "nice") to understanding the full array of human behavior. Higher social-emotional intelligence leads to greater tolerance of social demands and more mature coping strategies. Although the following indirect teaching strategies should not take the place of real-life social experience, they can serve as valuable supplements.

Dolls and Toy Figures

Symbolic and imaginary play provides children with very important opportunities to explore all sorts of social-emotional themes: fear, loss, rejection, conflict, anger, love, jealousy, and friendship. Although children should be allowed to experiment, parents can provide various age-appropriate items and facilitate pretend play as needed. For example, parents can assume the role of a toy figure but let the child direct the action.

Literature

The world of fiction, poetry, biography, and history provides a deep well of social learning and inspiration. A great book can be a child's best teacher. Parents should model a love of reading. Parents and children can read and discuss books together. Parents can ask, "Why did she do that? What would you have done differently?" Children will learn to apply lessons learned through literature to real-life situations.

Pets and Animals

Non-humans often allow children to experience extraordinary "interpersonal" connection. Furry friends may provide unconditional love and companionship. Pets give children the chance to understand and assume responsibility for another living being. But parents should carefully consider their child's developmental profile before bringing an animal into the home. Realistically, parents may still need to assume primary responsibility.

Social Skills Groups and Individual Therapy

Therapeutic Peer Groups

Children with ADHD, autism, and other developmental disorders are often referred to social skills groups. There are a plethora of approaches and providers but a paucity of evidence for effectiveness. Some children are in social skills groups to the exclusion of other more crucial therapies; for example, social skills groups should not take the place of medication for ADHD, CBT for anxiety, and individualized education programs for autism.

The biggest problem with social skills groups is carrying over the lessons learned in group out into the real world. Some children may actually adopt negative behaviors from other group members. But many children can benefit from real-time guided practice with peers, and form real friendships. The most effective social skills groups are led by experienced clinicians who take the time to screen and match participants. There should be a research-proven curriculum, parent and teacher involvement, practice homework, and outcome measures (Laugeson, 2013; Winner, 2019; Cannon, Kenworthy, Alexander, Adler Warner, & Anthony, 2018).

Individual Psychosocial Therapy

Most people would not think of one-on-one meetings between a child and a therapist as a social skills group. However, dyads are the most basic social unit. Important social learning can take place during a child's interaction with a psychologist, social worker, or speech-language therapist. The therapist can help the child preview challenging social situations, develop a plan, and give it a try. At the next visit, the child and therapist can review how it worked.

Another very valuable function of individual therapy is for someone with special expertise to get to know the child in a more in-depth way than others can. Then the therapist can help parents and teachers understand the child better. In this way, therapy isn't always concerned with changing the child.

Screens

Danger

Of course, electronic screens can isolate children and divide families. Modern media bombards developing minds with terrible messages, horrifying images, inappropriate models, and hateful speech. Parents should be very concerned about their children's exposure to aggression, violence, sexual objectification, drugs, racial stereotypes, poor nutrition, materialism, power, manipulation, and more.

Dancing with the Devil

All that being said, carefully selected TV shows, video games, and movies can provide opportunities for positive social modeling and family time. Some simulation games can give children practice with social thinking and social consequences. Some children with social delays learn better from visual-musical imagery than being talked at. If watched together, parents can use commercials or the pause button to talk about shared video: "Do you think that's really true?" "What would you do in that situation?"

E-Friends

Are cyber-friends real? Do chat rooms, instant-messaging, and text-messaging represent social interaction? As a supplement, yes, but let's not pretend that texting takes the place of face-to-face interaction (Turkle, 2016). The full depth and breadth of social reciprocity cannot be captured by a screen. Most social information is coded nonverbally as tone of voice, facial expression, gesture, posture, context, and touch. Electronic interaction that combines nonverbal with verbal communication can come closer to full connection.

Some children, adolescents, and adults with social challenges can benefit from this new culture of electronic connection. For some, Internet connection is much better than no social connection at all. There's more opportunity to modify the pace and complexity of interpersonal interaction, buying time to think or even receive on-the-spot coaching. In these ways, digital communication can jump-start or supplement natural face-to-face connection.

Family Rules

Parents, children, and teens need to weigh these digital pros and cons. Screens can be a source of connection for children who would otherwise be isolated—or a source of isolation for children who could otherwise be connected. Screens can confer a sense of belonging or impose unhealthy comparisons. Every parent must seriously consider how to the reap benefits of media age but avoid the undeniable potential for harm.

I strongly recommend proactive management. Parents, children, and adolescents should discuss rules and consequences. Electronic controls can be placed if a child will have difficulty with compliance. All of this can be done *with* the child or adolescent rather than *to* them (Pletter, 2019).

Social Change

On Relationships and Social Disability

So far, this discussion has focused on helping children find friendship. Companionship protects health, both emotional and physical. Social connection prevents anxiety and depression. It's definitely not okay to *feel lonely* most of the time. But is it okay to *be alone* some of the time?

Introverts

In his book *Galen's Prophecy* and throughout his career, Jerome Kagan (1997) showed how a reactive temperament in infancy naturally predisposes to an introverted personality type. Fussy babies can become withdrawn adults. Relatively less reactive temperament in infancy leans toward later extroversion. Easy babies are more likely to became gregarious. In *Quiet,* Susan Cain (2013) exposes and criticizes pro-extrovert/anti-introvert cultural bias. She makes a compelling case for the virtue of social reticence and the advantages of solitary thoughtfulness.

Being with other people can be energizing or exhausting, comforting or stressful. Some people need a break from socializing. Relationships need not be what life is *all* about. Periods of isolation allow time to read, play music, exercise, meditate, and think. This isn't a case for solitary existence, but a plea to define social success more broadly.

The Good Life

What if your child remains socially different? It's important to remember that many people are content not to socialize. This may run contrary to your idea of a "meaningful life." Most people think relationships are crucial to health and happiness. However, many of history's most admired and important individuals were not at all socially successful (Silberman & Sacks, 2015). Thanks largely to the growing importance of physics, science, computers, and the Internet, a relatively isolated existence is no longer synonymous with failure (Prizant & Fields-Meyer, 2016).

To quote Temple Grandin (D. Shapiro, personal communication, 2002), the most famous person with autism in the world: "You so-called normal people and your relationships! Don't give me an interview. Just look at my work portfolio. I don't need a marriage or even your idea of a friend. Just let me have my special interests and a good job." The autism pride and neurodiversity movements are based on the idea that our society needs to expand its narrow idea of success and meaning (Donvan & Zucker, 2016). This isn't to say that we should neglect to intervene where improvement of skills can improve quality of life. But sometimes accommodation is more realistic—and more respectful too.

Hidden Disability

In our assessment of others, we can be quick and harsh. Ironically, an insensitive rush to judgment can be more pernicious and problematic when the social impairment—or any disability—is relatively mild and hidden. It's not easy needing a white cane, a wheelchair, or a helmet. However, such specialized equipment is more likely to illicit a sympathetic reaction. What about children who "look normal" but act differently? They too are at risk for success deprivation, mental illness, and unemployment. Yet these children with subtle but significant social disabilities—and their parents—might be less likely to get a helping hand and more likely to incur blame, shame, reprimand, or punishment. Their relatively misunderstood behaviors don't usually inspire respect and compassion. All too often, children with subtle social disabilities are dealt exasperated reproaches, such as "What's your problem!" Note the exclamation mark instead of a question mark.

People with disabilities don't want pity, but they do need accommodation, no matter how mild or severe the impairment may seem. If the last chapter to be written in the civil rights movement is about disability rights, then perhaps the last pages will be about hidden impairments.

On "Us Versus Them"

The Evolution of Cooperation

As explained by Joshua Greene (2014) in *Moral Tribes,* human beings evolved for cooperation *within* groups but not *between* groups. In fact, human survival has always been about in-group cooperation and intergroup competition. Cooperation continues only if people can achieve more together than they can separately—conferring a survival advantage for that group. Within-group relationships endure only if the benefits outweigh the possible costs. The result: in-group bias, ethnocentrism, "us versus them."

Shibboleths

Arbitrary cultural practices and personal characteristics can bind or repel, unite or divide. From the Book of Judges, chapter 12, pronunciation of an initial "sh" sound was used to discriminate friend from foe.

And the Gileadites took the passages of Jordan before the Ephraimites. And it was so, that when those Ephraimites which were escaped said, "Let me go over," that the men of Gilead said unto him, "Art thou an Ephraimite?" If he said, "Nay," then said they unto him, "Say now Shibboleth." And he said, "Sibboleth," for he could not frame to pronounce it right. Then they took him and slew him at the passages of Jordan.

A shibboleth is any reliable marker of group identity that distinguishes "us versus them." This kind of "friend or foe" discrimination is a huge barrier to the neurodiversity and inclusion movement. Rigid cultural expectations create shibboleths of developmental difference. Involuntary movement and vocalization, dysregulated mood and behavior, learning variation, and other differences in socialization all represent markers of outsider status.

Isolation or Unification

Although a diagnosis of autism or other developmental differences can be isolating, such labels can also be unifying and empowering. Individuals and families that share a diagnosis often come together, online and in-person. Even if genetic testing doesn't—at the time of this writing—usually change management or outcome for individuals, families that share a specific genetic variation often do discover a wonderful sense of community and kinship. Local and worldwide advocacy groups have sprung up around a long list of specific diagnoses: Tuberous Sclerosis, Dup q 15 q, Down Syndrome, and Fragile X, to name just a few. Such neuro-villages can provide mutual emotional support and information, plus advocacy for research, education, and civil rights. Much of the extraordinary progress made by people with neurodevelopmental differences is the direct result of such parent and self-advocacy groups. In numbers, there is both strength and comfort.

To eliminate harmful distinctions between us and them, neurotypical and neurodiverse people need to find common ground. We need to build communities and broaden tribal identity. We need to include everyone in congregations, orchestras, dance troupes, apartment buildings, and political parties. This means not eliminating differences but identifying commonalties. After all, there's more than a little bit of developmental difference in all of us.

On the Golden Mean in Social Change

Human nature makes change difficult. I have tried to make case for accommodation. But not every school is ready to remake recess. Not every community is ready for inclusive housing. Not every congregation welcomes disruptive behavior. Not every soccer league allows two goalies on one team.

Walter was an elementary school student with autism. His teachers described him as "academically capable but socially inept." He did his schoolwork but had no friends. During recess, lunchtime, and between classes, he talked to himself, often spinning elaborate stories about comic book heroes. Walter engaged in self-absorbed play fights, imagining himself to be in the center of some intergalactic battle, thrusting his fists into the air. At first, other kids were confused. Then they were a little uncomfortable. Then they were entertained. Often, they huddled together to giggle and exchange comments. Finally, they were just bored and acted as if Walter didn't exist.

Walter's parents knew that he didn't have any friends. They asked Dr. Quito for help. After observing the class dynamic, Dr. Quito met with the teacher to suggest some social engineering. The teacher could announce a small group project and ask all the students to write down their partner preferences. Their preferences would be kept confidential. Dr. Quito and the teacher knew that the most popular kids would be listed on just about everybody's card, then there would be moderately popular kids on several cards, then there would be Walter. Not a single classmate would put him on their card. But then, the teacher could announce the small groups and deliberately pair Walter with one of the more popular (and kind) kids. Other classmates would see this pairing, wonder if the popular kid had chosen Walter, and perhaps see Walter in a different light.

But the teacher was uncomfortable with this idea. After all, the kid who was paired with Walter would know that she had not put him on her card. The teacher challenged Dr. Quito: "Shouldn't we respect the kids' choices?" This approach seemed unnatural, dishonest, and manipulative. Walter and the other kids had reached an understanding—a kind of equilibrium— about his outlier status. The teacher said Walter didn't seem unhappy. And didn't kids with autism prefer to be left alone? The principal, informed of Dr. Quito's suggestion, was concerned about kids going home and telling their parents that they were being forced to work with Walter. This kind of social engineering was not in Walter's IEP. After all, he was above grade level in all subjects. What did this have to do with his availability for learning? The public-school system didn't exist to help kids make friends.

This kind of pushback to social accommodation isn't unusual. How can we change social systems to accommodate neurodiverse individuals without stirring up too much resistance? If we push too fast and too hard, we run the risk of provoking social anxiety, instead of facilitating social reform.

Trail-End for Excursion 4

Our exploration of social engineering ends with a political question: As we work to break down social barriers, how do we avoid amplifying "us versus them" thinking? In the context of this book, resistance to accommodating developmental difference can be seen as a symptom of anxiety in a social system. Throughout history, social change has often been seen as a threat to be avoided. Referring back to Excursion 2, how can we apply parallel exposure therapy to this last frontier in the civil rights movement? On the playground and in the halls of Congress, for every individual and every community, what is the right balance between acceptance and change, accommodation and intervention, conformity and revolution? How do we mark a trail to achieve lasting change? In Excursion 5, by examining the important topic of sexuality and gender identity differences in individuals with autism, we suggest a framework for facilitating durable social change.

EXCURSION 5
Discover—Autism, Sexuality, and Gender Identity
with Aaron Shapiro, MD, MPH

———— ◆ ————

It's revolutionary for any trans person to choose to be
seen and visible in a world that tells us we should not exist.
—Laverne Cox

*Then came the most surprising thing of all. Suddenly, Raph, Dog,
and Turtle were not alone. Many other animals had been hiding
at the base of the mountain. They wanted to help. Some had tried
but failed. Some had gotten to the other side themselves, but knew
many of their friends weren't able to. Many had never even thought
about trying, but Raph's angry screeching had brought them out.
The sight of a bird, a dog, and a turtle all digging at the mountain
together inspired the other animals. Maybe there was a way to the
other side for everyone after all.*

*One by one, then by the dozens, and then by the hundreds, ani-
mals came, of every size and shape, to help dig a tunnel. Together,*

side by side, stone by stone, they punched their way through the center of the mountain.

With so many animals digging, it didn't take long. Joyfully, they pushed Raph to the front, insisting that he be the first one through the opening. And there, just as Raph remembered: Tambalacoque

trees. Tall and loaded with fruit. Plenty for everybody. Tambalaco-que fruit had never tasted so good.

Signposts for Excursion 5

This excursion is a detailed discussion of sexuality and gender in individuals with autism, including:

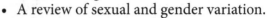

- A review of sexual and gender variation.
- Autistic differences in sexuality.
- Gender variation and autism.
- How to support neurodiversity, sexual diversity, and gender diversity for individuals and in society at large.

In Excursion 4, we discussed social engineering for individuals with autism. Here, in Excursion 5, we broaden our focus and tackle universal cultural reform for individuals with autism who also have differences in sexuality and gender.

Right up front, let's acknowledge that this is a sensitive and personal topic. Consciously or subconsciously, we are all subject to a lifetime of conditioning. Being a parent is largely a process of releasing the child you were conditioned to expect and accepting the child you actually have. For most parents, embracing autism is challenging enough. If, in addition to autism, a child has variant sexuality and/or gender, then even the most loving parents may feel confused, conflicted, afraid, and overwhelmed. They may even need time to grieve the loss of their "ideal" or expected child. Parents, teachers, and clinicians may have difficulty thinking outside of learned sex and gender boxes. In the discussion that follows, we suggest at least setting those boxes aside.

Readers of Excursions 1–4 will notice a change of tone with Excursion 5. Partly, this stems from the subject matter, but it is also due to the addition of Aaron's voice. Aaron is a gay physician who has focused much of his training on care for the LGBTQI community. Aaron approaches these issues as both a recipient and provider of LGBTQI-focused health care. Dan is a developmental-behavioral pediatrician with more general experience. He is also a proud father.

We cowrote this section, combining our clinical and personal backgrounds. We wanted to make a strong case for liberal, evidence-based thinking about sex and gender. As doctors from two different generations, we have worked hard to bring sensitivity to these pages. We understand that many parents are struggling to navigate new concepts and understand their children. We hope that this exploration of autism, sexuality, and gender helps people with autism and their families. We also wish to highlight how people with autism have much to teach the rest of us about intimate relationships, interpersonal differences, and cultural transformation. It is important to acknowledge that neither of us identifies as trans, nonbinary, or on the autism spectrum. We encourage readers to look for literature by authors—and live events with speakers—who are from these communities. Although we hope that this chapter helps elevate their voices, they speak for themselves better than we ever could.

Reed was a seven-year-old with autism. He was quirky and didn't have any friends. However, Reed was bright and did well in school. A few days before his routine check-up, Reed's parents sent an email to their pediatrician. They wanted Dr. Benjamin to know that Reed had been leaving the house every day with a long brown piece of construction paper clipped to the back of his head. Reed's father asked, "What's this?" Reed answered, "I want a ponytail like Emily's." Emily was a classmate. Reed's father took it off. Reed said, "Fine, I'll just make a new one at school." One of Reed's teachers emailed, "Do you want her to wear the ponytail in the class photo tomorrow?" The teacher's question and her use of a female pronoun startled Reed's parents.

Reed was not interested in sports. He had always preferred playing with a dollhouse. To Reed's parents, some of his mannerisms seemed effeminate. "At least," Reed's parents comforted themselves, "he's never said he wanted to be a girl." But this ponytail thing was no longer a private matter. Reed's parents started to have serious concerns about his future. Reed's father was very upset. He thought, It's because his mother babies him too much. Reed's mother hoped it was just a phase. They had hoped that autism would not make marriage impossible. But what about autism and whatever this turned out to be?

At the visit, Dr. Benjamin asked, "Reed, do you ever think about being a girl? Reed said, "No." Dr. Benjamin asked, "Have you ever wanted to change your name?" Again, Reed answered, "No," Then Dr. Benjamin announced, "He's probably not trans—just gay." Reed's parents were confused. In the weeks ahead, Reed's father pushed harder for Reed to join a soccer team. Reed refused. Reed's mother told her husband, "Back off. Can't you see you're just making things worse?"

Definitions

We are conditioned to think of sexuality and gender in "either/ or" terms: gay or straight, male or female. In real life, things are not so binary. Sexuality and gender are better thought of as fuzzy-edged continua, not sharply defined categories or boxes. There are many layers of nuance, complexity, and fluidity. It may take years to settle confidently into an identity. Consequently, it has become more customary to call such variability a "journey." If an individual is uncertain or ambivalent about sexuality or gender, this should not be seen as illness, deviance, or being inauthentic. Rather, exploration and questioning are necessary steps toward self-realization, all of which requires the passage of time.

What is the difference between *biological sex, gender identity, gender expression,* and *sexuality*? In brief, biological sex is reflected by your assigned sex at birth. Gender identity is who you are: intellectually, spiritually, socially, and politically. Gender expression is how you present your identity. And sexuality is who you're attracted to, who you want to have sex with, and/ or who you engage intimately with. Let us explain in a bit more detail (Hues, 2019).

But before moving on, an important disclaimer. As we emphasize the diversity of sexuality and gender, we recognize that people react to these various terms in different ways. The language used throughout this chapter isn't universally accepted. For starters, what initials should be used when referring to this portion of humanity? Here we use LGBTQI for lesbian, gay, bisexual, transgender, questioning or queer, and intersex. Others prefer different initials. Within and outside of the LGBTQI community, debate regarding definition of these and other terms will certainly continue. In the near future, the terminology we use here may be considered out-of-date and inaccurate. Still, one cannot begin to have a conversation without some kind of common vocabulary. Throughout this chapter we'll do our best to use words that are inclusive and respectful.

Assigned Biological Sex

Biological sex is a designation determined by physical appearance, genes, and hormones. Based on observable differences in the physical body, newborns are usually assigned a sex: male or female. However, some people don't fit so neatly into one box or the other. There can be nonbinary ambiguities in chromosomes, hormone levels, genitalia, or other physical features.

Although most people are born with XX (male) or XY (female) sex chromosomes, there are other chromosomal variants, such as XXY (Kleinfelter's syndrome), XO (Turner's syndrome), and many more. People born with differences in sexual differentiation may have visibly ambiguous genitalia or variant sex chromosome combinations. These individuals are also known as *intersex*.

Genes don't change. At least, we're not yet doing that kind of genetic engineering. But gene expression certainly can vary over time. The fascinating science of epigenetics describes how genes can be turned off and on by any number of environmental influences: cultural, chemical, educational, traumatic, etc.

In addition to genes, hormones affect biological sex and puberty. Certain hormones are feminizing (e.g. estrogen) and others are masculinizing (e.g. testosterone). The effect of hormones upon sex is most obvious with some endocrine disorders. For just one of many possible examples, congenital adrenal hyperplasia can cause ambiguous genitalia and early virilization in boys or girls. This means abnormally rapid growth, and premature development of pubic and armpit hair, deep voice, big muscles, and acne. Such "precocious puberty" can occur at a very young age, even two or three years old. Eventually, there are problems with fertility. The point here is that hormones affect assigned sex. Hormone levels and their effects certainly do change over time, either normally (think puberty, pregnancy, and menopause), abnormally (as in congenital adrenal hyperplasia and other endocrine disorders), or pharmacologically (such as with contraceptives, hormone supplements, or hormone blockers.)

The combined effects of genes and hormones usually results in male or female body types. But in some cases, a newborn's sex is hard to determine. Not too long ago, gender assignment surgery for newborns with ambiguous genitalia was considered a psychological emergency. As discussed further below, now we know that gender assignment should be delayed until a child becomes old enough to clarify their gender identity. It's better to follow a child's lead as they identify and express their gender than guess wrong and surgically give a girl a penis or a boy a vagina. Early in life, many children will start to express some gender variation. But gender identity can take years to realize.

At all ages, our body parts don't define our sex or gender. For various medical reasons, any individual's genitalia, pubic hair, facial hair, and breasts—plus their capacity for menstrual periods or ejaculation—can appear to be male, female, or not clearly one or the other. External genitalia usually allow a doctor, nurse practitioner, or midwife to accurately guess that newborn's sex. But sometimes, appearances can be misleading. Clinicians don't usually check chromosomes. Consequently, some people go a lifetime without knowing their genetic or natal biological identity.

In addition to chromosomal differences, there can be hidden differences in internal anatomy. For example, a girl can be born with normal vulva on the outside but have a blind vaginal pouch. Consider such a teenager with XX chromosomes who identifies as a female but has no menstrual periods. During adolescence, ultrasound or MRI (magnetic resonance imaging) evaluation show that the vagina ends with no cervix, uterus, or fallopian tubes. This is called müllerian agenesis (The American College of Obstetricians and Gynecologists, 2018). She will not be able to get pregnant but she is no less a young woman.

Gender Identity

Gender identity is who you know you are. You might be male, female, non-binary, fluid, or any other description that you know fits you best at any given time. If your gender identity matches your assigned sex at birth, then you're *cisgender*. "Cis" means "the same."

However, gender identity doesn't always match assigned sex at birth. Specifically, a person assigned male at birth might have a clear and definite female gender identity. Or, an assigned female at birth might feel that their gender fluidly migrates between male and female. When identities and bodies don't match, the individual is generally said to fall under the umbrella terms of a *gender-diverse, trans,* or *transgender* identity. "Trans" means "across boundaries," "opposite," or "different." Some people reject culturally normative gender categories altogether, living their truths as *gender-fluid, gender-non-binary,* or *queer.*

These categories need not be mutually exclusive. People can use multiple labels to help express how they identify. The distinction between "cis" and "trans" may be largely artificial and culturally determined. We all might be a complex and changing mix of both tendencies.

Gender Dysphoria

Imagine having a penis if you're a woman. Imagine menstruating if you're a male. Consider how extremely traumatic this could be. This kind of internal distress is called *gender dysphoria.* Transgender individuals may not be able to feel like themselves "in their own skin"—with their body parts and functions.

Individuals with gender dysphoria experience a number of stigmatizing experiences, both internally and externally. As a result, they can be at high risk for social and emotional problems. Minority stress theory refers to the stress that results from being different. It can cause a range of issues, including low self-esteem, anxiety, and depression. Subsequently, minority stress can also lead to risk-taking behaviors, such as substance use, self-harm, and suicide (van der Miesen, Nabbijohn, Santarossa, & VanderLaan, 2018; Blosnich et al., 2013).

Treatment of gender dysphoria might involve counseling, community support, speech therapy, hormone therapy, and/or gender-affirming surgery. Such surgery can include face reconstruction, breast implantation, or neo-genital construction. These treatments support a person's authentic gender identity and alleviate distress (AAP 2018).

To reiterate: Our body parts define neither our sex or gender. A 40-year-old man, assigned female at birth, who gave birth to children and underwent neither hormone therapy nor a mastectomy, is no less of a man than any other. Some trans women may feel that neovaginal surgery is central in their journey to being the women that they are. Others may be perfectly fine with their body as is. Many trans people experience huge financial and sociocultural barriers in their gender journeys, including the expense and stigma of transitioning from one's assigned sex to their true gender identity. As discussed further below, substantial progress toward social-cultural inclusion of trans and gender diverse individuals has taken place, but we still have a long way to go.

Gender Expression

If gender identity is who you are, then gender expression is how you present yourself. People often modify their gender presentation by changing their name, hairstyle, clothing, speech, culturally normative behaviors, or bodies via medical or surgical therapies. They may want to use pronouns that may not seem obvious: male ("he/him"), female ("she/her"), gender-neutral ("they/them" or "ze/zir"), or no pronouns at all (simply repeating their name instead of using a pronoun). If someone's pronouns are not known to you, it's generally acceptable to ask during introductions. You can also introduce yourself with your pronouns, to invite people to use theirs with you: "Hi, I'm Aaron and I use he/his pronouns." At first, some pronoun preferences might seem ungrammatical, foreign, or uncomfortable; with practice, it becomes more natural.

As discussed above, gender expression can be complicated. Someone may present as female in public, with long hair, mascara, and high heels. But the same person might tell you that his name is Ed and he uses he/him pronouns. For many reasons—temporary or permanent, driven by internal or external pressures—he may decide not to present as male. His female presentation doesn't make him any less of a man.

Gender as a Cultural Construct

Some gender-specific tendencies are inborn. Even in the most gender-neutral households, boys and girls may speak, play, and behave according to cultural stereotypes. But two boxes—male and female—don't contain all of humanity. To whatever degree, biological predisposition isn't carved in stone. Nor should it be.

Still, many parents buy blue jeans for their boys and pink skirts for their girls, condition their boys to play sports and their girls to look pretty. Advertisers reinforce binary gender stereotypes. Sexist cultural norms still encourage men to work in science, math, and technology, and women to work as teachers, nurses, and stay-at-home moms.

Let's take a hard look at this kind of binary bias and rigid thinking. When we encounter gender diversity and ambiguity,

339

we should consider the possibility that the rigid old classification system just doesn't work. As already stated, for many people, gender identity is a fluid journey, a developmental process, not a permanent trait. Just because someone used female pronouns the last time you saw them doesn't mean they will be using "she" today. Respect their journey. Follow their lead.

Well-intentioned people might have many questions. But no trans person owes us an explanation. We should not expect them to tell us about medications or surgeries that they may or may not have undertaken. We don't have a right to demand or require a label. On the contrary, if we are struggling to categorize someone as "male" or "female," it's we who need to unlearn the habit of putting people into artificial boxes.

Sexuality

Sexuality and gender are two different things. Sexuality is about your affinity—or lack of affinity—for others. But like gender, sexuality can be endlessly varied.

You may be sexually attracted to one gender and have romantic feelings for another. A person can be sexually or romantically attracted to males, females, neither, or both; or to various non-binary identities on this broad spectrum. Sexuality and attraction can be focused on gender identity, gender expression, or biological sex.

Many people don't have sexual or romantic attractions to speak of. Relative or absolute asexuality isn't rare, despite a steady barrage of cultural conditioning to the contrary. Determinations of gay (homosexual), straight (heterosexual), bisexual, pansexual, and asexual may or may not lend themselves to all-or-none/binary thinking.

Eddie spent most of his childhood in his room, learning electronics and computer programming. He resisted going to school and never did homework. Eddie's pediatrician, Dr. Gregg, thought he was on the autism spectrum, but Eddie's mother refused referral for expert assessment. Eddie got through school on raw brain power alone; he was able to pass tests without studying.

In high school, Eddie agreed to check out the robotics club. His parents were thrilled. Eddie programmed his team's robot to navigate a maze, and his team won a national competition.

For the first time in his life, Eddie had some friends. But when the guys in the robotics club talked about girls, Eddie felt uncomfortable. He was attracted to one of the other guys.

At a checkup, Dr. Gregg asked Eddie some routine screening questions about his sexuality and gender identity. Eddie said, "I'm pretty sure I'm gay." Eddie had not told his parents. He thought his dad would be okay with it, but he was worried about how his mother would react. Eddie asked Dr. Gregg, "My dad is in the waiting room. Could we tell him together?" They called Eddie's father back to the exam room. With some gentle encouragement from Dr. Gregg, Eddie said, "Dad, I'm gay." His father took a deep breath and said, "Eddie, thanks for telling me. Now there's something that I need to tell you. I'm bisexual." They cried and embraced.

With sexuality, as with gender, we should resist the rush to categorize. *Who are you? What are you?* For some, the answers are simple. But many people don't fit neatly into one column or another. Labels can change. "Masculine" girls and "feminine" boys might end up transgender, cisgender, homosexual, heterosexual, or somewhere in between. They might have one set of gender and sexuality inclinations during one phase of development, but then things might change and evolve. Again, this "journey" should not be seen as inauthentic—in fact, premature assignment of gender or sexuality can lead to a lifetime of alienation and psychiatric disorder. The suicide rate for such misclassified individuals is tragically high (Blosnich et al., 2013).

Now, let's take a detailed look at autism and *sexuality*. Then, autism and *gender diversity*.

Autism and Sexuality

Although our society has become much more open, many people still have trouble talking about relationships and sexuality. Old taboos and anxieties are especially strong with regard to the sexuality of individuals with autism. But autism and all neurodevelopmental disorders have a significant impact as children, youth, and adults navigate and explore their emerging sexual identities. Sexuality is a central aspect of being human, whether one is on the autism spectrum or not.

Despite many parents' discomfort around the topic, people

with autism have sexual identities and relationships too. There's no difference in the timing of puberty for people with and without autism (May, Pang, O'Connell, & Williams, 2017). Anxious parents tend to deny or underestimate the sexual experience of their sons and daughters with autism, forgetting that their children need not be sexually active or in a relationship to think about sex. This includes solo sexual experiences with masturbation and orgasm. Although older adolescents and young adults with autism usually have less partner experience than those in the general population, puberty and sexuality are important aspects of their growing development. It just may not happen in exactly the same way (Dewinter, De Graaf, & Begeer, 2017).

Autism and Intimacy

People with autism can have fulfilling sex lives. This point cannot be overemphasized. For stories of successful intimacy, we encourage interested readers to explore autobiographies of individuals with autism (Tammet, 2007; Hendrickx & Newton, 2007; Robison, 2008). Such stories of autistic romance reveal how healthy sexual relationships can flourish, not just despite neurodiversity but because of it.

A growing number of TV shows and movies explore this important topic. One beautifully done 2015 documentary, *Autism in Love,* tells the story of how four young adults on the spectrum deal with intimate relationships. They want love but don't always know how to get it.

The filmmakers begin with Lenny: autistic, unemployed, and single. His mother says, "Lenny's smart enough to know that he's different. And he doesn't like it." Lenny says, "I wish I could be a normal person." He is afraid of being in a relationship but despondent about not having a girlfriend. Bad sex ended one relationship; paying for sex seems gratuitous and unsatisfying. Lenny and his mom talk about him trying a dating website. He has rigid expectations and trouble with self-acceptance. His mother offers encouragement, but Lenny is very down on himself. He says, "I feel like I can't get a girl." By the end of the documentary, Lenny gets a job bagging groceries. One hopes that someday he might find the love he so desperately seeks.

Stephen and Gita, both with autism, had been in a long-term relationship. He likes playing along with the TV show *Jeopardy* but has significant problems with self-expression. He met Gita 20 years ago and recalls that first meeting in great detail. He fell in love with her; he explains that love means giving a kiss and a hug. His parents explain: "Gita was very verbal and that's what he was lacking. They complemented each other." They lived happily together for 17 years. They shared an apartment. Then she got ovarian cancer. She needed surgery and chemotherapy. She was not able to move back in with him. He lived independently, with parent support, and worked full-time stuffing envelopes at the post office. Between treatments, when they saw each other, she asked questions; he gave very short and simple answers. He remained hopeful about her health, but then she died. He misses her and thinks back on their relationship: "I gave Gita a hug. I put my arms around her."

Lindsey and Dave have been in a relationship for eight years. Both are on the autism spectrum. They have different interests and communication problems. Lindsay talks about her feelings, but awkwardly. Dave abruptly cuts her off to watch the weather forecast. Lindsey always knew she was different. She felt ashamed of being autistic and struggled with self-acceptance. She felt pressured to fit into the social norm. So, Lindsey learned how to be "a good actress." Of the many men she dated, Dave was the first who was also on the autism spectrum. Although it's difficult to love someone who doesn't understand you, Lindsey feels it's possible. They think about getting married, largely because of practical considerations. One day, he gets down on one knee and asks her to marry him. She is overwhelmed. Gently, he places a ring on her finger. They cry, and kiss. Reflecting back on the moment of his proposal, she reads a quote from Rumi: "Your task isn't to seek for love but merely to seek and find all the barriers within yourself that you have built against it." The documentary ends with Lindsey and Dave playing "Chopsticks" on the piano together.

As *Autism in Love* shows us, such stories should give people with developmental differences hope for intimacy and romance. However, these stories also demonstrate how disorders such as autism can make it harder to realize fulfilling sexual relationships. As we explore potential difficulties, it's important to keep in mind that such problems don't affect all people with autism. Also, people without autism can have similar problems too.

Common Experiences in Sexual Development

Not everybody goes through the same sexual stages, progression of sexual behaviors, sexual experiences, or sexual discoveries. Here are some common milestones in sexual development. This is just a list, not a suggestion of linear progression.

- Self-exploration, masturbating
- Orgasm
- Early mutual exploration (genital play)
- Outercourse (touching, hugging, kissing, French-kissing, petting, giving a hand job, receiving a hand job, fingering, mutual masturbation)
- Romantic feelings, crushes, falling in love
- Dating in groups, dating in pairs
- Intercourse (giving or receiving penetration; oral, anal, or vaginal)
- Other forms of sexual expression
- Dating, sexual and romantic relationships, falling in love
- Exploring sexual attraction and/or identity (gay, straight, bisexual, pansexual, asexual)

Let's consider how these same stages and experiences might be different for someone with autism or other developmental differences. If we superimpose the spectrum of differences associated with autism upon the normal development of sexuality, we reveal a wide range of sociosexual variation.

Factors Contributing to Autistic Differences in Sexuality

Ivy grew up going to special education classrooms for children with autism. From preschool through high school, she had few friends. She then went to the local community college, where she met a young man, Mitch, who was also on the autism spectrum. Right away, Mitch asked her, "Do you want to be my girlfriend?" She said, "Yes." Then he asked, "What's your name?" She told him but he soon forgot. Mitch just wanted to hold Ivy's hand and talk about space travel. She wanted to be his girlfriend but she didn't like being touched, and was not at all interested in listening to him go on and on about all the different Apollo rockets. After a few weeks, she decided not to hold his hand. He tried to kiss her. She hit him hard in the face. Stunned, he asked, "Don't you want to be my girlfriend anymore?" She said, "No."

Ivy took the bus home and told her mother, "My stomach hurts and I don't want to go to college anymore."

Autism represents a broad spectrum of abilities. Each person's social and sexual journey depends upon their individual profile and life circumstances. Some have it easier; others, harder. In some ways, the connection between autism and sexuality is obvious. In other ways, the effect of autistic differences on psychosexual development is more subtle.

In the following sections, we'll present an overview of some difficulties that people with autism *may* experience in sexual relations and experiences. Of course, there is a wide range of possible developmental trajectories. After discussing potential problems, we'll offer many ideas for promoting healthy sexual development and fulfillment.

Differences in Navigation of Psychosocial Stages

Sexual development happens within the context of social and personality development. In the discussion that follows, we'll consider how autism (and other developmental disabilities) affect different stages of development. Referring to the work of psychologist Eric Erickson (1993), let's take a careful look at how adolescents with autism are likely to resolve the developmental "crises" in two key psychosocial stages.

- Stage 5: Identity Versus Role Confusion (12 to 18 years)
- Stage 6: Intimacy Versus Isolation (19 to 40 years)

According to Erikson, stage 5, the crisis of Identity Versus Role Confusion, normally occurs in early and mid-adolescence. Erikson explains that the young teenager has a need for autonomy, individuation, and privacy. There is an evolving sense of self, separate from family. The teen is influenced by others outside the family and develops a "horizontal family" or "second family" of peers. There is experimentation, exploration, risk-taking, limit-testing, questioning of rules and authority, and a sense of invulnerability. Teens often have idealized views regarding social, religious, and political issues. They try on different roles and ask themselves, "Who am I?" Their ability to think in the abstract develops further, enhancing their capacity to think of themselves in relation to peers, family, community, and society as a whole.

Now, reread the last paragraph and ask yourself, *How much harder is all of this for someone with autism?* People with autism

345

go through their own version of this adolescent journey. Success in resolving each developmental crisis means an ability to stay true to yourself. Failure, all too common for teens with autism, means role confusion and a weak sense of self.

Next, consider Erikson's Stage 6. This crisis of Intimacy Versus Isolation normally occurs in late adolescence. During this time, older teens might begin to form intimate loving relationships with others, fusing their newly established identity with another person. They develop empathy and make commitments. There is further separation from the "vertical" or "first" family.

Again, reread the previous paragraph and ask yourself, *How much harder is this for someone with autism?* Success in resolving this crisis means the development of strong relationships. Here too, teens with autism face an increased chance of failure. This can mean further loneliness, social withdrawal, and even destructive wishes.

By understanding psychosexual stages, we can help individuals with autism anticipate challenges and move toward healthy relationships. Autism is complicated, with many contributing factors. Let's superimpose some common features of autism upon normal psychosexual development and see what we get.

Temperament Differences

Differences in temperament or behavioral style lie at the foundation of human development in general and of sexual development in particular. Whether there is autism or not, normal differences in temperament play an important role. Based on the pioneering work of Chess and Thomas (1990) and subsequent clinical applications by Carey (Chess & Thomas, 1995), the following aspects of temperament are considered essential to the study of human variation. Consider how each of the following might be a factor in sexual activity:

- Motor activity level (high, low)
- Regularity and predictability (high, low)
- Initial reaction (positive approach, negative withdrawal)
- Adaptability/flexibility (high, low)
- Sensory threshold (under-sensitive, over-sensitive)
- Intensity of reaction (high, low)
- Quality of mood (negative, positive)
- Attention span (short, long)

For a complete discussion of these differences in behavioral style—including detailed suggestions on how to help—see the "Gander Instruction Manual" in *Parent Child Journey* (Shapiro, 2016). But in brief, various combinations of temperament can be evaluated for "goodness of fit." For example, take a person with hyperactivity, negative initial reaction, inflexibility, high intensity of reaction, negative mood, and short attention span. In seeking a sexual relationship—depending upon the temperament of a potential partner—such an individual might have difficulty maintaining the necessary level of motor calmness, openness, reciprocity, equanimity, and engagement. Normal variations in temperament are amplified in autism. Adaptation is more challenging when the environment and other people dictate behavior that is out of sync with one's natural tendencies. This increases the risk of sexual incompatibility.

In addition to temperament, the Gander is a comprehensive assessment tool for the whole range of developmental differences. Here, we'll only survey how temperament and a few other selected aspects of development might affect sexuality in individuals with autism.

Sensory Differences

Sexuality involves all of the senses. Under-sensitivities and over-sensitivities significantly impact sexuality; again, especially for people with autism. Consider the obvious interplay of sensory threshold and sexuality regarding deep and light touch. Then consider the more subtle interplay of sexuality and sensitivity to taste, smell, hearing, sight, movement, and spatial positioning.

People with autism and heightened reactivity might experience sensory-sexual overload, which can result in anxious withdrawal, need for solitude, agitation, or even aggression. Others with autism and low reactivity might be under-responsive. They might react by turning off, seeking or even craving more amplified sensory stimulation. They might have unique or idiosyncratic sexual preferences. They might seem to want "inappropriate" or "selfish" sexual behavior, when it's really just a difference in how their sensory system processes stimuli.

Possible sensory incompatibilities can be resolved with mutual understanding, communication, accommodation, or compromise. It's a matter of understanding the source of the difficulties, talking about it openly and honestly, and practicing sensory-sexual awareness.

Motor Differences

The gross motor and fine motor deficits of many people with autism don't just affect performance on the athletic field or the classroom. Lack of motor tone, strength, and coordination may cause a degree of sexual clumsiness in the bedroom. There may be a lack of sexual energy and stamina that can be misinterpreted as insensitivity or lack of interest. Such motor deficits can also result in lack of sexual satisfaction for the partner.

Attention Regulation and Executive Function Differences

People with autism usually have complicated issues with attention regulation that can affect sex and intimacy. A core deficit in autism is poor joint or shared attention, which is crucial for generating intimacy in relationships. All facets of interpersonal relationships are affected if a partner is prone to perseveration, hyperfocusing, distractibility, impulsivity, or hyperactivity.

Think about romantic visual engagement, when partners have different eye-tracking preferences. People with autism may have a tendency to focus on geometric shapes instead of facial expressions, or on isolated features instead of the whole person. Mundane but crucial preparations for dating and intimacy can be sabotaged by legitimate difficulties with initiating, sustaining, inhibiting, shifting, planning, organizing, and time-tracking; all of which are commonly observed in people with autism.

Social (Nonverbal) Language Differences

Even when attentive and engaged, people with autism are at increased risk for misinterpreting nonverbal sexual cues. This lack of interpersonal savvy can result in confusion, bewilderment, obliviousness, or assault. People with autism may not understand certain cultural norms, expectations, or taboos. They may possess their own strong preferences or special interests and, as a result, appear to lack a sexual compass. They may have a very limited and restricted emotional code-book or sociosexual repertoire. They may be too ready to conform or too ready to act out. They may have difficulty relating to love and closeness. They may not understand the importance of being flexible, following the other person's lead, exerting self-control, asking important questions—including consent—or showing feelings. They may simply lack interpersonal communication skills.

Even with normal neuropsychological functioning, it's often difficult to manage sexual and emotional complexities. With autism, it's even harder. In general, people with autism have difficulty reading other people's thoughts and feelings. People with autism may be overly literal regarding expressive and receptive language. They may have poor inferential reasoning. They may think in "all-or-none" terms. They may have trouble reading situations and context. It can be harder for them to connect the dots and see the big picture. They may not understand why behavior that is okay in one setting is definitely not okay in another. They may confuse public and private norms. Internet porn may be more easily seen as a script for real life.

Despite all of these potential pitfalls, as discussed below, the social communication difficulties of people with autism can be a blessing in disguise.

It's important to note that people with autism may engage in sexual activity with others who are either on or off the autism spectrum. With either type of pairing, there are unique complexities. In some ways, neurotypical-neurodiverse couples have it easier; in other ways, sexuality in these "mixed" dyads may be more difficult. And as we discuss in more detail below, extended family and community biases may have a significant impact—positive or negative—on relationships involving people with developmental differences.

Psychiatric/Medical Issues

Many psychiatric and medical conditions commonly associated with autism significantly impact sexual development and intimate relationships. Because autism usually involves some combination of coexisting psychiatric issues, most teenagers and adults with autism take some kind of psychiatric medication; many take more than one (Spencer et al., 2013). Although a complete discussion of this topic is beyond the scope of this book, any of these medications, directly or indirectly, can have side effects that impact sexual function; drowsiness, emotional reactivity, or irritability; decreased libido (sex drive); issues around erection, ejaculation, arousal, or orgasm. Prescribers should be clear about sexual side effects. Patients should be fully informed before prescriptions are written. Many prescribers fail to ask about sexual side effects in typically developing patients, even more so in in patients with autism. Professional neglect may be due to false assumptions or subconscious biases about the sexuality of people with neurodevelopmental differences.

A number of medical conditions are commonly associated with autism. For example, sleep and gastrointestinal disorders can have an indirect but substantial bearing on eroticism and intimacy. Again, it's incumbent upon physicians to actively screen for these types of medical problems, ask about their possible impact upon sexual function, and treat as indicated.

Adaptive Behavior and Life-Skill Deficits

In addition to problems with social communication, people with autism often have other life-skill deficits. They may not be sufficiently concerned or capable regarding personal hygiene, self-care, home care, health, and safety, or too rigid and demanding about other people's personal habits. For teens with autism who are interested in finding a romantic partner, this is an important educational starting point. These skills are central to day-to-day functioning and establishing relationships with others.

Poor Sex Education

Often, people with developmental disabilities don't receive adequate sex education. This shortcoming can be due, in part, to their own social learning disabilities; but often, parents, teachers, and health professionals fail to provide a sufficiently individualized approach to sex education—if they provide any sex education at all. While comprehensive sex education is now standard in general education classrooms, this trend isn't usually matched in special education curricula. Again, professionals and parents have their own biases and fears.

Adults may not see people with autism as sexual beings who need—at least—the same level of sex education as everyone else. As a result, children and adults with disabilities often receive inconsistent or mixed messages about "appropriate" sexual thoughts and behaviors. Although these tendencies are gradually changing, family, culture, and media still rarely address the sexuality of people with developmental disability in meaningful ways.

Typically developing adolescents get their sex education from a variety of sources, including typically developing peers, parents, school-based health courses, and the Internet. For people with autism, the Internet is often the primary—if not only—source of sex education. Consequently, as mentioned above, porn is too often utilized as the sole guide to sexuality.

Developmental disability distorts the social learning environment. In special education classrooms, social skills groups, and other therapeutic settings, children with autism are more likely to spend their "wonder years" with others who possess a broad range of unusual or maladaptive behaviors. The 4:1 male: female ratio in special education and therapeutic settings is another difference from the usual mainstream environment. Consequently, many people with autism grow up segregated by both disability and gender.

Because of their social skills deficits, people with autism are much less likely to have opportunities for relationships that are intimate, healthy, and appropriate. More often, there is a high degree of social isolation and relationship deprivation. Peer-to-peer interaction is an important source of sex education for many, but people with autism are less likely to have those personal kinds of friendships. All of these factors make classroom-based sex education even more important for people with autism and other developmental differences.

Health-Care Deficiencies

Health-care providers may falsely assume that someone with autism isn't sexually active. As a result, they may fail to educate and screen regarding safe sex, including pregnancy prevention and sexually transmitted disease. At the very least, people with autism should receive the same anticipatory guidance as anybody else. As discussed further below, people with autism need more specialized instruction as well.

Potential Issues with Sex for People with Autism

The following sections can make for some difficult reading. However, individuals with autism and their parents should take heart. Serious sexual disorders are rare. Ordinary frustrations are common. By acknowledging the full range of potential issues, we can lower the risk of sexual problems. The purpose of this excursion is to help people with autism realize their most intimate hopes. To that end, let's face these real challenges head-on.

Lack of Sexual Fulfillment

Although controlled research is lacking, anecdotally, many people with autism lack interest in sex and might call themselves asexual. Other people with autism desire sex but have delayed first sex, less frequent sex, less satisfying sex, or remain lifelong virgins. Lack of sexual fulfillment can be one of many factors that erode self-image and self-confidence, and fuel anxiety or depression.

Avoidance

To avoid distress, people with autism may cope by avoiding sexual relationships altogether. This evading can set up a chronic and self-perpetuating cycle of increased withdrawal, lack of sexual intimacy, and lowered desire. Such individuals might rationalize away their longing by thinking, *It's not worth it. It's just too complicated. I don't really care anyhow.* Or their frustration might result in a heightened desire for sex, obsessive frustration with being a virgin, and despair about not having a relationship. Some individuals manage their sociosexual anxiety or depression with drugs, alcohol, Internet gaming, and/or porn.

Relationship Problems

Since people with autism, by definition, have more difficulty forming and sustaining mutually satisfying relationships, they are likely to struggle choosing partners well. Then they might be over-attached and dependent, detached and unresponsive, excessively demanding, brutally honest, or extremely reactive. They might have unusual ways of showing their love and affection. Or they might have sex but avoid the intimacy of relationships.

Verbal and Nonverbal Language Problems

Many people with autism have challenges with expressive and receptive language, both verbal and nonverbal. Consequently, when engaging in sexual activity people with autism may have difficulty reading and sending social cues. They may misinterpret or simply fail to register sexual signals. They may not have sufficient social skills to give consent, or to understand when sexual advances are unwanted. They may not have sufficient self-regulation to slam on the brakes when consent isn't given or is withdrawn.

Masturbation

Some individuals with autism may have difficulty controlling masturbation due to sensory differences, failure to understand social norms, and repetitive/perseverative behavioral tendencies. Although private masturbation should be considered normal and healthy, public masturbation can be a big problem. For some people with autism, masturbation and other sexual behaviors can become compulsive. Masturbation should be considered problematic if it becomes a source of significant distraction, self-injury, anxiety, shame, or misunderstanding.

Conversely, some individuals with autism seem unable to explore their bodies and learn to masturbate. This can increase their sexual frustration and leave them unaware of how their body responds sexually.

Sexual Obsessions

The overwhelming majority of people with autism have sexual deficits rather than excesses. However, aberrant sexual behavior can be a serious problem for a small minority of people on the autism spectrum.

Because of their tendency to perseverate and hyperfocus, some people with autism may develop sexual obsessions. Distorted sexual thoughts and fantasies may occur, sometimes driven by exposure to certain magazines, movies, or porn. People with autism may become more easily addicted to virtual Internet or phone sex. Some people with autism get in trouble through highly inappropriate sexual exhibitionism, flirtatiousness, and touching. There may be cases of promiscuity, staring, stalking, voyeurism, or harassment. They may even get into trouble for sexual aggression and assault. Sexual paraphilias and fetishes may include sexual excitement by a body part, object, or a specific personal characteristic; also, sadomasochistic behavior. According to one study, "inappropriate" sexual behaviors and paraphilias may be present in as many as one-fourth of individuals with autism, with higher rates in those with more severe overall impairment (Fernandes et al., 2016).

However, it should be noted, these sexual behaviors are explored and experienced by many people without autism and may not be unhealthy. For example, the explicit rules of BDSM culture (bondage and discipline, dominance and submission, and

353

sadomasochism) can be freeing. Such specific "dos and don'ts" may be especially helpful to some people with autism.

Victimization

People with developmental disabilities are far more likely to be sexual victims than perpetrators. Fifteen percent of parents reported that their children with autism had been sexually abused. Fifty percent of adults with autism reported having been sexually abused themselves (Harrell, 2017; Westcott & Jones, 1999). Predator-prey relationships can range from teasing and bullying to abuse, rape, and sex-slavery. Financial hardship may push some people into survival sex trade.

> In preschool, Frankie was diagnosed with autism. He didn't connect with the other children and he had poor self-control. Frankie's parents said, "It's like his motor runs super-fast. Then he crashes." In second grade, despite his parents' request for an autism program, Frankie was placed in a general education classroom. He refused to sit with the other kids. He refused to sit at all. He tore up his worksheets. Whenever his teacher tried to redirect him, Frankie had prolonged tantrums.
>
> One day at recess, a teacher found Frankie and another boy behind the school with their pants down, holding each other's penises. There was an emergency team meeting. Frankie was transferred to the public school autism program. There, things got worse. In the middle of class, he kept pulling his penis out of his pants and putting his finger in his anus. His meltdowns escalated. There was another meeting.
>
> The public school system agreed to pay his way to the local private school for children with autism. There he got one-on-one expert behavioral support. A child psychiatrist diagnosed a mood disorder and started him on medicine to control his mania. Gradually, his behavior improved. During the summer, he regressed. His mother had to stay right next to him at the neighborhood pool. But each year, he did better.

Toward Healthy Sexuality for People with Autism

Despite these serious concerns, it bears repeating that not all autistic sexual difference is worrisome or problematic. For many people with autism, sex can be a wonderful part of—often a key to—a meaningful relationship. Just like neurotypical sexuality, autistic sexuality can be complicated. Just because physical and emotional intimacy in autism might be different doesn't mean it should be feared, discouraged, or avoided. We can lower the odds of problems with autistic sexuality, but only if we deal with these issues head-on. By recognizing and acknowledging potential problems, we can help people with autism and other developmental differences toward experiencing the fullest lives possible.

Autism magnifies the extraordinary range of human diversity and variation. Compared to typically developing individuals, the sociosexual challenges of people with autism spectrum disorders may be different in degree but not so different in kind. All people—not just people with autism—can misread social cues, think in all-or-none terms, and objectify others. All people can have idiosyncrasies and quirks, peculiarities and eccentricities, sensory preferences and sensitivities. Autism simply shines a light on these individual differences and compels us to take note. Autism teaches us the importance of understanding, accepting, and enjoying each and every person as they are, not how we wish them to be. As discussed above, people with autism can struggle with sexual development. But in many ways, autism can have a positive effect on sex education, communication between sexual partners, and even cultural evolution.

Autism and Special Sex Education

The principles and content of a sex education curriculum for people with autism should be no different than sex education for neurotypical people. However, with autism, there is an even more compelling need to be explicit and individualize the approach— which can lead to better sex education for people with autism than is often provided to neurotypical people (Koller, 2000; Torisky & Torisky, 1985).

By analogy, sex education for people with autism is no different than reading instruction for people with dyslexia. Ultimately, we want people with dyslexia to read as well as anybody. They just need a different approach. As a result of specialized and intensive instruction, some people with dyslexia end up reading better than some without dyslexia. Furthermore, strong general educators use some of the same techniques developed for people with dyslexia to teach all of their students. At first glance, the following principles of special sex education may not seem quite as crucial for people without autism. On the other hand, what is good for autism may actually be good for everybody.

Often, when it comes to children and adolescents with disabilities, parents and health providers focus on a standard list of issues—activities of daily living, self-care, and other aspects of development and behavior—to the exclusion of sexual medicine. They forget that people with autism grow up to become sexual beings. Consequently, discussion regarding sexual pleasure and quality are often neglected—but sexual satisfaction and dysfunction should absolutely be a part of the sex ed conversation.

Sex education for people with autism should also include discussion of gender identity variation. In addition, same-sex attraction may be more common in people with autism, especially adult females (Fernandes et al., 2016). Gender and sexual diversity are no less important in sex education curricula for people with autism.

For special sex education, we apply the same techniques and strategies that guide special academic education, social skills training, and other therapeutic interventions. Because people with autism are at a higher risk for problems with sex and intimate relationships, their sex education must be more specialized, deliberate, and structured (Yulius Academy, 2010). This means:

- *More explicit.* From an early age, private body parts should be identified by their proper names: breast, vagina, vulva, clitoris, penis, testicles, etc. Sex acts should be described accurately: penis in vagina, fingers on clitoris, hand on penis, etc. Communication should be age-appropriate, regular, and consistent. Parents can actively model comfort and availability talking about sex. Taboos can be broken. Children and adolescents with autism—just like anybody—should know that no conversation is off limits.
- *More visual.* To teach body parts, interpersonal communication, and sexual behavior, there should be substantial reliance on visual explanation, including pictures, cartoons, and video. Too often, people with autism have only seen porn. They need more exposure to accurate representations of sexual behavior that is healthy and mutual (Rutgers, 2019). There are many excellent sex education picture books for children (Mayle, 1973). Parents should choose visually explicit material based

on their child's developmental—not chronological—age.

- *More scripted.* In general, people with autism may have a harder time with nuance, subtlety, and inference. Regarding sexuality, this natural tendency to follow rules can be helpful. People with autism do well with clearly stated do's and don'ts. This is especially important around discussion of consent.

  For example: *No means no. Yes means yes. This is okay in private, but not okay in public. This is okay in a close and intimate relationship, but not okay with an acquaintance. This is what it means to be in a close and intimate relationship. This is what it means to be an acquaintance.* People with autism often need help translating nonverbal cues into verbal language. *This kind of facial expression, tone of voice, and body language means yes. This kind of facial expression, tone of voice, and body language means no.* Whenever possible, clear rules help—even rules about what to do when there isn't a clear rule. For example: *When in doubt, stop and ask the person you're with, "Is this okay?"*

  A global reckoning with pandemic sexual assault and rape culture is gradually changing the standard regarding consent. Before initiating sex, individuals should ask for—and receive—clear, enthusiastic, and repeated consent. Misreading body language is no longer an acceptable excuse. As discussed above, people with autism are naturally rule-abiding, as long as they know the rules. With careful sex education, they can internalize specific scripts: *Go if and only if there is consent. Stop if and when consent is rescinded. No consent, no sex. A "yes" once doesn't equal a "yes" always.* Given their natural inclination toward consistency, habit, and specificity, people with autism may do even better than neurotypical people about asking for consent; neurotypical people might do well to act likewise, in a more rule-abiding manner.

- *More proactive.* When instinct doesn't serve as a reliable guide, it's that much more important to anticipate different sexual situations and do some advance planning. From an early age, deliberate education regarding body parts, sex, and where babies come from is essential. Sex education should not reinforce the heteronormative notion that sexual activity is purely for making babies. Rather, we should teach about family planning, avoiding unplanned pregnancies, and having healthy sexual relationships. Parents, teachers, and clinicians should model comfort talking about sex and answering questions. When young people reach an age of sexual maturation, talking remains crucial. People with autism may need more coaching and guided practice.

Reuben was a rule-abiding boy with autism. His rigidity made it hard for him to deal with the unexpected. However, once school routines were well-established, he did very well. Reuben's parents were not particularly religious but he was naturally attracted to Jewish rituals. He liked going to synagogue. He learned the order of the service and all the prayers. He was a regular at daily services and holiday celebrations, and fell comfortably into the rhythms of synagogue life.

When Reuben got older, a kindly new rabbi befriended him, and asked Reuben to join his family and friends for Friday-night dinners. There were a lot of people but Reuben loved the food and the singing. Week after week, the rabbi asked Reuben to join them. Reuben kept going. Then, the rabbi started asking Risa to come too. She was one of the young women in the congregation. And that's how it started. Each Sabbath at the rabbi's table, they sat across from each other, enjoying the songs and blessings. They didn't talk much. But gradually, they felt more comfortable being together.

One day, after Thursday-morning services, the rabbi asked Reuben if he was interested in marrying Risa. Reuben was nervous—but intrigued. He knew that this was expected.

The rabbi met with Reuben and taught him the orthodox ways of marriage, including sex. Reuben was fascinated and took comfort in having such a detailed script. One day, the rabbi asked Reuben and Risa to join him in his study. With the rabbi's encouragement and guidance, Reuben asked Risa to marry him. Risa said yes. According to custom, they had a wedding ceremony. According to custom, they had sex. According to custom, they had children, and raised their family within the synagogue community.

Sex Education Techniques for Autism

There are many excellent sex education curricula. For example, see *Our Whole Lives: Lifespan Sexuality Education* (The Unitarian Universalist Association, 2014). Such foundational programs are designed for all children, adolescents, and young adults. But they are also a very good place to start for people with autism. As supplements, there exist many programs and personal experience resources that are written for people with autism and other neurodevelopmental disorders (Henault, 2005; Center for Parent Information and Resource, 2018; Planned Parenthood, 2017; Newport & Newport, 2002). Although the goals are the same, specialized sex education may differ from general sex education in a number of ways.

Some individuals with autism and other neurological differences might need more remedial instruction—just as they might with math or history. For example, some people might need more explicit instruction on masturbation, including the when, where, and how. To satisfy normal sexual urges, private masturbation may feel easier and safer than navigating a relationship. It may be crucial to teach rules about public versus private behavior and other taboos. Titles of masturbation instruction manuals—such as "Finger Tips" and "Sex for One: The Joy of Self-Loving"—give some indication of content (RespectAbility, 2017).

To facilitate healthy and appropriate sexual behavior, some individuals may benefit from very direct guidance, even hand-on-hand instruction with experienced professional sex workers or sex therapists. Professional surrogate sexual partners teach intimacy, touching, and sexual cues (though this type of sex therapy isn't legal in all states). We shouldn't let our own discomforts interfere with finding effective sex education strategies for people with developmental differences.

Some individuals with autism who are interested in sex might need a higher level of relationship supervision. In theory, this can be provided by parents. In practice, it may be better if coaching and monitoring is provided by a mature friend or a professional therapist. Again, sexual situations should be anticipated. Visual communication, social stories, and cartoons can be applied to sex coaching just as they are used for other types of social skills training. Cognitive-behavioral therapy techniques can be applied to problem-solving about sex and private relationships. Previously learned strategies such as Unstuck and On-Target or Social Thinking can be applied to sexual situations (Cannon et al., 2018; Winner & Crooke, 2011). For example, "When you go over to Katie's apartment tonight, depending on how she responds, what's your

Plan A, Plan B, and Plan C?" Or, "What would be expected sexual behavior? What would be unexpected?" The sex/relationship coach must strike a delicate balance between ensuring safety and respecting autonomy. The goal is to avoid truly dangerous sexual behaviors while still allowing some room for individuals to learn from their own mistakes, just like anybody else.

When discussing sexuality with young people—including young people with developmental differences—it's critical to address our own hang-ups and anxieties. Neurotypical people often take for granted their ability to read social cues. But, especially when it comes to sex, we are usually not as skillful as we believe. Oblivious to our own conditioning, we may have difficulty leaving our discomforts and taboos at the door. Sex education for young people has to start with self-aware adults. Neurodiverse individuals compel parents, teachers, and clinicians to achieve a higher-than-usual level of self-understanding. Neurotypical adults who are comfortable with their own sexuality are better equipped to guide others and more likely to enjoy better communication in their own sexual relationships.

Autism and Communication Between Sexual Partners

Although the Internet may be a dangerous source of misinformation and predatory risk, it can also be a safe and accurate wellspring. People with autism may rely more heavily on the Internet for sexual modeling and experimentation. The Web can also be a comfortable place for intimate connection. Given their social skills deficits and relative isolation, people with autism are more likely to find potential partners online than at a bar or party. The Internet creates opportunities to consider responses carefully, receive coaching, and simplify social interaction. Online, people with autism can state their specific preferences and find others with shared interests. Internet communication can be more open and honest.

Before looking for a potential partner online, individuals with autism should carefully consider whether or not to share their diagnosis. Some people with autism might choose transparency about their need for a partner with compensatory strengths. Whether or not to disclose a diagnosis, online or in person, is up to the individual. With some coaching and experience, individuals will learn what works for them. Often, "birds of a feather" flock—and stay—together. As discussed above, many happy couples both have autism.

Relationship advice for people with autism should be no different than for everyone else. Everyone should be open and honest. Partners should give each other the gift of explicit communication. *Let's share specific sexual, sensory, and hygienic preferences. Here's what I like and don't like.* If you don't know or don't understand, stop and ask.

For example: Although it might not be easy to overcome significant sensory differences, just understanding their importance in sexual relations can go a long way toward relieving guilt, blame, and shame. Accurately labeling the source of a problem can free couples to discuss solutions. For some, sexual satisfaction might hinge upon showering with a certain type of soap and agreeing to a certain type of touching. With autism or not, sharing specific sensory preferences can help. With autism, such communication may be even more crucial.

Thanks to a lifetime of dealing with their own developmental differences, people with autism might actually be more conscious of the need for mutual acceptance and accommodation. At the center of their early development should be the fact that everyone is different and worthy of respect. People with autism may have more practice reading the thoughts and feelings of others, practicing sensitivity and flexibility. They may end up better than many neurotypical people regarding interpersonal awareness.

In my own (D.S.) practice, I evaluate children with developmental differences and provide long-term care. It has been an extraordinary privilege to watch these individuals grow from toddlerhood through adolescence. Young adults with autism are some of the most sensitive, compassionate, and unselfish people I have ever known. The ability of some people with autism to overcome developmental obstacles and lead wonderfully different lives should inspire us all. The sociosexual challenges of people with autism just amplify the importance of understanding, accepting, and enjoying the individual differences of all human beings.

Margie had always wanted to have a girlfriend. Although in-person interactions were painful, Margie found social connection online. There, she met Sally. They enjoyed the same video game. From halfway across the country, they played together for hours. At first it was just a few times a week. Then it was every day. Chatting back and forth, Margie and Sally got to know each other. Gradually, they experimented with cowriting sexual fantasies. After two years of intense online romance, they decided to get together—as Margie's father said—"the old-fashioned way." Their parents were supportive, even a bit excited.

Margie and her dad took a road trip. Margie knocked on Sally's door. Sally showed Margie the computer. They smiled at each other and settled right in, playing their favorite video game together. Margie's father and Sally's mother shrugged and smiled at each other too. Margie's father went to a coffee shop. Sally's mother also kept a respectful distance. Sally asked Margie if she wanted to have sex. Margie said, "Maybe next time." Sally said, "Okay." They continued playing the video game.

When it was time to go, Margie and Sally shared one kiss. Margie's father picked her up. When they got home, Margie ran straight to the computer and found Sally waiting for her. They picked up right where they left off: online and in love.

Autism and Cultural Evolution

Sexual Readiness

Sexual readiness should depend upon some minimum level of social development. But for people with autism spectrum disorders, our fears might lead us to set the level of prerequisite social skills too high. For some individuals, could safe sex actually represent a helpful first step toward the development of mature relationships? Could sex serve as a shared foundational interest, upon which a more complete relationship might be built?

In the past, social norms required three dates before a first kiss. Then it was three dates before sex. Today, it seems many people fall closer to having sex three times before a first date! Exploring sexual compatibility is a common way to explore intimacy. For people with autism, dinner and a movie might be a non-starter, but safe and successful sex might help bridge other interpersonal gaps and allow for an otherwise unimaginable depth of connection.

Taboos

Sex doesn't always mean traditional "lovemaking." Heteronormative and neurotypical taboos should be rejected. People with autism might find unique purposes for sex. They might experience sexual fulfillment in unconventional ways. Whether with autism or not, many people love being another person's special sexual interest. A person with autism may be more likely to fixate on a specific sexual motif or theme. This isn't necessarily a problem. Such sexual fixations may help some people fit in—safely, comfortably, and happily—with a certain kink or fetish community. If so, this should be both embraced and encouraged.

Sexual Disinterest

Many individuals with autism, on the other hand, truly have little or no interest in sex. They genuinely don't want a sexual relationship. We must be careful not to impose our own preconceptions regarding "normal" or "healthy" relationships. We must also be careful not to confuse lack of sexual interest with learned avoidance. Expert evaluation and counseling can be very helpful. As with all matters pertaining to sexuality, things can change over time.

Sexual Diversity

In his extraordinary book *The Evolution of Beauty: How Darwin's Forgotten Theory of Mate Choice Shapes the Animal World—and Us*, Richard Prum (2017) reminds us that autism, sexuality, and (as discussed in the next section) gender variation have little to do with natural selection and survival of the fittest. Rather, evolved beauty is simply about aesthetics—beauty for beauty's sake. The peacocks' brilliant feathers are attractive to potential mates but certainly not good camouflage from predators. Seen in this way, the existence of autistic, homosexual, and transgender people isn't at all contrary to evolutionary theory and should not be pathologized. Rather, variation is to be expected, celebrated, and protected.

Autism and Gender Variation

Now that we have discussed autism and sexuality, it's time to take a deeper look at autism and gender variation.

Ever since Nick was diagnosed with autism, his parents had been relentless advocates. They fought hard for his IEP at the public school, nurtured his extraordinary musical abilities, and embraced his autistic differences. Despite some significant challenges, their home was always filled with joy and a spirit of optimism.

One day, Nick's pediatrician commented lightheartedly on Nick's new hairstyle: "I like your man-bun, Nick!" Calmly, Nick's mother explained, "Well actually, that's a girl-bun. For the last eight months, Nick has let us know that he is a girl— oops, I mean, she is a girl." She laughed, "I'm still getting used to this myself. But she wants to be called she. She wants to keep her name. We're letting her teachers know. We're 100 percent cool with Nick whoever, whatever, however she is. We know that this is a journey. We're cool letting things unfold naturally. Just wanted you to know."

Background

"Disorder" Versus "Difference"

The term "gender identity disorder" is controversial. Although there may be associated distress and social stigmatization, gender identity variation isn't itself a disorder. The term "disorder" is used here with the understanding that our medical system requires a diagnosis to help individuals obtain insurance reimbursement for necessary interventions: hormonal, surgical, or psychotherapeutic. Also, scientific research and legal issues might depend upon using the language of disorder. Otherwise, we prefer the terms "gender variation" or "gender difference."

Prevalence

As defined in DSM5 (American Psychiatric Association, 2013), the prevalence of gender identity disorders in the population at large is somewhere between 0.002 and 0.014 percent. Since 2013, estimates of gender variance have gone up (Simons, Leibowitz, & Hidalgo, 2014). Individuals who are assigned male at birth are at the higher end of this prevalence range. Individuals who are assigned female at birth are less likely to identify as transgender or gender-variant.

Historically and currently, some cultures are more open to gender variance, such as Thailand and its "lady-boys," and parts of India. In such places, the rate of gender diversity is higher, suggesting a correlation with increased acceptance of sexual diversity.

Coexistence

Autism and gender difference can coexist. A growing body of research strongly suggests that, compared to the general population, people with autism have a higher prevalence of gender variation and people with gender variation have a higher incidence of autism (van der Miesen, Hurley, Bal, & de Vries, 2018; van der Miesen, de Vries, Steensma, & Hartman, 2018). Females with autism are less likely to identify with—and have positive feelings about—their gender, compared to males with autism and people without autism (Cooper, Smith, & Russell, 2018).

In 2010, researchers in Denmark reported that out of 115 boys and 89 girls referred to a gender disorders clinic (average age of 10.8 years), 7.8 percent had an autism diagnosis. In 2014, Dr. John Strang reported that more children expressed the desire to be acknowledged as the gender opposite to the sex they were assigned at birth if they had autism (5.4 percent), as compared to a control group with epilepsy or neurofibromatosis (1.7 percent) (Strang et al., 2014). Subsequently, the majority of studies have confirmed the association of autism with gender difference (Janssen, Huang, & Duncan, 2016; Jacobs, Rachlin, Erickson-Schroth, & Janssen, 2014). I have certainly seen it in my own clinical practice. (D.S.).

However, it should be noted that other studies question the strength—even the existence—of the association. Some even speculate that bullying, family rejection, and other minority stresses of transgender individuals might cause characteristics of autism and more false positives on autism screening instruments (Turban & van Schalkwyk, 2018; Nobili et al., 2018). While a debate has ensued (Strang et al., 2018; van Schalkwyk, Klingensmith, & Volkmar, 2015). What is beyond doubt is that both the prevalence of autism and gender identity variation have increased independently—as much as 2.5 and 1.0 percent, respectively. Whatever the strength of the connection between autism and gender variation, they will continue to overlap in a significant number of individuals (Glidden, Bouman, Jones, & Arcelus, 2016).

Possible Biological Factors Contributing to Gender Variation in Autism

Even if many in the research community feel that we are getting closer to proving that the association between autism and gender variation is more than coincidental, we don't yet understand the possible reasons. Safe to say, it's complicated. Could autism somehow predispose one to gender variation? Or could gender variation somehow predispose to autism? Probably neither. It's more likely that these conditions share some neurobiological pathways.

There are also probably multiple combinations of genes, environmental factors, and developmental factors at play (van der Miesen, Hurley, & de Vries, 2016). But all of this is just speculation, merely interesting hypotheses to be tested. Let's look at some possible biological factors first.

Genetic Factors

There is an increased incidence of autism in certain genetic and endocrine conditions that are also associated with differences in development of sex, and sometimes gender. For example:

- Kleinfelter's syndrome, people with XXY chromosomes, also known as testicular feminization syndrome
- Turner's syndrome, people with XO chromosomes, resulting in poor formation of the ovaries
- Congenital adrenal hyperplasia, with excess male hormones
- Fragile X syndrome, which is strongly associated with autism (and intellectual disability)

In Dr. Strang's study, greater gender variation was not solely associated with autism. More children with ADHD (4.8 percent) also expressed a wish to be the gender opposite to the sex they were assigned at birth. Why? First of all, there's a 4:1 male: female ratio in autism *and* ADHD. This suggests that each of these conditions might be linked with the X and/or Y chromosomes that help determine sex. Second, we know that ADHD and autism share a number of identifiable genes and thus commonly coexist. Different disorders with shared genes would have some shared features, possibly including more gender variation. Although other studies have not yet confirmed this possible association between ADHD and gender variation, the suggestion of genetic overlap in Dr. Strang's study is intriguing and relevant.

Endocrine Factors

In England, Simon Baron-Cohen (2004) has speculated that autism represents an "extreme male brain." By this, he means that people with autism have "systematizing" brains: good at physics, math, and visual-spatial problem-solving. In contrast, people with autism don't have female "empathizing" brains. Consequently, so the theory goes, they are less naturally understanding of, and less able to act upon, other people's thoughts and feelings.

Such autistic differences in male and female brain function have been suggested by brain scans as well. This theory hit the front pages when Larry Summers was fired as president of Harvard University for referring to Baron-Cohen's research and attributing gender imbalance in the higher echelons of STEM fields (science, technology, engineering, and math) to innate difference in sex. The hypothesis was that male-female brain differences in autism could be caused by higher in-utero testosterone levels and/or heightened embryologic sensitivity to this masculinizing hormone.

If true, such hormonal differences could link autism with differences in gender development. But there's a major problem with this theory. Greater testosterone exposure could explain the increased incidence of trans-males with autism, but it would not explain the increased incidence of trans-females with autism. In John Strang's study of children with autism and ADHD, the increased incidence of gender variation occurred equally in females and males.

Possible Psychosocial Factors

If biological factors in the coexistence of autism and gender variation are uncertain, psychosocial factors are even more tenuous—but no less intriguing.

Autism and "Distorted Thinking" About Gender

As discussed previously, one common feature of autism is the tendency to focus on isolated details and miss the broader context. People with autism often have difficulty "seeing the forest for the trees." Could the association between autism and gender variation be due to this type of autistic perseveration or "context-blindness"?

Some children with autism may obsessively glom onto a cross-gender detail, which could give parents the false impression that their child's obsession with the opposite gender is an early indication of gender variance. For example, a cisgender boy with autism might become fascinated by his mother's barrette or the floral pattern of his teacher's dress. A cisgender girl with autism might develop a very strong attachment to a specific football team logo. However, attachment to such objects could be completely unrelated to gender. A fragmentary autistic perseveration should not be confused with a more central and general expression of gender identity (Strang et al., 2018).

Could some children with autism mistakenly "carve into stone" some developmental ambivalence about gender? For example, what if a boy with autism has some normal and transient feelings about being a girl? Or a girl with autism entertains some thoughts about being a boy? Such exploration of an alternate gender identity is very common among all children—but most gender-nonconforming thoughts and behaviors don't mean a child is transgender. The more transitory the gender nonconformity, the less likely the child may identify as trans; the more persistent it is, the more likely the child may identify as trans. The excessively binary thinking of autism might lead one to conclude that they can't be a feminine man or a masculine woman.

Could stigma, poor self-image, and a sense of social isolation lead some individuals with autism to fantasize about a "better" transgender life? Might a transgender identity have special appeal to socially insecure and suggestible people with autism? For example:

- "I'm a boy with autism. If I become a girl, I won't have autism anymore."
- "It's better to be gender-nonconforming than socially disabled. I'd rather be known as trans than autistic."
- "I was rejected by the opposite sex. I don't fit with the same sex. Maybe being the other sex will be better."

An expert should be able to help an individual distinguish between obsessive thinking and gender identity conflict. Over time, parents, professionals, and children themselves may become more confident in understanding their gender identity and expression. But gender is fluid. And every child is different. Parents and clinicians should resist the urge to find the "right" gender. They should follow the child's lead, focus on what makes them happy, and support them in their journey.

Autism and Liberated Thinking About Gender and Sexuality

Young children with autism experience the social world differently. The nature, frequency, and depth of their social interactions may be out of the ordinary. As a result, they may be relatively free of societal stereotypes and expectations. Compared with typically developing peers, they may be less aware of gender-normative behavior and, thus, less inhibited in their expression of nonconforming thoughts and behavior. Interesting questions exist about this connection between autism and freedom from cultural norms.

Is it possible that LGBTQI people with autism are more likely to live their truths as compared to their neurotypical peers? If you identify as transgender or queer, could autism free you somewhat from debilitating social constructs and taboos? Could autism represent a social gift regarding self-realization? Is autistic context-blindness, social obliviousness, or extreme self-direction a blessing regarding self-liberation and not a curse? Can the autism pride and neurodiversity movements teach mainstream society to reject stigmatization and marginalization, thus paving the way for people to come out of the closet sooner, safer and more supported? Will people with autistic disregard for labels positively model how gender identity can change over time?

As John Strang said in a Slate interview: "Autistic people may be more bold and individualistic, less swayed by social expectations. Some of the front-line leaders of the trans rights movement have been trans and autistic—and there's a beautiful focus, for many of them, on being themselves and not bending to social expectations of what others expect them to be" (Urquhart, 2018).

To paraphrase some sexually liberated and gender-nonconforming patients of mine (D.S.) with autism:

- "I didn't care what people said. It just made more sense to not have a gender."
- "I just wondered what it would be like to be bisexual. I didn't feel like I had to be just one thing or another."
- "You're fixated on boys acting like boys and girls acting like girls. I've just never had any interest in all of that boy-girl stuff."

In these ways, individuals with autism normalize neurological and sexual diversity.

Parents, Autism, and Gender Variation

As previously emphasized, we all have preconceptions about what kinds of lives our children will have. For parents and families, the appearance of gender variation usually represents a challenging shift from old expectations to new realities. Most parents find it's helpful to reach out to others as they navigate this journey with their child. PFLAG, along with other groups and professionals, can be valuable sources of support and information.

Trans or Not?

Parents should not feel compelled to "collect evidence" and try to "prove" whether or not their child is transgender. Parents should make sure their child feels loved and supported—not analyzed, debated, or solved. They should not jump to any definitive assumptions. With or without the added complexity of coexisting autism, gender journeys need to unfold over time. As much as possible, parents and other adults should try to remain open-minded, neutral, and supportive. Remember, you're not parenting a gender; you're parenting a child. Parents should do their best to express unconditional love and acceptance.

Responding to Nonconformity

When a child first engages in stereotypically cross-gendered behavior—playing, dressing, or speaking like the "opposite sex"—parents should try to remain steadfast in their positive regard. There are some special issues that arise when autism and gender nonconformity coexist. For example, behavioral intervention for delayed play skills shouldn't just teach boys to play with trucks and girls to play with dolls. Sensory therapies for hypersensitivity to clothing shouldn't just teach boys to tolerate blue jeans and girls to wear dresses. And as previously stated, gender variation should not be mistaken for—and treated as—a pathological autistic obsession. Such gender-nonconforming preferences might be due to gender identity differences, not autism.

Unconditional Support and Love

Parents and clinicians need to be very mindful of their own social conditioning and biases. Children can pick up on a parent's discomfort. Whatever their social or sexual development, children need to be loved for who they are. Unflagging parental support frees kids to experiment with different modes of expression and identity. Parents can provide the foundation upon which a child builds an identity; the safe harbor from which they explore their own truth. Children should feel trust and comfort throughout their developmental journey—unconditional acceptance, regardless of how they express themselves.

Data from a longitudinal study of 433 individuals in Toronto (Travers 2012) shows that trans youth with strong parental support for their gender identity and expression (compared to trans youth with unsupportive parents) report: higher life satisfaction (72 percent versus 33 percent), higher self-esteem (64 percent versus 13 percent), better mental health (70 percent versus 15 percent), and more secure housing (100 percent versus 45 percent). Families are the entire game when it comes to keeping gender-exploring individuals healthy and alive (Seibel 2018).

Gender-Neutral Parenting

At all ages, individuals need freedom to explore and discover their gender without shame. All parents, whether or not they suspect gender identity differences in their children, can create a home that accepts gender variation. All children should feel comfortable exploring and expressing their truth. Together, parents and children can read Jazz Jennings's picture book *I Am Jazz*—or watch her TV show of the same name. They can send a message of non-binary acceptance by buying clothing from Chellum Man's new clothing line or following Geena Rocero's style. They can read Janet Mock's and Jacob Tobia's memoirs, or Alok Vaid-Menon's poetry. They can watch television and films that feature trans and nonbinary actors like Laverne Cox, Daniella Vega, MJ Rodriguez, Indya Moore, and Angelica Ross. They can watch Caster Semenya's Olympic races.

Most homes are filled with discussions about film, television, books, and sports. Incorporating trans people into these ordinary conversations normalizes transgender existence for children, allowing them to see themselves reflected in the world.

Comprehensive Treatment of Gender Dysphoria

Throughout the gender journey, expert clinicians can help in many ways. Professional teams should include individuals with expertise in both autism and gender variation. All clinicians should be attuned to the fact that having one condition doesn't preclude having the other. On the contrary, those who work in autism clinics should screen carefully for gender diversity, and those who work in gender clinics should screen carefully for autism.

As already emphasized, treatment of gender dysphoria is essential to mental health, including suicide prevention. Beyond the scope of this book but worth emphasizing, a comprehensive approach to assessment and treatment is crucial for psychiatric well-being and promotion of positive self-image (American Academy of Pediatrics Section on Adolescent Health, 2018; Durwood, McLaughlin, & Olson, 2017). Decisions to treat should be made in close consultation with a team of experts. Most large communities now have transgender subspecialty clinics. If expert help isn't available locally, families should give serious consideration to traveling for up-to-date care. For individuals and their families, transitioning is a lot to undertake, even when it's a necessity. In addition to expert medical intervention, it is essential that clinicians provide a high level of psychosocial support.

Puberty Blockers

Hormone blockers are a cornerstone of management for gender dysphoria (Mahfouda, Moore, Siafarikas, Zepf, & Lin, 2017). These medications are well-studied, safe, and effective. Leuprolide (Lupron) is a commonly used hormone injection that halts the progression of puberty (Lopez, Solomon, Boulware, & Christison-Lagay, 2018) and, with expert management, its effects are largely reversible. Scientific progress also continues regarding fertility preservation (Cheng, Pastuszak, Myers, Goodwin, & Hotaling, 2019). Delaying puberty gives a child more time to explore their gender identity while protecting them against going through the wrong puberty (Connolly, Zervos, Barone, Johnson, & Joseph, 2016). For example, a child, assigned female at birth and subsequently diagnosed with autism, consistently states a preference for male clothing and hairstyle. The child starts asking to be called by a "boy name." Parents and clinicians are not sure if this represents autistic obsession, gender expression, or some combination of the two. In such a case, leuprolide would give the child time to "try out" a different gender with support, and without puberty forcing the issue. At any time, that child could stop the hormone-blocker and opt out of surgery or other hormone therapy.

Gender Affirmation

Down the line, decisions can be made regarding gender-affirming interventions, including speech therapy, gender-affirming hormones, surgery, psychotherapeutic support, and more (Byne et al., 2012).

Without question, my (A.S.) favorite part of gender clinic is that each and every person is completely different. Each person has a different relationship to their sex assigned at birth, different family dynamics, different mental health histories, and different ways of navigating self-expression in society. Likewise, each person has different goals and levels of confidence about those goals.

Part of our job is to make sure people know that they are not alone in their journey (Lopez, Marinkovic, Eimicke, Rosenthal, & Olshan, 2017). Their gender expression goal may never change, or it may change countless times over the course of a lifetime. No matter what, tools exist to help individuals find happiness with their gender (Hembree et al., 2017; Wesp & Deutsch, 2017; Gorton & Erickson-Schroth, 2017).

Parallel Exposure Therapy for Sociocultural Change

For developmentally diverse individuals, there has never been a better time to be alive. Through early identification and intervention, progress is being made in preparing children with autism for the road ahead. In parallel, LGBTQI individuals are now better prepared for their road as well. We have come a long way in supporting both neurodevelopmental and sexuality-gender minority individuals—but there's still a long way to go.

The following story demonstrates application of parallel exposure therapy to system-wide anxiety. Here, we combine many of the principles discussed throughout this book. This is just one example of how to break down cultural barriers for neurodevelopmental and gender-diverse individuals.

Ellie's Story

As an infant, Elliott was extremely irritable. Every sound seemed to send him through the roof. He always seemed to be looking past his mother's face, over her head at lights or fans on the ceiling. He didn't play peek-a-boo.

As a toddler, Elliott was late talking. He didn't play with toys the usual way. For example, instead of moving cars across the floor, he just stared at the wheels going around and around. Morning and evening routines felt impossible. It seemed like every transition brought on a tantrum.

Elliott wore out a path in the rug by running back and forth along the same line. He became obsessed with the dishwashing machine. Elliott's parents became more upset and confused. He was so different from their friends' kids. At age two, they called for an evaluation.

A psychologist told them that Elliott was on the autism spectrum. He was referred to the developmental pediatrics program at the local university hospital, where a doctor confirmed the diagnosis of autism and suggested that there were also red flags for ADHD and anxiety.

Elliott's parents were in shock, but they were determined to do everything possible to help their son. He was enrolled in a special preschool program. He received speech-language therapy, occupational therapy, and applied behavior analysis therapy. His parents joined a support group. Over time, the combination of public and private services seemed to make a difference. Elliott's parents learned a lot. He was still a kid with special needs, but Elliott made progress.

Slowly, Elliott's parents realized that there was something else going on. In addition to his social disability and obsessions, Elliott was not acting like a typical boy. More and more, Elliott played and dressed like a girl. He was not at all interested in sports. He liked dolls and ballet. He put on his mother's jewelry and high heels, and asked to wear her makeup. Sometimes he tried to tuck his penis back between his thighs. One day, he announced that everyone should call him Ellie instead of Elliott.

Elliott's/Ellie's parents were worried sick. Was this an autistic obsession? Or, on top of the autism, could he really be gay or transgender? Life was going to be hard enough for him with just the autism. If he was also gay or trans, how could he ever have a normal life? It was hard enough finding a school for a *kid with autism. What school could deal with this transgender stuff too? And what about life after high school—relationships, jobs? They could not imagine a world where their son—or daughter?!—would fit in.*

Despite substantial progress, neurodevelopmental and LGBTQI minorities still lack opportunity and acceptance. Although people with autism have a much better chance of graduating from high school than a generation ago, their job prospects remain poor. People with sexuality and gender differences are coming out of the closet in significantly larger numbers. However, people with autism and people identifying as LGBTQI remain members of disenfranchised communities. Cultural resistance to inclusion of people with developmental differences persists. They still face higher rates of violence, mental illness, suicide, and discrimination than the general population.

At the suggestion of a friend, they made an appointment with a gender specialist. With the doctor's help, Ellie's parents were able to see their daughter as a trans-girl with autism. She began to receive comprehensive support for social disability. Ellie spent lots of time online connecting with similar kids. Her parents joined a PFLAG support group. Ellie wore dresses all the time, styled her long hair, and began to wear makeup. She received leuprolide injections to block male pubertal changes and got her first training bra at the same time as her peers.

Despite their ongoing discomfort with these changes, her parents listened very carefully when the gender identity specialists warned about depression and suicide risk. They didn't want her to feel like she couldn't be her true self. And they had to admit, since Ellie had laid claim to her trans identity, a cloud had lifted. Ellie was still on the autism spectrum, but she was happier.

Historically, across various civil rights movements, tension between revolution and incrementalism has existed. In African-American history, Malcolm X's call for violent overthrow is often contrasted with Martin Luther King, Jr.'s peaceful protest. In the gay rights movement, Peter Staley from ACT-UP sparred with both Mark Harrington from Treatment Action Group and Cleve Jones from the NAMES Project AIDS Memorial Quilt over the level of confrontation necessary to effect change for people dying from AIDS. In the disability rights movement, the 1977 sit-in for physical accessibility led by Frank Bowe was much more visible than the Shriver family's quiet establishment of the Special Olympics and the piecemeal but landmark disability rights laws passed during the last half-century.

> To the kids at school, Ellie's autism was a bigger deal than her being trans. She was just so quirky and in her own world. She made odd movements with her hands and went on and on about YouTube videos for much younger kids. But teachers and other parents were okay with Ellie's autism, whereas the idea of a boy-body and a girl-mind was a whole different thing. The idea of a child with a penis being in the girls' restroom bothered more than a few people in the school community. They called the principal's office, circulated a petition, and threatened to sue the school for violating their children's rights to a safe environment. The principal, Mr. Jones, knew that Ellie had a right to safety and acceptance. But there was a storm brewing. Mr. Jones feared that things could get out of hand.

Avoidance and resistance are the main symptoms of anxiety—just as true of anxiety in social systems as within individuals. Whether cultural or personal, change requires a certain amount of stress. Not enough anxiety can mean stagnation and failure to make progress. However, too much anxiety can lead to paralysis or even regression. Progress requires strategic consideration of these opposing forces (Sunstein, 2019). Preparing the road for the child doesn't mean neglecting to prepare the child for the road. Making a case for gradual exposure doesn't necessarily represent a case against revolution. It's just that individual intervention without social accommodation, and radical activism without cross-cultural sensitivity, are less likely to work. We need both.

> Mr. Jones met with Ellie and her parents. He emphasized that the school was 100 percent behind them. He sought their advice on how to handle the bathroom issue. Whatever other kids and parents thought about LGBTQI issues, Mr. Jones knew that Ellie had a right to go to the bathroom. Ellie explained that, when she went to the girls' room, she always minded her own business. She didn't talk with anybody, but just went straight to

a stall and quickly closed the door. But she was always nervous about stares or possible teasing, and tried to "hold it" as long as she could. Ellie got a urinary tract infection as a result.

When preparing the road for the child, when is it appropriate to start low and go slow? When is it better to leap boldly ahead? In Excursion 2, we discussed gradual exposure for treatment of anxiety, in both individuals and systems.

Remember the swimming pool metaphor? Anxiety is, for some, best overcome through incremental habituation—gradual exposure to the water, one toe at a time. If a fearful child is thrown into the deep end of the pool, they might be so overwhelmed that they either drown or never get in a pool again. But for others, such a slow and measured introduction can backfire by prolonging the torture. Consider the child who remains paralyzed, crying at the edge of the pool. If such a child possesses relatively good adaptability despite their negative initial reaction, then they may be better off just jumping into the deep end all at once. They might scream at first. But then, given the opportunity, they can adapt. Similarly, decisions about how to overcome anxiety in larger systems--gradual or cold turkey--should be based on what is going to work best.

Given the current culture of his school, Mr. Jones knew that he needed to proceed cautiously. He explained to Ellie and her parents that there was a private restroom in the nurse's office, which Ellie could use. Ellie was relieved to hear that this was an option. They all agreed to make this change but keep it low-key. Mr. Jones sent a confidential notice to the teachers and nurse, so they wouldn't say anything if she was using their restroom.

Ellie and her parents didn't want to make anyone else uncomfortable. They appreciated Mr. Jones's support and sensitivity.

Still, Mr. Jones knew there was more to do. Ellie's gender nonconformity was creating irrational fear for too many parents and even teachers. He wanted to make the school safer for Ellie and other kids like her. But he also didn't want to risk making Ellie the center of a potentially larger backlash.

Social change might come quickly or slowly, dramatically or ploddingly, inexorably or in spurts. For adoption of a new cultural paradigm, public opinion must reach a threshold or tipping point (Gladwell, 2002). More often than not, it's "everyday" people—parents, youth, community members—who are tired of the status quo and urgently build movements to make that tipping point come sooner.

Mr. Jones knew that the school had to become a more welcoming place, not just for Ellie but for all autistic and LGBTQI people. Ellie's IEP already included a social skills group with the school counselor. Mr. Jones brainstormed new ways to help Ellie and shift the school culture.

He had recently learned about peer-to-peer programs in which age-matched typically developing children or older children with autism served as mentors and facilitators. Given her strong academic abilities, he thought that Ellie could be a tutor for kids in lower grades. Wouldn't it be great if she could be on the giving instead of the receiving end for a change? He also learned about programs for structuring up recess activities and other social opportunities. He could start some after-school clubs in Ellie's special areas of interest, which would benefit other kids as well.

Then, he found a transgender consultant who specialized in helping change school environments to be more LGBTQI-inclusive and welcoming. The consultant helped Mr. Jones start a gay-straight alliance and bring in a guest speaker for the next parent-teacher organization meeting. They placed a few posters around the school with messages about inclusion and diversity. And, although Ellie still preferred to use the private restrooms, they put up a sign by one of the public restrooms that said: "This is a gender-neutral restroom with multiple stalls. It's open to users of any gender identity or expression. If you prefer a gender-specific restroom, there are boys' and girls' restrooms at the other end of the hall."

Mr. Jones figured that these changes would make some of the students, teachers, and parents uncomfortable. But, if he implemented them one at a time, gradually exposing the community to new ideas and feelings, he hoped to raise awareness without inviting too much reaction. Mr. Jones wanted to set a new tone in the school without starting a groundswell of opposition. Meanwhile, he continued to make sure that Ellie was getting the support she needed.

It's much easier to evaluate what works in individuals than in systems. In Excursion 2, I emphasized the need to individualize the type and level of support. When it comes time to face fears and make changes, some people will have a harder time than others. To reach the summit, different members of the hiking party might need to take different trails, travel at different speeds, and use different tools along the way. And some people might not want to change at all. A goal that is important and attainable for some might be undesirable and/or too difficult for others.

How should we resolve different needs and different desires across different people and different systems? Here we venture into the minefield of cross-cultural conflict.

> *Mr. Jones knew that other changes would be harder. He felt that the whole district needed to do a better job of serving autistic and gender/sexuality minority students. More and more children were coming out. Around the country, other school systems had a broader range of programs for children on the autism spectrum. In Ellie's school, there were programs for children with more severe autism but not for academically capable—albeit socially awkward—students like Ellie. The history and social studies curricula didn't really address the disability and gay rights movements. There could be at least a brief unit on each.*
>
> *Mr. Jones was also concerned about the sex education program. As it stood, there was only passing reference to homosexuality and no mention of nonbinary gender variance. Mr. Jones knew that it would be hard to sell to his district school board building out its autism program, expanding the civil rights curriculum, and providing more inclusive sex education. But he knew it was worth a try.*

Previously, I suggested choosing targets for change based on the highest level of shared motivation, whether anxious resistance exists in individuals, families, schools, communities, or nations. Motivation for change is determined by weighing importance against difficulty. The chance of successful parallel exposure increases with the number of people buying into the project. Remember, goals of high shared importance and low shared difficulty are going to be the most motivating. Even if difficult, goals of sufficiently high shared importance might also reach a critical level of shared enthusiasm. Then, cascades of interest—even passion—can gain momentum.

But what if too many people in a system feel that the goal is unimportant or undesirable, that change would be much too costly or problematic?

As careful and strategic as he tried to be, Mr. Jones didn't anticipate such a strong backlash. Although many in the school community were supportive or indifferent, just as many were openly opposed. A few students, teachers, and parents were especially angry and vocal. Some children didn't like being paired with Ellie for academic or recess activities. One of the parents protested that this was "Communist-style" social-engineering. Another parent posted the following comment on social media: "Our kids should be allowed to play with whoever they want and not be forced to play with some Autistic Fairy!" They wanted the gender-neutral restroom sign taken down.

Mr. Jones met with anybody who wanted to talk. He listened respectfully, and acknowledged their concerns. One conversation at a time, he helped them feel heard. But he also helped them consider what it must feel like for someone like Ellie and her family.

Minority inclusion takes root if outliers are welcomed into the majority community. But more commonly, change comes about when outliers demand their due. Then, "Them" becomes "Us." Irrational fears become less prevalent. What is considered unfamiliar and threatening turns into a new cultural norm.

Mr. Jones kept the restroom sign up. One family withdrew their child from the school. Slowly and steadily, Mr. Jones successfully implemented other changes schoolwide. He attended school board meetings and presented his case in measured tones, while reminding those in power about potential violations of civil rights law, bigger legal battles, and damage to their reputations as advocates for all children. Gradually, students and teachers acclimated.

Thanks to Mr. Jones and the school counselor, Ellie made a friend, but she still felt like an outsider. One day, her English teacher assigned the kids a project: to make an autobiographical video. At first, Ellie was nervous about the project. But then, she started putting together pictures of herself, from infancy to the present. With her face in a square at the top of the screen, Ellie narrated her story:

"This is a picture of me when I was just born. I had boy parts. These are pictures of me when I was still really little. I dressed like a girl and wore my hair like a girl and played like a girl. This is because I always was a girl. Here's me with my best friend, the dishwasher. I didn't really have anybody to play with. I didn't know how to play like other kids. I didn't choose to be trans. And I didn't choose to be autistic. It would be easier if I wasn't either one! But my parents love me for being me. Anybody else out there?"

She put her cell phone number at the end. The day after Ellie showed her autobiographical video to the class, Ellie got a text message. It was from one of the popular girls at school. Did Ellie want to come to her birthday party?

The Future of Neurodiversity, Sexual Diversity, and Gender Diversity

In just the last generation, the world is a radically better place for individuals with social and sexual nonconformity. The inclusion movement has meant more direct exposure of children with autism to typically developing peers, and more direct exposure of mainstream society to atypical individuals. The same is true for LGBTQI individuals. As more queer and gender-nonconforming individuals come out, more straight people discover that family members, friends, and coworkers are gay or trans. Rising prevalence estimates for autism, sexuality, and gender variation are largely the result of increased awareness, familiarity, and acceptance. With less fear of danger and stigmatization, more people are out. The fact that we are all in it together is becoming increasingly difficult to deny.

Gradually but dramatically, autistic and LGBTQI people have found their way into mainstream culture. Beyond direct and personal contact, there is much more frequent and regular exposure to human diversity through TV shows, movies, literature, media coverage, "out" celebrities, school curricula, restroom signs, gay-straight alliances, gay pride and autism pride marches, peer-mentoring programs, and more. Across all facets of modern society and at many cultural touchpoints, the neurodiversity and LGBTQI movements have arrived. Unapologetic and proud, speaking for all minorities, the Autism Self Advocacy Network has declared, "Nothing about us without us!"

Social norms have changed. Especially for younger generations, it's no longer okay to discriminate against people with disabilities. Although sadly weaker in some countries than others, there is growing global consciousness around not discriminating against LGBTQI individuals. Increasingly, bigots are called out for ignoring new social standards.

Cultural institutions have changed too. Over the last half-century or so, legislation has been passed in countries all across the world recognizing the rights of individuals with developmental disabilities and LGBTQI identities. In the United States, individuals with disabilities have been protected against discrimination and guaranteed the right to an education. At the turn of the century, several Supreme Court rulings protected homosexuals, struck down sodomy laws, overturned part of the Defense of Marriage Act, and legalized same-sex marriage. In 1973, the American Psychiatric Association removed "homosexuality" as an illness from the Diagnostic and Statistical Manual. In the 2013 DSM, gender identity disorder was changed to gender dysphoria, emphasizing that gender nonconformity itself isn't a disease, even though depression and anxiety can result from cultural expectations and discrimination. And in 2019 the World Health Organization removed "transgender" as a category of mental disorder.

These legal, medical, and other cultural changes are the direct product of bold activists, loving parents, and brave children. That being said, transgender women of color are still being killed at outrageous rates, LGBTQI people regularly experience discrimination, and individuals with autism are often denied the support they deserve. Even so, slowly but surely, Them is becoming Us.

Trail-End for Excursion 5

And so, our last excursion ends. Here, we have sought not just to describe or accommodate human diversity, but to celebrate it. Old boxes no longer hold all of us—they never really did. Taboos are to be broken, assumptions discarded, biases questioned. People with developmental variations help us broaden our thinking and soften our hearts. It's our differences that make us stronger.

Conclusion

Like my first book, *Parent Child Journey,* this has been a book about "and" versus "or." All too often, we think about developmental difference too simplistically. Is it ADHD *or* anxiety? Is the problem in the child, the family, the school, *or* the culture? Do we need to prepare the child with autism for "real life" *or* change our schools and society for the child? To me, it's obvious: We need to address all of these issues. It's "and," not "or."

We need to help children with ADHD achieve better self-control *and* grant them more freedom. We need to help children with anxiety face their fears *and* face our own fears too. We need to help children with autism toward more improved social flexibility *and* work toward a less rigid world within which they can thrive. We need to help sexual- and gender-minority children embrace their true selves *and* create a world that embraces all individuals for who they are.

Sometimes, we should focus more on helping the child change. Other times, we must work harder to change the child's environment. Over the years, we prepare the child for the road *and* prepare the road for the child. All along the way, we stop, go, balance, change, and discover.

Appendix

Teacher Questionnaire

Thanks very much for taking the time to complete this form.

Child's name: _____ Date: _____

Teacher's name: _____

Class: _____

School: _____ Grade: _____

School address: _____

Schoolphone:_____Fax:_____

Please describe this child's strengths, special abilities, and interests:

_____

_____

_____

_____

_____

_____

Please describe any weaknesses, difficulties, or areas of concern:

_____

_____

_____

_____

Please describe briefly this child's present educational program (including size and nature of the classroom, time outside of regular classroom, special help, etc.):

_____

_____

_____

_____

Vanderbilt Rating Scale

Please circle the most appropriate number. Thank you.
    0 = never; 1 = occasionally; 2 = often; 3 = very often

1.	Fails to give attention to details or makes careless mistakes in school work	0	1	2	3
2.	Has difficulty sustaining attention to tasks or activities	0	1	2	3
3.	Does not seem to listen when spoken to directly	0	1	2	3
4.	Does not follow through on instructions and fails to finish schoolwork	0	1	2	3
5.	Has difficulty organizing tasks and activities	0	1	2	3
6.	Avoids, dislikes, or is reluctant to engage in tasks that require sustained mental effort	0	1	2	3
7.	Loses things necessary for tasks/ activities (assignments, pencils, books, etc.)	0	1	2	3
8.	Is easily distracted by extraneous stimuli	0	1	2	3
9.	Is forgetful in daily activities	0	1	2	3
10.	Fidgets with hands or feet or squirms in seat	0	1	2	3
11.	Inappropriately leaves seat in classroom or in other situations	0	1	2	3

12.	Inappropriately runs about or climbs excessively	0	1	2	3
13.	Has difficulty playing or engaging in leisure activities quietly	0	1	2	3
14.	Is "on the go" or acts as if "driven by a motor"	0	1	2	3
15.	Talks excessively	0	1	2	3
16.	Blurts out answers before questions have been completed	0	1	2	3
17.	Has difficulty waiting turns	0	1	2	3
18.	Interrupts or intrudes on others (e.g. butts into conversations or games)	0	1	2	3
19.	Argues with adults	0	1	2	3
20.	Loses temper	0	1	2	3
21.	Actively defies or refuses to comply with adults' requests or rules	0	1	2	3
22.	Deliberately annoys people	0	1	2	3
23.	Blames others for his or her mistakes or misbehaviors	0	1	2	3
24.	Is touchy or easily annoyed by others	0	1	2	3
25.	Is angry and resentful	0	1	2	3
26.	Is spiteful and vindictive	0	1	2	3
27.	Bullies, threatens, or intimidates others	0	1	2	3
28.	Initiates physical fights	0	1	2	3
29.	Lies to obtain goods for favors or to avoid obligations (i.e. "cons" others)	0	1	2	3
30.	Is truant from ("skips out of") school	0	1	2	3
31.	Is physically cruel to people	0	1	2	3
32.	Has stolen items of nontrivial value	0	1	2	3
33.	Deliberately destroys others' property	0	1	2	3
34.	Is fearful, anxious, or worried	0	1	2	3
35.	Is self-conscious or easily embarrassed	0	1	2	3
36.	Is afraid to try new things for fear of making mistakes	0	1	2	3
37.	Feels worthless or inferior	0	1	2	3
38.	Blames self for problems, feels guilty	0	1	2	3
39.	Feels lonely, unwanted, or unloved	0	1	2	3
40.	Is sad, unhappy, or depressed	0	1	2	3

Academic Performance

Leave blank if not applicable. Use back for additional comments. Thanks.

	Problematic		Average		Above average	Comments
Reading	1	2	3	4	5	
Understanding spoken language and instructions	1	2	3	4	5	
Written expression	1	2	3	4	5	
Oral expression	1	2	3	4	5	
Spelling	1	2	3	4	5	
Writing mechanics/ fine motor skills	1	2	3	4	5	
Memory	1	2	3	4	5	
Gross motor skills/ athletics	1	2	3	4	5	
Foreign language	1	2	3	4	5	
Mathematics	1	2	3	4	5	
Computers	1	2	3	4	5	
Arts/crafts	1	2	3	4	5	
Music	1	2	3	4	5	
Science	1	2	3	4	5	
Organization skills/ time management	1	2	3	4	5	
Assignment completion	1	2	3	4	5	

Teacher's additional comments:

_____

_____

_____

_____

Thank you very much! Please feel free to call if there is anything that you would like to discuss.

References

Adesman, A. (2015) "ADHD Medication Guide." Retrieved from www.north-well.edu/sites/northwell.edu/files/d7/ADHD-Medspercent20Guide.pdf.

Alvord, M. K., & McGrath, A. (2017) *Conquer Negative Thinking for Teens: A Workbook to Break the Nine Thought Habits That Are Holding You Back.* Instant Help.

Amaral, D. G. (2017). "Examining the Causes of Autism." *Cerebrum: The Dana Forum on Brain Science.*

American Academy of Pediatrics. (2019) "Bright Futures Guidelines and Pocket Guide." Retrieved July 22, 2019, from https://brightfutures.aap.org/materials-and-tools/guidelines-and-pocket-guide/Pages/default.aspx.

American Academy of Pediatrics Section on Adolescent Health. (2018) "AM. STARs LGBTQ Youth: Enhancing Care for Gender and Sexual Minorities." *Adolescent Medicine. State of the Art Reviews.* (D. M. Forcier, D. J. D. Brown, & D. R. T. Brown, Eds.) American Academy of Pediatrics.

The American College of Obstetricians and Gynecologists & Committee on Adolescent Health Care. (2018) "Müllerian Agenesis: Diagnosis, Management, and Treatment—ACOG." Retrieved July 19, 2019, from www.acog.org/Clinical-Guidance-and-Publications/Committee-Opinions/Committee-on-Adolescent-Health-Care/Mullerian-Agenesis-Diagnosis-Management-and-Treatment.

American Psychiatric Association. (2013) *Diagnostic and Statistical Manual of Mental Disorders (DSM-5).* American Psychiatric Pub.

Baio, J., Wiggins, L., Christensen, D. L., Maenner, M. J., Daniels, J., Warren, Z., Dowling, N. F. (2018) "Prevalence of Autism Spectrum Disorder Among Children Aged 8 Years—Autism and Developmental Disabilities Monitoring Network," 11 Sites, United States, 2014. *Morbidity and Mortality Weekly Report.* Surveillance Summaries (Washington, DC), 67(6), 1–23.

Barkley, R. A. (1997) *ADHD and the Nature of Self-Control.* New York: The Guilford Press.

Barkley, R. A. (2018a) "ADHD Likely Reduces Estimated Life Expectancy by Young Adulthood." Retrieved from www.russellbarkley.org/factsheets/ ADHD_Likelypercent20_Reduces_Estimated_Life_Expectancy_Barkley.pdf.

Barkley, R. A. (2013) "A Plea to Rename Sluggish Cognitive Tempo (SCT) as Concentration Deficit Disorder (CDD)." *The ADHD Report, 21*(7), 1–4.

Barkley, R. A. (2018b) *Barkley Sluggish Cognitive Tempo Scale—Children and Adolescents.* New York, NY: The Guilford Press.

Barkley, R. A. (2018c) "Focus on the Side Effects of Psychosocial Treatments for Children and Teens with ADHD: A Special Issue." *The ADHD Report, 26*(1), 1–4.

Barkley, R. A. (2019) "Neuropsychological Testing isn't Useful in the Diagnosis of ADHD: Stop It (or Prove It)!" *The ADHD Report, 27*(2), 1–8.

Barkley, R. A. (2013) *Taking Charge of ADHD: The Complete, Authoritative Guide for Parents* (3rd edition). New York: The Guilford Press.

Barkley, R. A., & Benton, C. M. (2010) *Taking Charge of Adult ADHD.* New York: The Guilford Press.

Baron-Cohen, S. (2004) *The Essential Difference: Male and Female Brains and The Truth About Autism* (reprint edition). New York: Basic Books.

Baron-Cohen, S. (1997) *Mindblindness: An Essay on Autism and Theory of Mind* (revised edition). Cambridge, MA: A Bradford Book.

Bascom, J. (2012) *Loud Hands: Autistic People, Speaking.* Washington, DC: Autistic Self Advocacy Network.

Bazelon, E. (2013) *Sticks and Stones: Defeating the Culture of Bullying and Rediscovering the Power of Character and Empathy.* New York: Random House.

Beek, T. F., Cohen-Kettenis, P. T., Bouman, W. P., de Vries, A. L. C., Steensma, T. D., Witcomb, G. L., ... Kreukels, B. P. C. (2016) "Gender Incongruence of Adolescence and Adulthood: Acceptability and Clinical Utility of the World Health Organization's Proposed ICD-11 Criteria." *PLoS ONE, 11*(10).

Blosnich, J. R., Brown, G. R., Shipherd, J. C., Kauth, M., Piegari, R. I., & Bossarte, R. M. (2013) "Prevalence of Gender Identity Disorder and Suicide Risk Among Transgender Veterans Utilizing Veterans Health Administration Care." *American Journal of Public Health, 103*(10), e27–32.

Buber, M. (1971) *I And Thou.* (W. Kaufmann, Trans.). New York: Touchstone.

Byne, W., Bradley, S. J., Coleman, E., Eyler, A. E., Green, R., Menvielle, E. J., ... American Psychiatric Association Task Force on Treatment of Gender Identity Disorder. (2012) "Report of the American Psychiatric Association Task Force on Treatment of Gender Identity Disorder." *Archives of Sexual Behavior, 41*(4), 759–796.

Cain, S. (2013) *Quiet: The Power of Introverts in a World That Can't Stop Talking.* New York: Broadway Books.

Cannon, L., Kenworthy, L., Alexander, K. C., Adler Werner, M., & Anthony, L. (2018) *Unstuck and On Target!: An Executive Function Curriculum to Improve Flexibility, Planning, and Organization* (second edition). Baltimore, MD: Brookes Publishing.

Center for Parent Information and Resource. (2018) "Sexuality Education for Students with Disabilities." Retrieved August 1, 2019, from www.parentcenterhub.org/whatiscpir/.

Centers for Disease Control and Prevention. (2017a) "ADHD Awareness." Retrieved June 7, 2019, from www.cdc.gov/features/adhd-awareness.

Centers for Disease Control and Prevention. (2018) "ADHD Treatment Recommendations." Retrieved June 7, 2019, from www.cdc.gov/ncbddd/adhd/guidelines.html.

Centers for Disease Control and Prevention. (2017b) "Behavior Therapy First for Young Children with ADHD." Retrieved July 31, 2019, from www.cdc.gov/features/adhd-awareness.

Centers for Disease Control and Prevention. (2016) "Data and Statistics About ADHD." Retrieved June 7, 2019, from www.cdc.gov/ncbddd/adhd/data.html.

Chang, Z., Quinn, P. D., Hur, K., Gibbons, R. D., Sjölander, A., Larsson, H., & D'Onofrio, B. M. (2017) "Association Between Medication Use for Attention-Deficit/Hyperactivity Disorder and Risk of Motor Vehicle Crashes." JAMA Psychiatry, 74(6), 597–603.

Chansky, T. (2004) Freeing Your Child from Anxiety: Powerful, Practical Solutions to Overcome Your Child's Fears, Worries, and Phobias. New York: Harmony.

Cheng, P. J., Pastuszak, A. W., Myers, J. B., Goodwin, I. A., & Hotaling, J. M. (2019) "Fertility Concerns of the Transgender Patient." Translational Andrology and Urology, 8(3), 218–219.

Chess, S., & Thomas, A. (1995) Temperament in Clinical Practice (reprint edition). New York: The Guilford Press.

Chess, S., & Thomas, A. (1990) "The New York Longitudinal Study (NYLS): The Young Adult Periods." Canadian Journal of Psychiatry. Revue Canadienne De Psychiatrie, 35(6), 557–561.

Connolly, M. D., Zervos, M. J., Barone, C. J., Johnson, C. C., & Joseph, C. L. M. (2016) "The Mental Health of Transgender Youth: Advances in Understanding." The Journal of Adolescent Health. Official Publication of the Society for Adolescent Medicine, 59(5), 489–495.

Cooper, K., Smith, L. G. E., & Russell, A. J. (2018) "Gender Identity in Autism: Sex Differences in Social Affiliation with Gender Groups." Journal of Autism and Developmental Disorders, 48(12), 3995–4006.

Dewinter, J., De Graaf, H., & Begeer, S. (2017) "Sexual Orientation, Gender Identity, and Romantic Relationships in Adolescents and Adults with Autism Spectrum Disorder." Journal of Autism and Developmental Disorders, 47(9), 2927–2934.

Dewinter, J., Vermeiren, R., Vanwesenbeeck, I., & Van Nieuwenhuizen, C. (2016) "Parental Awareness of Sexual Experience in Adolescent Boys with Autism Spectrum Disorder." Journal of Autism and Developmental Disorders, 46, 713–719.

Donvan, J., & Zucker, C. (2017) In a Different Key: The Story of Autism (reprint edition). New York: Broadway Books.

Durand, V. M. (2013) Sleep Better!: A Guide to Improving Sleep for Children with Special Needs (revised edition). Baltimore, MD: Brookes Publishing.

Durkheim, E. (2007) On Suicide. A. Riley, Ed., R. Buss, Trans. (translation edition) London: Penguin Classics.

Durwood, L., McLaughlin, K. A., & Olson, K. R. (2017) "Mental Health and

Self-Worth in Socially Transitioned Transgender Youth." *Journal of the American Academy of Child and Adolescent Psychiatry*, 56(2), 116–123.

Egolf, A., & Coffey, B. J. (2014) "Current Pharmacotherapeutic Approaches for the Treatment of Tourette Syndrome." *Drugs of Today* (Barcelona, Spain, 1998), 50(2), 159–179.

Eichenstein, R. (2015) *Not What I Expected: Help and Hope for Parents of Atypical Children*. New York, New York: TarcherPerigee.

Elgar, S. (1985) "Sex Education and Sexual Awareness Building for Autistic Children and Youth: Some Viewpoints and Considerations—Response to the Responses." *Journal of Autism and Developmental Disorders*, 15(2), 224–227.

Elkind, D. (2006) *The Hurried Child* (25th anniversary edition). Cambridge, MA: Da Capo Lifelong Books.

Erikson, E. H. (1993) *Childhood and Society* (reissue edition). New York: W. W. Norton & Company.

Evans, S. W., Owens, J., & Bunford, M. N. (2014) "Evidence-Based Psychosocial Treatments for Children and Adolescents with Attention-Deficit/Hyperactivity Disorder." *Journal of Clinical Child and Adolescent Psychology: The Official Journal for the Society of Clinical Child and Adolescent Psychology*, American Psychological Association, Division 53, 43(4), 527–551.

Ferber, R. (2006) *Solve Your Child's Sleep Problems*. (revised, expanded edition). New York: Touchstone.

Fernandes, L. C., Gillberg, C. I., Cederlund, M., Hagberg, B., Gillberg, C., & Billstedt, E. (2016) "Aspects of Sexuality in Adolescents and Adults Diagnosed with Autism Spectrum Disorders in Childhood." *Journal of Autism and Developmental Disorders*, 46(9), 3155–3165.

Fraiberg, S., Adelson, E., & Shapiro, V. (1975) "Ghosts in the Nursery: A Psychoanalytic Approach to the Problems of Impaired Infant-Mother Relationships." *Journal of the American Academy of Child Psychiatry*, 14(3), 387–421.

Gardner, H. (2011) *Frames of Mind: The Theory of Multiple Intelligences* (3rd edition). New York: Basic Books.

Gilovich, T., Keltner, D., Chen, S., & Nisbett, R. E. (2015) *Social Psychology* (4th edition). New York: W. W. Norton & Company.

Gladwell, M. (2002) *The Tipping Point: How Little Things Can Make a Big Difference*. Boston: Back Bay Books.

Glidden, D., Bouman, W. P., Jones, B. A., & Arcelus, J. (2016) "Gender Dysphoria and Autism Spectrum Disorder: A Systematic Review of the Literature." *Sexual Medicine Reviews*, 4(1), 3–14.

Gorton, R. N., & Erickson-Schroth, L. (2017) "Hormonal and Surgical Treatment Options for Transgender Men (Female-to-Male)." *The Psychiatric Clinics of North America*, 40(1), 79–97.

Green, M., & Solnit, A. J. (1964) "Reactions to the Threatened Loss of a Child: A Vulnerable Child Syndrome—Pediatric Management of the Dying Child, Part III." *Pediatrics*, 34(1), 58–66.

Greene, J. (2014) *Moral Tribes: Emotion, Reason, and the Gap Between Us and Them* (reprint edition). New York: Penguin Books.

Greenhill, L., Kollins, S., Abikoff, H., McCracken, J., Riddle, M., Swanson,

J., … Cooper, T. (2006) "Efficacy and Safety of Immediate-Release Methylphenidate Treatment for Preschoolers with ADHD." *Journal of the American Academy of Child and Adolescent Psychiatry*, 45(11), 1284–1293.

Greenspan, S. I., & Salmon, J. (1994) *Playground Politics: Understanding the Emotional Life of Your School-Age Child*. Reading, MA: Da Capo Lifelong Books.

Grinker, R. R. (2008) *Unstrange Minds: Remapping the World of Autism*. New York: Basic Books.

Haidt, J. (2013) *The Righteous Mind: Why Good People Are Divided by Politics and Religion* (reprint edition). New York: Vintage.

Hamed, A. M., Kauer, A. J., & Stevens, H. E. (2015) "Why the Diagnosis of Attention Deficit Hyperactivity Disorder Matters." *Frontiers in Psychiatry*, 6.

Hamilton, S. P. (2015) "The Promise of Psychiatric Pharmacogenomics." *Biological Psychiatry*, 77(1), 29–35.

Hansen, S. N., Schendel, D. E., & Parner, E. T. (2015) "Explaining the Increase in the Prevalence of Autism Spectrum Disorders: The Proportion Attributable to Changes in Reporting Practices." *JAMA Pediatrics*, 169(1), 56–62.

Harrell, E. (2017) "Bureau of Justice Statistics (BJS)—Crime Against Persons with Disabilities, 2009-2015—Statistical Tables." Retrieved August 1, 2019, from **www.bjs.gov/index.cfm?ty=pbdetail&iid=5986.**

Heath, C., & Heath, D. (2010) *Switch: How to Change Things When Change Is Hard*. New York: Crown Business.

Hechtman, L., Swanson, J. M., Sibley, M. H., Stehli, A., Owens, E. B., Mitchell, J. T., … MTA Cooperative Group. (2016) "Functional Adult Outcomes 16 Years After Childhood Diagnosis of Attention-Deficit/Hyperactivity Disorder: MTA Results." *Journal of the American Academy of Child and Adolescent Psychiatry*, 55(11), 945–952.

Hembree, W. C., Cohen-Kettenis, P. T., Gooren, L., Hannema, S. E., Meyer, W. J., Murad, M. H., … T'Sjoen, G. G. (2017) "Endocrine Treatment of Gender-Dysphoric/Gender-Incongruent Persons: An Endocrine Society Clinical Practice Guideline." *The Journal of Clinical Endocrinology & Metabolism*, 102(11), 3869–3903.

Henault, I. (2005) *Asperger's Syndrome and Sexuality: From Adolescence through Adulthood*. London; Philadelphia: Jessica Kingsley Publishers.

Hendrickx, S., & Newton, K. (2007) *Asperger Syndrome—A Love Story*. London; Philadelphia: Jessica Kingsley Publishers.

Huebner, D. (2005) *What to Do When You Worry Too Much: A Kid's Guide to Overcoming Anxiety*. Washington, DC: Magination Press.

Hues. (2019) "An Adorable, Accessible Way to Explain a Complicated Concept » The Genderbread Person." Retrieved July 19, 2019, from **www. genderbread.org.**

Jackson, L. (2002) *Freaks, Geeks, and Asperger Syndrome: A User Guide to Adolescence*. London; New York: Jessica Kingsley Publishers.

Jacobs, L. A., Rachlin, K., Erickson-Schroth, L., & Janssen, A. (2014) "Gender Dysphoria and Co-Occurring Autism Spectrum Disorders: Review, Case Examples, and Treatment Considerations." *LGBT Health*, 1(4), 277–282.

Janssen, A., Huang, H., & Duncan, C. (2016) "Gender Variance Among

Youth with Autism Spectrum Disorders: A Retrospective Chart Review." *Transgender Health*, 1(1), 63–68.

Kagan, J. (1997) *Galen's Prophecy: Temperament in Human Nature*. New York: Westview Press.

Kaplan, G., & McCracken, J. T. (2012) "Psychopharmacology of Autism Spectrum Disorders." *Pediatric Clinics of North America*, 59(1), 175–187, xii.

Kendall, P.C., & Braswell, L. B. (1994) *Cognitive-Behavioral Therapy for Impulsive Children*. New York: Guilford Publications, Inc.

Kendall, P. C., & Hedtke, K. A. (2006) *Cognitive-Behavioral Therapy for Anxious Children: Therapist Manual* (3rd edition). Ardmore, PA: Workbook Publishing.

Kendall, P. C., & Hedtke, K. A. (2006) *Coping Cat Workbook* (2nd edition). Ardmore, PA: Workbook Pub Inc.

Kluth, P. (2010) *"You're Going to Love This Kid!": Teaching Students with Autism in the Inclusive Classroom* (2nd edition). Baltimore, MD: Brookes Publishing.

Koller, R. (2000) "Sexuality and Adolescents with Autism." *Sexuality and Disability*, 18(2), 125–135.

Laugeson, E. A. (2013) *The Science of Making Friends: Helping Socially Challenged Teens and Young Adults* (PAP/DVDR edition, with DVD). San Francisco: John Wiley & Sons Inc.

Lebowitz, E. R., Omer, H., Hermes, H., & Scahill, L. (2014) "Parent Training for Childhood Anxiety Disorders: The SPACE Program." *Cognitive and Behavioral Practice*, 21(4), 456–469.

Levine, M. (1993) *Developmental Variation and Learning Disorders* (2nd edition). Cambridge, MA: Educators Pub Svc Inc.

Levine, M. (2008) *The Price of Privilege: How Parental Pressure and Material Advantage Are Creating a Generation of Disconnected and Unhappy Kids* (reprint edition). New York: Harper Perennial.

Lopez, C. M., Solomon, D., Boulware, S. D., & Christison-Lagay, E. R. (2018) "Trends in the Use of Puberty Blockers among Transgender Children in the United States." *Journal of Pediatric Endocrinology & Metabolism. JPEM*, 31(6), 665–670.

Lopez, X., Marinkovic, M., Eimicke, T., Rosenthal, S. M., Olshan, J. S., & Pediatric Endocrine Society Transgender Health Special Interest Group. (2017) "Statement on Gender-Affirmative Approach to Care from the Pediatric Endocrine Society Special Interest Group on Transgender Health." *Current Opinion in Pediatrics*, 29(4), 475–480.

Lukianoff, G., & Haidt, J. (2018) *The Coddling of the American Mind: How Good Intentions and Bad Ideas Are Setting Up a Generation for Failure*. New York: Penguin Press.

Maglione, M. A., Gans, D., Das, L., Timbie, J., Kasari, C., for the Technical Expert Panel, & Network, H. A. I. R.-B. (2012) "Nonmedical Interventions for Children With ASD: Recommended Guidelines and Further Research Needs." *Pediatrics*, 130(Supplement 2), S169–S178.

Mahajan, R., Bernal, M. P., Panzer, R., Whitaker, A., Roberts, W., Handen, B., ... Autism Speaks Autism Treatment Network Psychopharmacology

Committee. (2012) "Clinical Practice Pathways for Evaluation and Medication Choice for Attention-Deficit/Hyperactivity Disorder Symptoms in Autism Spectrum Disorders." *Pediatrics*, 130 Suppl 2, S125–138.

Mahfouda, S., Moore, J. K., Siafarikas, A., Zepf, F. D., & Lin, A. (2017) "Puberty Suppression in Transgender Children and Adolescents." *The Lancet. Diabetes & Endocrinology*, 5(10), 816–826.

Majdandžić, M., Lazarus, R. S., Oort, F. J., van der Sluis, C., Dodd, H. F., Morris, T. M., ... Bögels, S. M. (2018) "The Structure of Challenging Parenting Behavior and Associations with Anxiety in Dutch and Australian Children." *Journal of Clinical Child and Adolescent Psychology—The Official Journal for the Society of Clinical Child and Adolescent Psychology, American Psychological Association, Division 53*, 47(2), 282–295.

March, J. S. (2011) "The Preschool ADHD Treatment Study (PATS) as the Culmination of Twenty Years of Clinical Trials in Pediatric Psychopharmacology." *Journal of the American Academy of Child & Adolescent Psychiatry*, 50(5), 427–430.

May, T., Pang, K. C., O'Connell, M. A., & Williams, K. (2017) "Typical Pubertal Timing in an Australian Population of Girls and Boys with Autism Spectrum Disorder." *Journal of Autism and Developmental Disorders*, 47(12), 3983–3993.

Mayle, P. (1973) *Where Did I Come From?* New York: Lyle Stuart Inc.

McCabe, S. E., Dickinson, K., West, B. T., & Wilens, T. E. (2016) "Age of Onset, Duration, and Type of Medication Therapy for Attention-Deficit/ Hyperactivity Disorder and Substance Use During Adolescence: A Multi-Cohort National Study." *Journal of the American Academy of Child and Adolescent Psychiatry*, 55(6), 479–486.

McCracken, J. T., McGough, J. J., Loo, S. K., Levitt, J., Del'Homme, M., Cowen, J., ... Bilder, R. M. (2016) "Combined Stimulant and Guanfacine Administration in Attention-Deficit/Hyperactivity Disorder: A Controlled, Comparative Study." *Journal of the American Academy of Child & Adolescent Psychiatry*, 55(8), 657-666.

McPheeters, M. L., Warren, Z., Sathe, N., Bruzek, J. L., Krishnaswami, S., Jerome, R. N., & Veenstra-Vanderweele, J. (2011) "A Systematic Review of Medical Treatments for Children with Autism Spectrum Disorders." *Pediatrics*, 127(5), e1312–1321.

Mischel, W. (2014) *The Marshmallow Test: Mastering Self-Control* (1st edition). New York: Little, Brown Spark.

Morton, C., & Morton, G. (2015) *Why Johnny Doesn't Flap: NT Is OK!* London; Philadelphia: Jessica Kingsley Publishers.

Moser, L. (2015) "Parents of Behavior-Challenged Kids Wait Years to Get in and See This Doctor. Here's His Secret." Retrieved June 7, 2019, from www.washingtonian.com/2015/08/09/feel-like-a-failure-as-a-parent-theres-a-doctor-for-that/.

Myles, B. S., Trautman, M. L., & Schelvan, R. L. (2004) *The Hidden Curriculum: Practical Solutions for Understanding Unstated Rules in Social Situations*. Shawnee Mission, KS: Autism Asperger Publishing Company.

Myers, S. M., & Johnson, C. P. (2007) "Management of Children with Autism

Spectrum Disorders." *Pediatrics*, 120(5), 1162–1182.

National Autism Center. (2015) "National Standards Project, Phase 2." Retrieved July 21, 2019, from www.nationalautismcenter.org/national-standards-project/phase-2/.

National Institute of Mental Health. (2009) "The Multimodal Treatment of Attention Deficit Hyperactivity Disorder Study (MTA): Questions and Answers." Retrieved June 7, 2019, from www.nimh.nih.gov/funding/clinical-research/practical/mta/the-multimodal-treatment-of-attention-deficit-hyperactivity-disorder-study-mta-questions-and-answers.shtml.

National Institute of Mental Health. (2019) "Research Domain Criteria (RDoC)." Retrieved July 21, 2019, from www.nimh.nih.gov/research/research-funded-by-nimh/rdoc/index.shtml.

National Resource Council, Committee on Educational Interventions for Children with Autism. (2001) *Educating Children with Autism*. (J. P. McGee & C. Lord, Eds.). Washington, DC: National Academies Press.

Newport, J. & Newport, M. (2002) *Autism-Asperger's & Sexuality: Puberty and Beyond*. Arlington, TX: Future Horizons.

Nigg, J. T. (2017). *Getting Ahead of ADHD: What Next-Generation Science Says about Treatments That Work—And How You Can Make Them Work for Your Child*. New York: The Guilford Press.

Nisbett, R. E. (2004) *The Geography of Thought: How Asians and Westerners Think Differently … and Why* (reprint edition) New York: Free Press.

Nobili, A., Glazebrook, C., Bouman, W. P., Glidden, D., Baron-Cohen, S., Allison, C., … Arcelus, J. (2018) "Autistic Traits in Treatment-Seeking Transgender Adults." *Journal of Autism and Developmental Disorders*, 48(12), 3984–3994.

Odom, S. L., Boyd, B. A., Hall, L. J., & Hume, K. (2010) Evaluation of Comprehensive Treatment Models for Individuals with Autism Spectrum Disorders. *Journal of Autism and Developmental Disorders*, 40(4), 425–436.

Offit, P. A. (2013) *Do You Believe in Magic?: The Sense and Nonsense of Alternative Medicine* (reprint edition). New York: Harper.

Ogundele, M. O., & Ayyash, H. F. (2018) "Review of the Evidence for the Management of Co-Morbid Tic Disorders in Children and Adolescents with Attention Deficit Hyperactivity Disorder." *World Journal of Clinical Pediatrics*, 7(1), 36–42.

Orban, S. A., Rapport, M. D., Friedman, L. M., & Kofler, M. J. (2014) "Executive Function/Cognitive Training for Children with ADHD: Do Results Warrant the Hype and Cost?" *The ADHD Report*, 22(8), 8–14.

Owens, J. A., & Mindell, J. A. (2005) *Take Charge of Your Child's Sleep: The All-in-One Resource for Solving Sleep Problems in Kids and Teens*. New York: Marlowe & Company.

Pinker, S. (2019) *Enlightenment Now: The Case for Reason, Science, Humanism, and Progress* (reprint edition). New York: Penguin Books.

Planned Parenthood. (2017) "Sexuality Education for Youth on the Autism Spectrum." Retrieved July 19, 2019, from www.plannedparenthood.org/planned-parenthood-massachusetts/local-training-education/parent-buzz-newsletter/parent-buzz-e-newsletters/

sexuality-education-youth-autism-spectrum.

Pletter, Adam. (2019) "Become a Savvy Digital Parent—With Child Psychologist Dr. Adam Pletter." Retrieved July 19, 2019, from https://iparent101.com/.

Pollan, M. (2019) *How to Change Your Mind: What the New Science of Psychedelics Teaches Us About Consciousness, Dying, Addiction, Depression, and Transcendence* (reprint edition). New York: Penguin Books.

Pozzi, M., Carnovale, C., Peeters, G. G. A. M., Gentili, M., Antoniazzi, S., Radice, S., ... Nobile, M. (2018) "Adverse Drug Events Related to Mood and Emotion in Pediatric Patients Treated for ADHD: A Meta-Analysis." *Journal of Affective Disorders*, 238, 161–178.

Prum, R. O. (2017) *The Evolution of Beauty: How Darwin's Forgotten Theory of Mate Choice Shapes the Animal World—and Us*. New York: Doubleday.

Putnam, R. D. (2001) *Bowling Alone: The Collapse and Revival of American Community* (1st edition). New York: Touchstone Books by Simon & Schuster.

Rapee, R., Wignall, A., Spence, S., Lyneham, H., & Cobham, V. (2008) *Helping Your Anxious Child: A Step-by-Step Guide for Parents* (2nd edition). Oakland, CA: New Harbinger Publications.

RespectAbility. (2017) Sexual Education Resources. Retrieved August 1, 2019, from www.respectability.org/resources/sexual-education-resources.

Robertson, M. M., Eapen, V., Singer, H. S., Martino, D., Scharf, J. M., Paschou, P., ... Leckman, J. F. (2017) "Gilles de la Tourette Syndrome." *Nature Reviews. Disease Primers*, 3, 16097.

Robison, J. E. (2008) *Look Me in the Eye: My Life with Asperger's* (reprint edition). New York: Three Rivers Press.

Rogers, C. (1995) *On Becoming a Person: A Therapist's View of Psychotherapy* (2nd edition). New York: Mariner Books.

Ross, L. & Nisbett, R. (2011) *The Person and the Situation: Perspectives of Social Psychology* (2nd edition). London: Pinter & Martin Ltd.

Roy, A., Hechtman, L., Arnold, L. E., Sibley, M. H., Molina, B. S. G., Swanson, J. M., ... MTA Cooperative Group. (2016) "Childhood Factors Affecting Persistence and Desistence of Attention-Deficit/Hyperactivity Disorder Symptoms in Adulthood: Results From the MTA." *Journal of the American Academy of Child and Adolescent Psychiatry*, 55(11), 937–944.

Rutgers. (2019) Sensoa Flag System. Retrieved August 1, 2019, from www.flagsystem.org.

Sacks, O. (1996) *An Anthropologist on Mars: Seven Paradoxical Tales*. New York: Vintage.

Sapolsky, R. M. (2018) *Behave: The Biology of Humans at Our Best and Worst* (reprint edition). New York: Penguin Books.

Seibel, B. L. (2018) "The Impact of the Parental Support on Risk Factors in the Process of Gender Affirmation of Transgender and Gender Diverse People". *Front Psychol*, 9(399).

Shapiro, D. (2016) *Parent Child Journey: An Individualized Approach to Raising your Challenging Child*. CreateSpace Independent Publishing Platform.

Silberman, S. (2016) *Neurotribes: The Legacy of Autism and the Future of Neurodiversity* (reprint edition). New York: Avery.

Simons, L. K., Leibowitz, S. F., & Hidalgo, M. A. (2014) "Understanding Gender Variance in Children and Adolescents." *Pediatric Annals*, 43(6), e126–131.

Soke, G. N., Maenner, M. J., Christensen, D., Kurzius-Spencer, M., & Schieve, L. A. (2018) "Prevalence of Co-occurring Medical and Behavioral Conditions/Symptoms Among 4- and 8-Year-Old Children with Autism Spectrum Disorder in Selected Areas of the United States in 2010." *Journal of Autism and Developmental Disorders*, 48(8), 2663–2676.

Solomon, A. (2013) *Far From the Tree: Parents, Children, and the Search for Identity* (reprint edition). New York: Scribner.

Solomon, Andrew, & Audible Studios. *New Family Values*. Audible Studios.

Spencer, D., Marshall, J., Post, B., Kulakodlu, M., Newschaffer, C., Dennen, T., ... Jain, A. (2013) "Psychotropic Medication Use and Polypharmacy in Children with Autism Spectrum Disorders." *Pediatrics*, 132(5), 833–840.

Stixrud, W., & Johnson, N. (2019) *The Self-Driven Child: The Science and Sense of Giving Your Kids More Control Over Their Lives* (reprint edition). New York: Penguin Books.

Strang, J. F., Janssen, A., Tishelman, A., Leibowitz, S. F., Kenworthy, L., McGuire, J. K., ... Anthony, L. G. (2018) "Revisiting the Link: Evidence of the Rates of Autism in Studies of Gender Diverse Individuals." *Journal of the American Academy of Child and Adolescent Psychiatry*, 57(11), 885–887.

Strang, J. F., Kenworthy, L., Dominska, A., Sokoloff, J., Kenealy, L. E., Berl, M., ... Wallace, G. L. (2014) "Increased Gender Variance in Autism Spectrum Disorders and Attention Deficit Hyperactivity Disorder." *Archives of Sexual Behavior*, 43(8), 1525–1533.

Strang, J. F., Powers, M. D., Knauss, M., Sibarium, E., Leibowitz, S. F., Kenworthy, L., ... Anthony, L. G. (2018) "'They Thought It Was an Obsession': Trajectories and Perspectives of Autistic Transgender and Gender-Diverse Adolescents." *Journal of Autism and Developmental Disorders*, 48(12), 4039–4055.

Strohl, M. P. (2011) "Bradley's Benzedrine Studies on Children with Behavioral Disorders." *The Yale Journal of Biology and Medicine*, 84(1), 27–33.

Subcommittee on Attention-Deficit/Hyperactivity Disorder, & Steering Committee on Quality Improvement and Management. (2011) "ADHD: Clinical Practice Guideline for the Diagnosis, Evaluation, and Treatment of Attention-Deficit/Hyperactivity Disorder in Children and Adolescents." *Pediatrics*, 128(5), 1007–1022.

Sunstein, C. R. (2019) *How Change Happens*. Cambridge, MA: The MIT Press.

Swanson, J. M., Arnold, L. E., Molina, B. S. G., Sibley, M. H., Hechtman, L. T., Hinshaw, S. P., ... MTA Cooperative Group. (2017) "Young Adult Outcomes in the Follow-Up of the Multimodal Treatment Study of Attention-Deficit/Hyperactivity Disorder: Symptom Persistence, Source Discrepancy, and Height Suppression." *Journal of Child Psychology and Psychiatry, and Allied Disciplines*, 58(6), 663–678.

Tammet, D. (2007) *Born on a Blue Day: Inside the Extraordinary Mind of an Autistic Savant* (reprint edition). New York: Free Press.

Torisky, D., & Torisky, C. (1985) "Sex Education and Sexual Awareness Building for Autistic Children and Youth: Some Viewpoints and Considerations: Response." *Journal of Autism and Developmental Disorders,* 15(2), 221–223.

Travers R, Bauer G, Pyne J, Bradley K, for the Trans PULSE Project (2012); Gale L, Papadimitriou M. "Impacts of Strong Parental Support for Trans Youth: A Report Prepared for Children's Aid Society of Toronto and Delisle Youth Services."

Truong, D. (2019, July 16) "More Students Are Being Bullied Online, Federal Report Says." *Washington Post.* Retrieved from www.washingtonpost.com/local/education/more-students-are-being-bullied-online-federal-report-says/2019/07/15/0f19f7d0-a71d-11e9-9214-246e594de5d5_story.html.

Turban, J. L., & van Schalkwyk, G. I. (2018) "Gender Dysphoria and Autism Spectrum Disorder: Is the Link Real?" *Journal of the American Academy of Child and Adolescent Psychiatry,* 57(1), 8–9.

Turkle, S. (2016) *Reclaiming Conversation: The Power of Talk in a Digital Age* (reprint edition). New York: Penguin Books.

Twenge, J. M. (2017) *iGen: Why Today's Super-Connected Kids Are Growing Up Less Rebellious, More Tolerant, Less Happy—and Completely Unprepared for Adulthood–and What That Means for the Rest of Us* (reprint edition). New York: Atria Books.

The Unitarian Universalist Association. (2014) "Our Whole Lives: Lifespan Sexuality Education." Retrieved July 19, 2019, from www.uua.org/re/owl.

Urquhart, E. (2018, March 21) "A Disproportionate Number of Autistic Youth Are Transgender. Why?" Retrieved July 18, 2019, from https://slate.com/human-interest/2018/03/why-are-a-disproportionate-number-of-autistic-youth-transgender.html.

van der Miesen, A. I. R., Cohen-Kettenis, P. T., & de Vries, A. L. C. (2018) "Is There a Link Between Gender Dysphoria and Autism Spectrum Disorder?" *Journal of the American Academy of Child and Adolescent Psychiatry,* 57(11), 884–885.

van der Miesen, A. I. R., de Vries, A. L. C., Steensma, T. D., & Hartman, C. A. (2018) "Autistic Symptoms in Children and Adolescents with Gender Dysphoria." *Journal of Autism and Developmental Disorders,* 48(5), 1537–1548.

van der Miesen, A. I. R., Hurley, H., Bal, A. M., & de Vries, A. L. C. (2018) "Prevalence of the Wish to be of the Opposite Gender in Adolescents and Adults with Autism Spectrum Disorder." *Archives of Sexual Behavior,* 47(8), 2307–2317.

van der Miesen, A. I. R., Hurley, H., & de Vries, A. L. C. (2016) "Gender Dysphoria and Autism Spectrum Disorder: A Narrative Review." *International Review of Psychiatry (Abingdon, England),* 28(1), 70–80.

van der Miesen, A. I. R., Nabbijohn, A. N., Santarossa, A., & VanderLaan, D. P. (2018) "Behavioral and Emotional Problems in Gender-Nonconforming Children: A Canadian Community-Based Study." *Journal of the American Academy of Child & Adolescent Psychiatry,* 57(7), 491–499.

van Schalkwyk, G. I., Klingensmith, K., & Volkmar, F. R. (2015) "Gender Identity and Autism Spectrum Disorders." *The Yale Journal of Biology and Medicine,* 88(1), 81–83.

Vasa, R. A., Mazurek, M. O., Mahajan, R., Bennett, A. E., Bernal, M. P., Nozzolillo, A. A., … Coury, D. L. (2016) "Assessment and Treatment of Anxiety in Youth with Autism Spectrum Disorders." *Pediatrics*, 137(Supplement 2), S115–S123.

Vermeulen, P. (2012) *Autism as Context Blindness*. Shawnee Mission, KS: AAPC Publishing.

Weinfeld, R., & Davis, M. (2008) *Special Needs Advocacy Resource Book: What You Can Do Now to Advocate for Your Exceptional Child's Education*. Waco, TX: Prufrock Press.

Wesp, L. M., & Deutsch, M. B. (2017) "Hormonal and Surgical Treatment Options for Transgender Women and Transfeminine Spectrum Persons." *The Psychiatric Clinics of North America*, 40(1), 99–111.

Westcott, H. L., & Jones, D. P. (1999) "Prevalence of Abuse of Disabled Children—A Chronology."

Wilens, T. E., Adler, L. A., Adams, J., Sgambati, S., Rotrosen, J., Sawtelle, R., … Fusillo, S. (2008) "Misuse and Diversion of Stimulants Prescribed for ADHD: A Systematic Review of the Literature." *Journal of the American Academy of Child and Adolescent Psychiatry*, 47(1), 21–31.

Wilens, T. E., & Hammerness, P. G. (2016) *Straight Talk about Psychiatric Medications for Kids* (fourth edition). New York: The Guilford Press.

Winner, M. G. (2019) "Socialthinking—Home." Retrieved July 31, 2019, from **www.socialthinking.com**.

Winner, M. G., & Crooke, P. (2011) *Socially Curious and Curiously Social: A Social Thinking Guidebook for Bright Teens and Young Adults*. Great Barrington, MA: North River Press.

Wolf, M., & Bowers, P. G. (1999) The Double-Deficit Hypothesis for the Developmental Dyslexias. *Journal of Educational Psychology*, 91(3), 415–438.

Wolpe, J. (1992) *The Practice of Behavior Therapy* (4th edition). Boston, MA: Allyn & Bacon.

Wong, C., Odom, S. L., Hume, K. A., Cox, A. W., Fettig, A., Kucharczyk, S., … Schultz, T. R. (2015) "Evidence-Based Practices for Children, Youth, and Young Adults with Autism Spectrum Disorder: A Comprehensive Review." *Journal of Autism and Developmental Disorders*, 45(7), 1951–1966.

Yulius Academy. (2010) "Tackling Teenage Project." Retrieved July 19, 2019, from **www.ikpuber.nl/en/content/tackling-teenage**.

Zucker, B. (2016) *Anxiety-Free Kids: An Interactive Guide for Parents and Children* (2 edition). Waco, TX: Prufrock Press.

Zwaigenbaum, L., Bauman, M. L., Choueiri, R., Kasari, C., Carter, A., Granpeesheh, D., … Natowicz, M. R. (2015) "Early Intervention for Children with Autism Spectrum Disorder Under 3 Years of Age: Recommendations for Practice and Research." *Pediatrics*, 136 Suppl 1, S60–81.

About the Authors

Dr. Dan Shapiro is a native of East Lansing, Michigan. He moved to Washington, DC, to attend the George Washington University School of Medicine and stayed for pediatric residency training at Children's National Medical Center. Dr. Shapiro practiced primary-care pediatric and adolescent medicine in Silver Spring, Maryland, before shifting his focus to developmental and behavioral pediatrics. Currently, in addition to his office practice, Dr. Shapiro observes children and collaborates with educators at dozens of Washington, DC, and suburban Maryland schools. He developed the Parent Child Journey program and offers behavior-management training groups throughout Greater Washington. (For more information, go to ParentChildJourney.com.) He is a fellow of the American Academy of Pediatrics and a member of the Society for Developmental and Behavioral Pediatrics. Dr. Shapiro is married, with four children and two grandchildren. He is the author of *Parent Child Journey: An Individualized Approach to Raising Your Challenging Child.*

Dr. Aaron Shapiro is currently a resident in Primary Care Social Internal Medicine at Montefiore Medical Center in The

Bronx, New York. He received his M.D. from the Alpert Medical School of Brown University and his M.P.H. in Health Leadership and Management from the Johns Hopkins Bloomberg School of Public Health. He is the founder of Citizen Physicians (a non-partisan non-profit organization dedicated to increasing civic engagement in the medical community), a National Health Service Corps Scholar, and a Global Health Corps Alumnus. He is the third of Dr. Dan Shapiro's four sons.

About the Illustrator

John Watkins-Chow was born in New Jersey and has three degrees from MIT. John has been drawing all his life. He has worked in animation, comics, and sketch card art on properties such as Star Wars, Lord of the Rings, and Marvel Comics—and his own comic, *Talismen*. John was also the illustrator for Dr. Shapiro's first book, *Parent Child Journey: An Individualized Approach to Raising Your Challenging Child*. During the day, John teaches math at a private school in suburban Maryland. John is married and has two daughters.

CPSIA information can be obtained
at www.ICGtesting.com
Printed in the USA
LVHW082302150321
681644LV00039B/806